THE IMPACT OF ATOMIC ENERGY

A History of Responses by Governments, Scientists, and Religious Groups

THE
IMPACT
OF
ATOMIC ENERGY

Erwin N. Hiebert

Faith and Life Press
Newton, Kansas

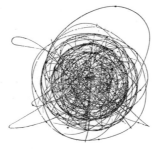

PREFACE

Down through history the Christian church has related itself to new conditions in varying ways and with varying degrees of effectiveness. Once people believed that the earth stood motionless in the center of the universe. The discovery of the earth's movement caused men to radically change their thinking. Once slavery was an accepted and honored social form. Today that institution is viewed as an abomination.

Today nuclear power is a reality only fifteen years old. It is causing us to rethink our whole relationship to power. For this awesome power now in the hands of men puts mankind's future in the balance. It is a power which can be used for good or for evil.

Because of this new factor in today's life, the Christian church needs both to have the factual information and to seek to address herself to this new condition in a Christian way. The Peace and Social Concerns Committee of the General Conference Mennonite Church's Board of Christian Service has sought to do this. Dr. Erwin N. Hiebert, associate professor of the History of Science at the University of Wisconsin, presented a lengthy paper to this committee on the nuclear question. His impressive work inspired the decision to publish this book. Further, this effort to face the question of nuclear power brought forth a statement of position regarding nuclear power which was adopted at the 1959 session of the General Conference held at Bluffton, Ohio.

Mr. Hiebert reviews the facts of the development of the atomic bomb and the reactions to this power on the part of scientists, the political community, nations, and the church. From this, one can gain an insight into the moral implications involved.

The author of this work comes eminently qualified for this task. Originally a Canadian, he did undergraduate study at Tabor College and Bethel College in Kansas. During the war he was a research chemist on the Manhattan Project. He did graduate work at the University of Chicago and received his doctorate in chemistry and in the history of science at the University of Wisconsin.   He has taught at San Francisco State College and Harvard University and was a Fulbright visiting lecturer at the Max Planck Institute, Goettingen, Germany.

The Peace and Social Concerns Committee commends this book to your careful study.   It comes from the hands of a scholar deeply concerned about nuclear power and one who can speak with authority.   An informed and sensitive Christian conscience is essential if the church is to speak to the new world being born.

ESKO LOEWEN, CHAIRMAN
PEACE AND SOCIAL CONCERNS COMMITTEE

ACKNOWLEDGMENTS

Of the many friends and colleagues to whom I am indebted for the completion of this work, I should like to single out a few for special mention. Dr. Albert J. Meyer, professor of physics at Goshen College, Goshen, Indiana, and Dr. Frederick J. White of the Knolls Atomic Power Laboratory at Schenectady, New York, have given me both counsel and criticism which was of great value. Dr. James F. Crow, professor of medical genetics at the University of Wisconsin, read an early draft of chapter four and made a number of pertinent suggestions. Father Joseph E. Brown of Madison, Wisconsin, and Mr. Clarence Bauman, European Peace Section representative of the Mennonite Central Committee, Bonn, Germany, supplied information vital to chapter nine. To the members of the Peace and Social Concerns Committee of the General Conference Mennonite Church I am especially grateful. Without their continuing encouragement and support this study would never have been begun or completed. Thanks are also extended to Mr. Maynard Shelly, the associate executive secretary of the Board of Education and Publication, whose efficient and patient editorial assistance and splendid co-operation greatly benefited this book.

It is also a pleasure to acknowledge the indispensable assistance offered by the general secretaries, executive directors, and directors of public relations of a number of church councils and organizations. I must content myself with naming the organizations which they have served so well: World Council of Churches (Geneva); The National Council of the Churches of Christ in the U.S.A.; The American Council of Christian Churches; The National Association of Evangelicals; The National Conference of Christians and Jews, Inc.; The Union of American Hebrew Congregations; The Central Council of American Rabbis; The Catholic Worker; American Friends Service Committee; Brethren Service Committee; Mennonite Central Committee; and the International Fellowship of Reconciliation (London).

To Mrs. Loretta Freiling and Mrs. Nelia Smith I offer my thanks for help in preparing the manuscript.

My wife, Elfrieda Franz Hiebert, has helped in the preparation of this work at every stage, but most of all by providing an environment in which the writing of a book was possible.

Madison, Wisconsin
October, 1960   E.N.H.

CONTENTS

part I

A HALF CENTURY
OF UNPRECEDENTED
ADVANCE IN
ATOMIC ENERGY

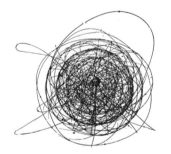

chapter 1

THE SCIENTIFIC AND TECHNOLOGICAL TASK

Toward the end of the nineteenth century, classical mechanics, thermodynamics, and electromagnetic theory had been worked out so completely that many scientists envisaged the future of physical science merely as a refinement of what was already known. Professor A. A. Michelson of the University of Chicago, America's first Nobel prize winner (1907), said in his Lowell Lectures of 1899: "The more important fundamental laws and facts of physical science have all been discovered, and these are now so firmly established that the possibility of their ever being supplanted in consequence of new discoveries is exceedingly remote. . . . Our future discoveries must be looked for in the sixth place of decimals."[1] Ten years later, no scientist would have dared to make such a statement; less than fifty years later, the energy of the nucleus had been released in an atomic bomb.

Before the end of the nineteenth century X rays had been discovered by Roentgen in Germany, natural radioactivity by Becquerel in France, and electrons (as discrete particles of negative charge and small mass) by J. J. Thomson in England. Proof that the electron was a constituent of all atoms gave the first definite line of attack on the constitution of the atom. The alpha particle, which was found to be one of the decay products emitted from radioactive elements, became for Ernest Rutherford, first, the object of study, and then, a tool for the experimental investigation of the nucleus of the atom. By 1911 he was able to argue convincingly that the atom was not a homogeneous blob of matter, but rather that it possessed a dense positively charged nucleus surrounded by electrons.

In 1913 Niels Bohr of Copenhagen proposed a satisfactory planetary model for the hydrogen atom. By 1919 Rutherford

[1]A. A. Michelson, *Light Waves and Their Uses* (Chicago, 1903), pp. 23, 24.

had shown by means of probing alpha particles that the nucleus of an atom could be completely transmuted by head-on impact. Rutherford suggested that this discovery might possibly have a greater effect on the outcome of world events than the war. This suggestion coming from a British scientist working in the seclusion of the Cavendish Laboratory may have sounded preposterous forty years ago, although it no longer seems so today. By 1925 it had been verified that Rutherford had converted nitrogen into oxygen and hydrogen by head-on collisions with alpha particles. The transmutation of one element into another thereafter became quite commonplace.

Some of the things which were being accomplished in physics and chemistry after the First World War were as wild as they could be. These accomplishments initiated changes in theoretical physics which brought a revolution in the definitions of motion, space, energy, and matter. No one seemed to mind the progress of scientific knowledge at that time; no one was aware of the potentially explosive ideas with which scientists were toying. It was, as everyone knew, in political science and sociology that new ideas had caused trouble. The average person did not, after all, claim to know very much about nuclear science, whereas he frequently maintained the right to be considered an expert in politics and human behavior. Since the days of Rutherford's fundamental researches, the steady advancement of nuclear physics and chemistry has opened up vast new areas of investigation which are both marvelous and sinister to contemplate. To be sure, the history of atomic energy is stranger than fiction.

In the early 1930's American scientists at the University of California were designing an electromagnetic machine, the cyclotron, for accelerating fundamental particles such as protons (hydrogen nuclei—so named in 1920), deuterons (heavy hydrogen nuclei—discovered in 1932), and alpha particles. By bombarding various kinds of matter with the accelerated particles from these machines, it was hoped that the projectiles would penetrate into the nuclei of atoms and that a study of the disintegration products would reveal information concerning the detailed structure of the nucleus of various atoms. The experiments, in fact, disclosed a great deal about nuclear structure.

In 1932 James Chadwick, working under Rutherford in Cambridge, discovered that an uncharged particle was emitted when alpha particles collided with the light metal beryllium. This new particle, which was called the neutron, was the last of the three fundamental particles which comprise the basic building blocks of all matter, *i.e.*, electrons, protons, and neutrons. Now, just as alpha particles had been used by Rutherford as projectiles to probe into the nucleus of the atom, so Chadwick's neutrons were to become an even more powerful tool for studying the nucleus.

In the same year Enrico Fermi, working in Rome with essentially no high-powered equipment, but with a great passion for the new nuclear studies, came upon the idea of using Chadwick's newly discovered neutrons to achieve the same objective being sought with the aid of the cyclotron, namely, the study of the nuclei of atoms by means of particle penetration experiments. Fermi was extraordinarily fortunate because neutrons have no electric charge and for that reason are able to wiggle into the nuclei of atoms where protons, deuterons, and alpha particles normally fear to tread. Because his results deviated so radically from what he had expected, Fermi did not know that he had accomplished the fission of uranium. These results were not readily interpreted by Fermi even when he reported them to the Italian Academy of the Lincei in Rome in 1934. He thought he had prepared a new element which did not exist in nature. Later he remarked that neither he nor his colleagues had had enough imagination to think that a different process of disintegration might occur in uranium than in any other element; nor had they known enough chemistry to separate the products of uranium disintegration from one another.

No one had any ideas about nuclear fission at that time. As late as 1936, the year of Rutherford's death, it was argued that the possibility of gaining useful energy by artificial processes of nuclear transformations did not appear to be promising. The new knowledge concerning the behavior of uranium, although exciting to scientists, seemed to elicit only academic interest. Uranium metal at that time had virtually no practical value beyond its use in minute quantities to impart a brilliant yellow color to pottery and glass.

RESEARCH TAKES ON AN INTERNATIONAL CHARACTER

After January 1939 this picture changed almost overnight. Experimental scientists, it was said, were afraid to leave their laboratories over the lunch hour for fear that they would miss witnessing fundamental breakthroughs in nuclear science. Fermi's experiments were repeated and studied in detail around 1937 in various laboratories, but especially under Otto Hahn and Friedrich Strassmann in the radioactivity laboratory of the Kaiser Wilhelm Institute for Chemistry in Berlin-Dahlem— located less than three miles from Hitler's chancellery. Among the products of the reaction, these chemists identified the element barium, the nucleus of which is only half the size of the nucleus of uranium. This was an indication to Hahn, who had once worked on radioactivity with Rutherford in Montreal (1905), that the atom had been split in two.[2] The discovery was announced in *Die Naturwissenschaften* in January 1939.

The correct interpretation of the uranium experiments of Hahn and Strassmann came from two scientists who had taken refuge from the Nazis in other countries. One of these was the Viennese Jewess, a mathematical physicist, Lize Meitner, who had been protected for a number of years by Hahn in Berlin at the Institute. While working on uranium-neutron experiments in Stockholm, Dr. Meitner conceived the idea late in 1938 (after having met Fermi who had just received the Nobel prize and who was on his way to America) that the uranium atom was absorbing the neutron and splitting into roughly equal fragments. Her nephew, Austrian-born Otto Frisch, another refugee, who was then at the Niels Bohr Institute for Theoretical Physics at Copenhagen, came to similar conclusions at the same time. A joint experiment in Copenhagen proved that uranium had split into two nuclei of roughly equal size—barium and krypton. Because of the similarity between the nucleus-splitting experiment and the process by which biological organisms reproduce themselves, the nuclear process was described by Frisch with an expression which had already been used in biology—viz., fission.

Meitner and Frisch promptly communicated their conjecture to the Danish physicist Niels Bohr, who was just preparing to leave for the Institute for Advanced Study at Princeton to discuss theoretical problems with Albert Einstein. The news of uranium fission reached American scientists through a lecture by Niels Bohr in Washington, D. C., in January of 1939. Some physicists left that meeting to test the conclusion in their laboratories even before Bohr had finished his lecture. Within a short time

[2]See Otto Hahn, *New Atoms* (New York, 1950).

the demonstration of large energy pulses due to fission fragments had been verified. Thus, in January 1939 the discovery and interpretation of the fission of uranium, which had been made abroad in November of 1938, was confirmed in the United States. The implications were the release of nuclear energy and the possibility of a neutron chain reaction. By the end of the year, some hundred papers relating to nuclear experiments had been published, and the fissioning of uranium had been verified in Copenhagen, Paris, Berlin, Vienna, Berkeley, New York, Baltimore, and Washington.

Meitner and Frisch first published their interpretations in the British scientific journal *Nature* in February of 1939. The burst of energy accompanying the fission was correctly interpreted by them on the basis of Einstein's mass-energy equation. A letter to *Nature* early in 1939, signed by von Halban, Joliot-Curie, and Kowarski in Paris, reported that the number of neutrons in a solution containing uranium was greater than the number of neutrons which had been introduced into it by immersing a neutron source in it. This suggested that enough extra neutrons were given off in the process to possibly sustain a chain reaction for the fission, once begun. Experiments under Sir George Thomson at the Imperial College of Science in London seemed at this time to indicate the near impossibility of a fission reaction which would be rapid enough to release its energy before pushing the fissioning materials apart. The most distinguished physicists of Germany seemed to have reached the same conclusion. If correct, this notion would have excluded the possibility of a self-sustaining chain reaction; and there would have been no atomic bomb. For ordinary natural uranium their conclusion was valid.

By the end of 1939 German troops occupied Czechoslovakia, and Poland had been invaded. While Germany was engaged in violent pogroms and Europe was generally at war, America, England, France, and Denmark became the homes of an international constellation of atomic scientists who had fled from their countries for reasons of political and religious persecution. Never before, perhaps, had there been such fruitful scientific communication in any one specialized area of science at this high level. The birth of atomic energy was truly brought about by an international effort on the part of scientists and was not, as a common myth would have it, discovered and developed in

the United States during World War II. Any account of even
the most American phases of the history of atomic energy will
bear a remarkable international character. The English, for
example, in spite of the disaster of Dunkirk and the German
mass bombings of English cities, accomplished a great deal between 1939 and 1941. In the final stages, the United States
was aided primarily by scientists from England, Canada, France,
Italy, and Germany, but many smaller countries contributed far
beyond what one would expect from their size.[3]

In March 1940, Peierls and Frisch in England pointed out
that the impossibility of a bomb from ordinary uranium did
not exclude the possibility of a bomb from the lighter uranium
atoms, namely the 235 isotopes of uranium (U-235). The Committee for the Scientific Study of Air Warfare was approached
in March 1940 with a scheme for a bomb. Experiments were
undertaken at Liverpool under James Chadwick, at Birmingham,
and at the Cavendish Laboratory. It was not long thereafter
that atomic research was driven underground in the interests of
the allied war effort, chiefly after the German invasion of France
in June 1940. A number of French scientists had already joined
the British research teams by then; and, just before Paris fell,
Frederic Joliot-Curie (Nobel prize winner with his wife, 1935)
sent his associates von Halban and Kowarski with about 224
pounds of heavy water to England. In July of 1940, R. H.
Fowler was given the assignment of communicating to the
American government the collected British information on nuclear energy.

To return to the history of the atomic energy program in our
own country, we find that in August 1939 Italian-born Enrico
Fermi and two Hungarian scientists, Leo Szilard and Eugene
P. Wigner, had drafted a two-page letter which they persuaded
Albert Einstein to sign. The letter addressed to President Roosevelt drew attention to the fact that the possibility of a nuclear
chain reaction in a large mass of uranium indicated extremely
powerful bombs. As a result of urgent appeals from other
scientists, Roosevelt appointed an Advisory Committee on Uranium to look into the question of a joint allied special atomic
weapons research project. There were some fears at the time

[3]An excellent and eminently fair summary of the part played by European scientists is given by Gordon Dean, former chairman of the AEC,
in his *Report on the Atom* (New York, 1953).

that enemy powers were already actively engaged in atomic research. It was learned later that Hitler's scientists had not been able to convince him of the feasibility of undertaking atomic research in terms of the time which was available. The free exchange of atomic ideas came to a halt in April of 1940, mostly by voluntary censorship on the part of scientists. In June 1940 Roosevelt's Advisory Committee on Uranium was placed under the newly created National Defense Research Council (NDRC). After Pearl Harbor, development of an atomic bomb was given top priority.

ORGANIZATION OF THE MANHATTAN PROJECT

After a number of preliminary scientific tests had gotten under way in various European, Canadian,[4] and American laboratories (primarily at Columbia University and the University of California), the United States government, just before Pearl Harbor in December of 1941, decided to broaden greatly its whole uranium program by transferring the responsibility for these matters to the Office of Scientific Research and Development (OSRD) under a Top Policy Group. By August of 1942 the army had by directive of Secretary of War Henry L. Stimson established a new district in its Corps of Engineers which was named the "Manhattan Engineer District" and which in September was placed under the direction of Major General (then Brigadier General) Leslie R. Groves. A tremendous top secret project was undertaken by this directive, with Oak Ridge, Tennessee (known as "Dogpatch"), and Hanford, Washington, being selected as the sites for processing of isotopes, and Los Alamos, as the place for the bomb development. At Los Alamos, New Mexico, on a mesa twenty miles from Santa Fe and accessible only by a winding country road, Robert Oppenheimer was in charge of 4,500 workers and a 600 million dollar plant which imported incredible quantities of equipment and materials without apparently producing anything to be shipped out.

In the same year, a group of scientists working under the direction of Enrico Fermi (who had left Fascist Italy late in 1938) ushered in the atomic age proper with an *experimentum*

[4]For a summary of Canada's wartime participation in the atomic energy program, see *Bulletin of Atomic Scientists,* Nov. 1947, pp. 325-328, and May 1950, pp. 139-141.

crucis executed in the Metallurgical Laboratory of the University of Chicago and located in the converted squash court beneath the stands of Stagg Field—the football field of a university which under Chancellor Robert M. Hutchins had abolished football. It was there on December 2, 1942, that "man achieved . . . the first self-sustaining chain reaction and thereby initiated the controlled release of atomic energy."[5] This experiment, which showed that a self-maintaining nuclear reaction was possible, marked the turning point in research which resulted in the atomic bomb. It was also on the basis of what was learned here about one "microgram" of the new element plutonium, that the government went ahead with a plant at Hanford, Washington, for the large-scale production and separation of the metal. The original chain reaction pile was so small that on the assumption that one bomb would require 100 kilograms of plutonium, the pile would have to be kept going for seventy thousand years to produce a single bomb.

The accomplishment of this small experimental chain reactor was a major hurdle after which the decision came to forge ahead in a more unified manner in all areas of the project. That first hurdle turned out to be merely the beginning of a long sequence of difficult technical and theoretical problems which demanded almost immediate solution. Industrial and university laboratories and facilities were used in assignments which required highly specialized scientific know-how. Technical personnel from all branches of science and from various parts of the world were recruited by the Manhattan project as quickly as possible and were brought together to work in a relatively small number of laboratories and industrial installations. This was the time, for example, when Niels Bohr was smuggled by fishing boat from Copenhagen to Sweden and from there taken by the Royal Air Force to the United States.

On the Manhattan project, money flowed freely. Raw materials and equipment were channeled in at the highest level of priority. The Manhattan District took precedence over all demands for manpower and materials; two billions in dollars were expended and 120,000 people were engaged directly in the undertaking. Uranium for bombs was produced. Only time was at a premium. Major General Groves has mentioned that

[5]After the war a plaque containing this inscription was erected on the west end of the University of Chicago football stadium.

the bomb was ready six days after enough material was ready for the test. Twenty-four days after the New Mexico test, two bombs had been dropped on Japan. To accomplish the deadlines which the project had set for itself demanded the collaboration of a wide variety of skills—scientific, industrial, political, and military.

On July 1, 1945, two weeks before the first atomic bomb was tested in New Mexico, the United States War Department printed a report by H. D. Smyth, containing the story of the American part of the development of the atomic bomb.[6] Insofar as the national security permitted at the time, the report included the administrative history of the project and the basic scientific knowledge on which the several developments were based. In the general summary we read:

> A weapon has been developed that is potentially destructive beyond the wildest nightmares of the imagination, a weapon so ideally suited to sudden unannounced attack that a country's major cities might be destroyed overnight by an ostensibly friendly power. This weapon has been created not by the devilish inspiration of some warped genius but by the arduous labor of thousands of normal men and women working for the safety of the country. Many of the principles that have been used were well known to the international world in 1940. To develop the necessary industrial processes from these principles has been costly in time, effort, and money, but the processes which we selected for serious effort have worked and several that we have not chosen could probably be made to work. We have an initial advantage in time because, so far as we know, other countries have not been able to carry out parallel developments during the war period. We also have a general advantage in scientific and particularly in industrial strength, but such an advantage can easily be thrown away.[7]

The Smyth report—as it came to be called—was available for distribution in August of 1945 after the bombs had been dropped on Japan. According to this report, "the mass of uranium-235 required to produce explosive fission under appropriate conditions can hardly be less than two kilograms nor greater than 100 kilograms."[8] In other words, the uranium of the atomic bomb weighed somewhere between 4½ and 450 pounds, according to the War Department.

[6]H. D. Smyth, *A General Account of the Development of Methods of using Atomic Energy for Military Purposes under the Auspices of the United States Government 1940-1945* (Washington, D. C., 1945). Much of the factual information presented here is taken from this official report.
[7]Smyth, *loc cit.,* Section 13.2.
[8]Smyth, *loc cit.,* Section 4.49.

We will recognize how extraordinarily fast events moved at the time when we recall that only three years had elapsed between the uranium splitting experiments of Otto Hahn in 1939 in Berlin and Fermi's accomplishment of a controlled chain reaction in 1942 in Chicago. In less than three additional years, two atomic bombs had been released over Japan. Thus, in the course of some four to six years, scientists had realized the large-scale release of nuclear energy which the experiments had suggested in 1939.

It has always been a puzzle that before 1939 scientists could have missed detecting the tremendous amounts of energy which can be released from matter. Albert Einstein wrote in 1946: "The answer is simple enough: so long as none of the energy is given off externally, it cannot be observed. It is as though a man who is fabulously rich should never spend or give away a cent: no one could tell how rich he was."

ENERGY FROM THE LOSS OF MASS

A word of explanation is in order here concerning the expression *atomic energy*. Because the magnitude of energy changes involved in nuclear disintegrations is greater by a factor of over a million than ordinary chemical reactions and most other energy changes with which we are all familiar, it is almost a misnomer to speak of atomic energy as one might speak of mechanical, electrical, or chemical energy. When scientists use the expression *atomic energy,* they are speaking of orders of magnitude which fall completely outside of the "energies" which accompany non-nuclear processes. If, for example, all the atoms in a kilogram (2.2 pounds) of uranium-235 were to undergo fission, the total mass annihilation would be approximately 0.1 per cent of one kilogram, or one gram (.0022 pounds). According to Einstein's equation, this corresponds approximately to the energy liberated by the explosion of 20,000 tons (40,000,000 pounds) of TNT.

Without entering into any of the more technical details here, let us make a summary statement of the natural source materials which can be considered potential fissionable stock, i.e., atomic fuels. Pure uranium (U) as extracted from its ore contains only 0.7 per cent of isotope U-235. This is the only natural occurring uranium isotope which will release large amounts of energy with the neutrons available from the fission process.   The remaining 99.3 per cent of natural uranium, which is predominantly U-238, can be converted, by the absorption of a neutron in the atomic pile, into U-239.   It is unstable and, by losing an electron, decays to form a new element not known in nature, called *neptunium* (Np-239).   This element similarly decays and gives rise to another new element called *plutonium* (Pu-239).

Plutonium is fissionable like U-235.   In addition, thorium-232 (Th-232), which is more abundant in nature than uranium, is a potential fissionable material because it can be converted by the absorption of a neutron into Th-233, which is unstable and decays by the emission of electrons first into protactinium-233 and then into uranium-233.   U-233 in turn is just as fissionable as U-235 and Pu-239.   At the very high neutron "temperatures" of an H-bomb, U-238 can also be made to release large amounts of energy in fission, but this requires a U-235 or a Pu-239 bomb to set off an H-bomb, which in turn causes the otherwise inert and ordinarily nonfissionable U-238 to fission.   Apart from these "fission" reactions, we know today that enormous quantities of energy can also be released in the so-called atomic "fusion," and we must say something about this reaction which has been harnessed in the hydrogen bomb, also called the H-bomb, or the thermonuclear bomb.

A number of years ago, scientists came to the conclusion that the enormous quantities of energy released by the sun could not possibly be accounted for by known processes such as the expansion and contraction of gases or the chemical combustion of fossil fuels.   While the sun's surface temperature was known to be close to 6000 degrees Centigrade, its interior, as well as that of many stars, was believed to be closer to 20 million degrees. Hans Bethe and C. F. von Weizsäcker in 1939 had suggested a sequence of nuclear changes involving hydrogen which theoretically accounted for the large continuing energy output of the sun.   The net over-all result was thought to be the synthesis by fusion of four hydrogen atoms into a single helium atom, with a net loss of mass.   It was reasonable to assume that the light hydrogen atoms, which exist in the sun in superabundance, were combining to form heavier atoms by the thermonuclear process, which, according to the Einstein mass-energy equation, would be accompanied by the release of very large quantities of energy. While the theoretical feasibility of attaining energy from thermonuclear fusion was therefore predicted, there was no conceivable method of producing in the laboratory the 20 million degree temperatures which were necessary in order to start that reaction. The atomic bomb provided such high temperatures. It was accordingly possible to create the conditions of thermonuclear fusion (the H-bomb) by housing hydrogen in a conventional fission A-bomb and allowing the high temperatures (20 million degrees) achieved in the detonation of the A-bomb to set off the thermonuclear reaction.

In practice it turns out that the two heavy isotopes of hydrogen, deuterium, and tritium, combine at somewhat lower temperature in a fusion reaction than ordinary hydrogen. Deuterium is found in nature, and tritium does not occur naturally, but can be made in atomic reactors. Small amounts of a mixture of these elements are sufficient to start the reaction and raise the temperature to the level at which lithium metal will react readily with pure deuterium. Lithium is cheap, deuterium is relatively cheap, and there are almost inexhaustible amounts of the latter available in the oceans, where there is one deuterium atom for every 6,400 ordinary hydrogen atoms.

To summarize what happens in all nuclear reactions, we could say that tremendous amounts of energy are released whenever the heaviest atoms split or "fission" into middle-sized atoms and whenever the lightest atoms combine or "fuse" into middle-sized atoms. In either case, the nuclear processes occur because middle-sized atoms are more stable than either very light or very heavy atoms. To use a crude analogy, heavy atoms, like overgrown empires, are held together only by special effort. They are ripe for dissolution. The unstable light atoms, on the other hand, are like small communities which fuse together to attain mutual stability. Heavy atoms give up their energy by subdivision, while light atoms give up their energy by union. In both cases, fission and fusion, it has been verified experimentally that a loss of mass takes place during the process. The lost mass shows up as energy. The mathematical equation ($E = mc^2$), which predicts the relationship between lost mass "m" and gained energy "E," was already enunciated by Einstein in 1905 when he deduced it as a theoretical consequence of his theory of relativity. The "c" in this equation is the velocity of light. The atomic bombs and the H-bombs are instances in which the equation has been shown to be precisely verified.

GERMANY AND THE ATOMIC BOMB

Before leaving this subject, let us take a look at a number of foreign reactions to the achievement of the release of atomic energy through the Manhattan project.

A recent controversial and intensely stimulating history of atomic science by the German journalist Robert Jungk[9] purports to bring into the clear for the first time a considerable number of hitherto obscure facts and interpretations concerning the earliest phases of European nuclear research in the 1920's and 1930's. It is the story of how the peaceful and academic international pursuits of nuclear scientists were transformed after 1939 into a secret and cruel technology capable of destroying mankind. Jungk suggests that the nuclear scientists heading German uranium research consciously and consistently evaded working on atomic energy projects as a kind of conspiracy against Hitler. It is an established fact, for example, that Max von Laue was an outspoken opponent of the Nazi regime and that he resigned in 1943 from the Kaiser Wilhelm Institute in Berlin where he and a group of scientists were engaged in atomic research. Jungk's book has become the focus of a bitter controversy over the implication that the European scientists exercised a degree of moral sensitivity to atomic bomb research which was all but absent in American scientists who, overcome by the desire to accomplish a brilliant technical achievement, were persuaded into signing a pact with the devil.

Scientists have described Jungk's analysis as a *post factum* rationalization which is devoid of honest evidence that the Germans did sabotage atomic bomb development. In general, American scientists now would agree that the German failure to develop atomic energy was due not to moral scruples on the part of her scientists, but was based on a realistic appraisal of the difficulties involved in developing the atomic bomb as compared, for example, with the almost certain advantage of rockets as a valuable weapon to the war. The physicist Samuel Goudsmit, who led the United States investigation of the German uranium program, has described a number of recordings of the conversations of captured German scientists who had just heard of the Hiroshima explosion.[10] These recordings, made without the

[9]Robert Jungk, *Brighter Than a Thousand Suns* (New York, 1958).
[10]Samuel Goudsmit, *Alsos* (New York, 1947).

knowledge of the scientists, indicated that the Germans had been
unsuccessful in their attempts to make an atomic bomb and had
convinced themselves that it was theoretically impossible. Goudsmit has reported that the German uranium efforts were on a
ludicrously small scale.

On the other hand, one reviewer of Jungk's book, viz., the
physicist Herbert Jehle, has said:

> The most disputed of Jungk's conclusions—his claim that leading Ger-
> man physicists in 1939-1945 deliberately stalled the development of
> German atomic bombs—has been checked and verified by personal
> investigation and inquiry by this reviewer. It was in detail documented
> to this reviewer through K. F. Bonhoefer and Max von Laue, that they
> and Hahn, Heisenberg, von Weizsäcker and Jensen actually did (with
> some differences in motivation), do the best they could to prevent the
> attempt by Hitler's Germany to build atom bombs. They not only
> succeeded in this, but also risked their lives in an unsuccessful attempt to
> convince Niels Bohr in 1941 and 1942 (and through him the Western
> physicists) of the lack of need to develop atomic weapons in the Allied
> world—the urgency of this development of the atom bomb by the Allies
> having been entirely based on the fear of atom bombs being constructed
> in Nazi Germany.[11]

Dr. von Weizsäcker in a recent World Council of Churches
study document has not denied that the Germans were working
on the problem of nuclear energy. He says, "It is true that our
German group then came to know clearly that we would not be
able to make bombs; and that relieved our consciences without
forcing the decision upon us."[12]

In his reply to criticisms of the book, and especially to those
of E. U. Condon's scathing review,[13] Jungk wholeheartedly
endorses Condon's suggestion that a team of historians ought to
write the history of the atomic bomb as soon and as objectively
as possible. When that is done, says Jungk, "I am convinced
that such a team will not only find fault with me but will also
find some merit in my having unearthed some facts which until
now have been buried under the bouquets of professional cour-
tesy and veiled by the mist of nationalistic thinking."[14]

ANGLO-AMERICAN CO-OPERATION

The history of Anglo-American co-operation in the area of

[11]Herbert Jehle, *SSRS Newsletter,* Jan. 1959.
[12]C. F. von Weizsäcker, *Christians and the Prevention of War in an
Atomic Age*—A Theological Discussion, Aug. 27, 1958, p. 12.
[13]E. U. Condon, *Science,* Dec. 26, 1958, p. 1619.
[14]R. Jungk, *Science,* May 1, 1959, p. 1192.

atomic energy is also worthy of our mention here. According to Leonard Bertin, science correspondent of the London *Daily Telegraph*,[15] many British scientists have long entertained some feelings of bitterness toward America for having accepted the aid of foreign atomic scientists without proper recognition and without subsequently making atomic knowledge available to other countries. Bertin's attitude is not rabidly partisan and his account is a sincere presentation of the British side of the controversy over security. According to his argument, America by the end of the war in 1945 possessed a virtual monopoly in the area of atomic energy which was far beyond the stage required for the production of atomic bombs.

Sometime in the fall of 1942 the transatlantic atomic partnership between the United States and Britain broke down. It coincided in time approximately with the appointment of Major General Groves to the Manhattan District. Groves was later accused by some scientists in this country of having hobbled and frustrated the Anglo-American co-operation. A conference in Quebec in 1943 brought the British back into the running again, but only to a limited extent. American politics somehow got in the way of co-operation. Mr. Bertin points out that in 1943, when the possibility of atomic fission seemed highly probable, the British scientists were so upset at being denied access to information that Churchill, who lost his temper over not being consulted in policy matters, sent a strongly worded note to the White House, saying that if atomic data were not shared more fully, England would organize her own research program.

Agreements for postwar exchange of information were reached between Roosevelt and Churchill, but by 1946 Congress had passed legislation prohibiting the release of atomic information to any nation. American legislation through its unilateral termination of collaboration thereafter not only excluded Britain from a fair share of the results of wartime collaboration, but also forced a wartime ally to develop the peacetime aspects of atomic energy on her own at great cost of effort and money. In specific instances, Britain later had to purchase from American industrial concerns some of the ideas which she was responsible for developing during the war. There were some important changes in this situation after the introduction of the atoms-for-peace program

[15]Leonard Bertin, *Atom Harvest, A British View of Atomic Energy* (San Francisco, 1957).

late in 1953. But, unfortunately, by that time England and
other countries such as Norway, France, and the Soviet Union
had already achieved many of the same objectives. England
actually stood in the lead in industrial atomic power. In the
Soviet Union and England, there had been atomic and thermonuclear bomb tests as well.

STATUS OF RUSSIAN ATOMIC RESEARCH IN 1945

There are varying reports of how the Soviet Union learned
about American attempts to produce atomic bombs. None of
them add any more information than Truman's own account.
Truman reports that on July 24, 1945, while at Potsdam, he
casually mentioned to Stalin that the United States "had a new
weapon of unusual destructive force." To this Stalin said merely
that he was glad to hear it and he hoped that the United States
would make "good use of it against the Japanese."[16]

After the first atomic bomb had been dropped on Hiroshima,
Ambassador to Russia Averell Harriman reported, from conversations with Stalin and Molotov, that Stalin had shown "great
interest in the atomic bomb and said that it could mean the end
of the war and aggression, but that the secret would have to be
kept well." Stalin also said at the time that they "had found,
in Berlin, laboratories in which the Germans were working on
the breaking of the atom, but that they did not find that they
had come to any results." Stalin added that "Soviet scientists
had also been working on the problem but had not been able
to solve it."[17]

Such nuclear research as there was in the U.S.S.R. in the
1930's was primarily undertaken by or under the responsibility
of the Russian Academy of Sciences.[18] Indeed, the academy was
the Soviet government's chief co-ordinator for all official scientific investigations. A uranium project was centrally co-ordi-
nated by the academy between 1939 and 1940, but this was
interrupted by the German invasion. It is more than likely,
however, that during the war Soviet industry was taxed to its

[16]Harry Truman, *Memoirs,* Vol. I. *Year of Decisions* (New York,
1955) p. 416.

[17]Truman, *loc. cit.* pp. 425, 426.

[18]There are two main compilations on Soviet achievements in atomic
energy: Arnold Kramish, *Atomic Energy in the Soviet Union* (Stanford,
1959); George A. Modelski, *Atomic Energy in the Communist Bloc*
(Melbourne, 1959).

limit without having to engage in the development of atomic bombs. In this respect the Soviet scientists were very much in the same position as the Germans. They probably could not have proceeded very far on technical grounds even if they had been fully aware of the theoretical feasibility of atomic bombs. Beyond this, military sanction to work in these areas would have been necessary. We know that even with all of its scientific resources and industrial potential the United States managed only to complete the bomb after Germany had already surrendered. During the war, therefore, the Soviet leaders likely were not deeply concerned over America's lead in atomic energy.

Although it has been said that only chance gave the atomic bomb to the West instead of to the Communists and Nazis, there never was an actual atomic weapons race in the early 1940's, as is commonly asserted.

ATOMIC ENERGY—THE OUTCOME OF PURE RESEARCH

Our brief historical resumé of the development of atomic energy in this chapter should help to convince us that the pioneering investigations concerned with the structure of the nucleus were undertaken neither by a group of single-track minds in relentless pursuit of knowledge regardless of social consequences, nor by a clique of cold-blooded, calculating, scientific demons plotting the end of the world in their secluded laboratories. For fifty years, physical scientists studied the structure of the atom. It was the work of ordinary men humbly and earnestly engaged in studying one of the most fascinating and challenging problems on the frontier of physical science.

All of the money in the world combined could not have produced an atomic bomb before 1939. Even a group of superbly trained scientists with high priority on materials and equipment cannot solve any and every technical problem which faces mankind unless there is a scientific understanding of certain fundamental relationships in nature. Basic advances in science are not bought at a cheap price nor at the behest of immediate and mundane objectives. Atomic energy became a reality only after the considerable effort of sustained preliminary investigations which were conceived almost entirely in the minds of scientists engaged in pure research for its own sake. It certainly would be unfair to maintain, as some have, that the scientists who lent their knowledge and skill to the development of atomic energy were led to prostitute their science. Perhaps someone will say that mankind ought to proclaim a moratorium on atomic research for a century or so. How blindly unrealistic that would be, and how utterly impossible in practice in the modern world in which we live!

Any human being who wants to create something new is bound to be some sort of menace. Lord Rayleigh has said that there is no possibility of telling whether the issue of scientists' work will prove them to be fiends or dreamers or angels. We cannot with any degree of certainty predict the character of the technological advances which modern theoretical science will bring about. Nor can we predict the character of the advances in theoretical science which modern technology will bring about.

In the following chapters we shall have an opportunity to examine the circumstances of the connection between pure science and the military use and testing of atomic weapons since 1945. Thereafter we shall consider how the more positive peace-time applications of atomic energy may be balanced off against the potentialities for destruction. The most important point to bear in mind is that atomic energy *per se* is neither good nor evil. The whole problem, we shall discover, is tremendously complicated by the fact that the military and peacetime uses of atomic energy are not easily and sharply divided. The concept of atomic energy for war, and the concept of atomic energy for peace are oversimplified concepts which do not lead to any easy and unambiguous course of action. But that is no excuse for unconcern or complacency.

Although much has been said about the atom in magazines, newspapers, and popular books and pamphlets on the subject, it is questionable whether the facts and implications have really sunk in. Some of us have witnessed the birth of the atomic age, but it is surprising how easily we forget recent events of great importance. Santayana has said that "those who cannot remember the past are condemned to repeat it." We hope that the future has some lessons to learn from the past, and that in the area of atomic energy there are some experiences which mankind would scarcely choose to relearn by repetition. Some historical accounts, we would maintain, should teach moral principles and political wisdom. Lord Bolingbroke said that history is "philosophy teaching by example."

chapter 2

MILITARY ASPECTS OF ATOMIC ENERGY IN WORLD WAR II

The atomic bomb was not a chance product of an overactive imagination. It was a by-product of the scientific and engineering developments which form the basis of our technologically oriented twentieth century. The discovery and control of methods of rearranging the protons and neutrons inside the nucleus of the atom was accompanied by the release of energies which exceed by a factor of a million the energies of chemical reactions of fossil fuels like coal and oil upon which the industrial civilization of the nineteenth century was built. The fact that atomic energy was first developed and made use of as a military weapon was an accident of history which we want to examine.

On the whole, we should recognize that various individuals who were responsible for making the high-level decisions and who were calling the shots in our government before and during the war were motivated according to what must have seemed the wisest long-range policy for their country in terms of the circumstances.[1] Indeed, the records show that presidents, secretaries of defense, and generals frequently gave their official support to undertakings concerning which they personally had grave misgivings. Responsible public servants enmeshed in the machinery of government would hardly be representing the total concensus of opinion of the people and of their cabinets and advisory experts if they were to attempt to act solely on the basis of their own beliefs and opinions. If they did, their action would be dictatorial. It is easy to criticize in retrospect. It is not so easy to dogmatically insist that any one of us in the same situation would have been able to radically change the course of events in order to conform to our own ideals.

[1]See e.g., "The story General Marshall told me. Hitherto unpublished views on fateful decisions of World War II," *U. S. News* & *World Report,* Nov. 2, 1959, pp. 50-56.

Nineteen-forty-five was the atomic bomb year. In February of that year the Big Three—Roosevelt, Churchill, and Stalin—met at Yalta to plan the final defeat and occupation of Germany. It is unlikely that anyone at Yalta was counting on the use of atomic bombs to bring the war with Germany to a close. In fact, it is not certain that Roosevelt ever mentioned the atomic bomb project to Stalin—although there were private sessions between Roosevelt and Stalin during which such matters could have been aired. Available evidence points to the contrary.

By the end of April 1945, President Roosevelt was dead, Mussolini had been executed, and Hitler had committed suicide. The war with Japan was still on. Truman was totally unaware of the Manhattan project when he inherited the presidency on April 12, 1945. It was a miracle, he thought, that so vast an enterprise (100,000 persons) had been kept secret even from the members of Congress. Momentous decisions were reached at top-secret and high-level discussions during the four months leading up to Hiroshima.[2] The precariousness of those days for President Truman are revealed in scattered remarks in his *Memoirs*. "Being a President," he said, "is like riding a tiger. A man has to keep on riding or be swallowed."[3]

Military men high in command were convinced at this stage of the war that nothing short of an enormous invasion of the Japanese mainland would end the war. Most of the military knew nothing about the Manhattan project. Massive bombing raids on the Japanese were in progress, but Intelligence estimates placed the strength of the Japanese at five million well equipped men—two million in the home islands, two million in Korea, China, Formosa, and Manchuria, and one million scattered elsewhere. The Japanese had lost their naval and air superiority in the Pacific theater, but the raids of their suicide pilots (kamikaze) were on the increase.

DELIBERATE, PREMEDITATED DESTRUCTION

During May and June an Interim Committee of military officials and scientists was called together by Secretary of War

[2]For a day by day account of events just prior to Hiroshima, see Michael Amrine, *The Great Decision, the secret history of the atomic bomb* (New York, 1959).
[3]Harry Truman, *Memoirs,* Vol. 2, *Years of Trial and Hope* (New York, 1956), p. 1.

Henry L. Stimson to discuss general atomic policy, and more specifically to decide whether and how the atomic bomb was to be used against the Japanese. Stimson was then already deeply concerned about the postwar relations with Russia. He had thought long enough about the potential atomic weapon to wonder how it would "appear in the long view of history." General George C. Marshall felt that he personally would be opposed to using the new weapon against the Japanese if the United States felt that it could keep the bomb a secret after the war. Later, in Berlin, the commander-in-chief of the combined forces in Europe, General Dwight D. Eisenhower, expressed much the same opinion. Dr. Karl T. Compton, a member of the committee, raised the question of the possibility of arranging a nonmilitary demonstration with the intention of showing the Japanese the uselessness of continuing the war. There were serious technical difficulties involved with that alternative, not the least of which was the uncertain character of delivering a bomb at an announced time to a specified place with the sure knowledge that its intricate mechanism would really work. Even if successful, would Japan's fanatic militarists be sufficiently convinced to stop the war?

The committee voted for the military use of the bomb, but Stimson had not yet accepted that decision as final.[4] Scientists on the Manhattan project were working up some rather strong feelings on the question of the use of the bomb at about this time.[5] Fleet Admiral William D. Leahy, the president's personal chief of staff, when informed about the potential atomic weapon through James F. Byrnes, was highly dubious about the whole thing. In any case, he regarded the alleged potential destructiveness of such weapons contrary to the civilized laws of war. The British, it seems, were not consulted at all about atomic policy, but on July 4, 1945, Churchill sent a message containing the formal British consent to use the bomb. The records show that Churchill approved of the military use of the atomic bomb from the start. He had even gone over the question of atomic policy matters with his political opponent, Clement Attlee of the Labor Party, before the latter replaced him at the Potsdam conference.

Three weeks after the United Nations Organization charter

[4]Henry L. Stimson and McGeorge Bundy, *On Active Service in War and Peace* (New York, 1948), Chap. XXIII.
[5]This subject is discussed in chapter 8.

had been signed, the first atomic bomb was tested on July 16, 1945, at Alamogordo Air Base, 120 miles southeast of Albuquerque, New Mexico. According to the Smyth report, the detonation was followed by a huge multicolored surging cloud which boiled with tremendous power to an altitude of over 40,000 feet in about five minutes. During the time of the test, the president and his advisers were in Potsdam for the last of the Big Three wartime conferences. The atmosphere was quite different from that of Yalta. An atomic bomb had been successfully exploded. With Truman in place of Roosevelt, and Clement Attlee taking over Churchill's position after the latter's defeat in Britain's parliamentary elections of July 23, Generalissimo Stalin remained as the only member of the original Big Three.

The Potsdam Declaration on July 26 invited Japan to surrender. The invitation was rejected by Japan on July 28. Nothing seemed to remain but to use the atomic bomb. It was argued that this would give the Japanese emperor an excuse for ending the war. Scientists by that time had sent a number of alternative suggestions to Washington. To this day no one quite knows by whom and when these suggestions were examined. Time was too short for negotiations, and atomic bombs were too rare. The number of atomic bombs possessed by the Allies was top secret at the time, but early in 1947 it was revealed by Stimson that "the two atomic bombs which we had dropped were the only ones we had ready and our rate of production at the time was very small."[6]

The temptation to make a final show of strength must have been almost irresistible. Undoubtedly there were thoughts about retribution for Pearl Harbor. Might the army have felt that the success of a two billion dollar project had to be exploited? Some day the circumstances may be known. Much vital information which is still secret would be needed to reconstruct the whole picture. Stimson wrote in 1947: "The decision to use the atomic bomb was a decision that brought death to over a hundred thousand Japanese. No explanation can change that fact and I do not wish to gloss it over. But this deliberate, premeditated destruction was our least abhorrent choice."[7]

[6]Henry L. Stimson, *Harper's Magazine,* Feb. 1947, p. 105. This article contains a careful record of Stimson's personal connections with the decision of the U.S. to use the atomic bomb against Japan.
[7]Stimson, *Ibid.,* p. 107.

Three weeks after the test explosion in New Mexico and four days after the termination of the conference in Potsdam, one airplane, the Enola Gay, a B-29 manned by eleven men, left from the tiny island of Tinian located among the Marianas in the Pacific. To avoid premature detonation, the atomic bomb was not assembled until the plane was in the air. Two observation planes followed. On Monday morning, August 6, while Truman was in mid-Atlantic returning to America aboard the U.S.S. Augusta from Potsdam, the atomic bomb was dropped over Hiroshima at an altitude of 31,600 feet. It exploded when it reached a height of 2,000 feet.[8]

The bomb, whose fissile material was uranium 235, was equivalent to 20,000 tons of TNT. Fifty thousand people were killed immediately and at least that many lingered over death as lethal gamma radiation took its final toll. Four and one-tenth square miles out of seven were completely obliterated—in all, 160,000 people were killed and injured, 200,000 rendered homeless. Why had Hiroshima been singled out? American Intelligence reports had it that 40,000 troops were making their military headquarters there, although this figure has never been substantiated.

Soon after the bomb, word reached Washington that the prepared statements should be released to the press. Truman announced by radio on August 6: "It is an atomic bomb. It is the harnessing of the basic power of the universe. The force from which the sun draws its power has been loosened against those who brought war to the Far East." Albert Einstein, who had been deeply concerned that the potential locked up in the atom be used for human good, and who had allowed his name to be used in 1939 to convince President Roosevelt of the military value of atomic energy, was horrified when the Americans dropped the first bomb on Hiroshima.

The Hiroshima bomb was followed by regular bombing attacks and the dropping of millions of leaflets with a special message to the Japanese people. The message announced the explosiveness of the newly developed atomic bombs and outlined the consequences of an "honorable surrender." It was suggested that steps be taken to cease all military resistance,

[8]See the report of Merle Miller and Abe Spitzer, *We Dropped the A-bomb* (New York, 1946).

otherwise, we shall resolutely employ this bomb and all our
other superior weapons to promptly and forcefully end the war."

While the Japanese Supreme War Council was in session, the
same air force mission was repeated over Nagasaki, the home of
the Mitsubishi Works. Kokura had been the number two target
on the list of cities to receive an atomic bomb, but three unsuccessful attempts to find a hole in the clouds through which to
drop the bomb on that city were followed up by a trip to Nagasaki where the sky was found to be clear. That was on August
9, three days after Hiroshima, while Truman was still aboard
the Augusta; it was the day after Russia had declared war on
Japan and had invaded Manchuria. This second bomb, whose
fissile material was plutonium 239, exhausted the total Allied
stockpile of atomic weapons in 1945. We see that the American
threat of a resolute employment of atomic bombs could not have
been carried out beyond this point.

WE HAVE SOWED THE WHIRLWIND

Japan offered to surrender on August 14. Three weeks after
the Potsdam Declaration, the war was over, and the United
States stood in the position of world leadership. American science
was the bastion of a powerful and victorious nation. The two
atomic bombs, even if they had not ended the war by defeating
Japan (since that, in a sense, had already been accomplished),
did provide an excuse and the occasion to draw the combat to a
close. We do not know whether the Japanese would have
surrendered on terms satisfactory to the Allies within a three-
week interval if the atomic bombs had not been used. It is
understandable that various military services should feel that the
atomic bomb had diverted attention from the more important
but less spectacular contributions to the war's end. Officials
who had a hand in planning military strategy in the Pacific
Theater have been divided as to whether the atomic bombs
added to the over-all war effort. Some have felt that it merely
brought Russia into the war. The opinion has also been voiced
that the atomic bombs forced Russia prematurely into an all-out
military atomic energy program. But these are all uncertain
and conjectural retrospections. There is no end to the number
of "if" questions that can be raised in connection with the events
of history, but most such discussions are not very profitable.

It can hardly be disputed that it was a rude thrust into international morality which took place above Hiroshima and Nagasaki within a span of three days. Neither city could really have been very important as a military target. In retrospect, it would even seem somewhat cynical to justify the American claim that the atomic bomb shortened the war, especially in light of other alternatives which scientists on the Manhattan project had suggested. The Japanese, it seems, would have surrendered somewhat sooner if they had been given earlier assurance that their emperor would be respected even though the government was to be changed. The majority of Japan's warships had been sunk, and the lifeblood of her economy was severely crippled through loss of merchant vessels. Her air force was decimated and her army, though large, was broken down in Burma and scattered in China. Russia was poised close at hand and ready to pounce on her with all of her strength. The U.S. Strategic Bombing Survey estimated that certainly prior to December 31, 1945, and in all probability prior to November 1, 1945, Japan would have surrendered without the atomic bomb, even if Russia had not entered the war, and even if no invasion had been undertaken. In any case, it is almost impossible to envision what kind of coercive necessity would have motivated the Allies to strike Nagasaki before the Japanese War Council had sufficient time to consider the proposed "honorable surrender."

It has been argued that America's daily war expenditure was about 250 million dollars at that time. If the two atomic weapons used on Japan shortened the war by as much as ten days and saved $2\frac{1}{2}$ billion dollars, this would have been sufficient to write off the total cost of the wartime Manhattan project. Perhaps it was to save American lives. That may have been true, if one accepts the military estimate that to quell the Japanese resistance man to man might have required the loss of a million American lives and half that number of British. One must suppose that the most convincing argument for the use of a second atomic bomb was to show Japan that the Allies really meant business.

The fact remains that the surprise attack with atomic weapons not only demolished two cities, but as we have learned since, also shattered the moral authority of the United States. For, if the bombing was an unnecessary tragedy which might have been avoided, certainly the United States had laid bare the question

of its moral prestige.   Hiroshima and Nagasaki were camps of
unprecedented and sudden mass murder, and the hideous spec-
tacle of lingering radiation deaths provided material for horrid
tales.   Hanson W. Baldwin, of the *New York Times,* said the
day after Hiroshima: "[The atomic bomb's] use will probably
save American lives, may shorten the war materially, may even
compel Japanese surrender.   Yet when this is said, we have
sowed the whirlwind . . . we have been the first to introduce a
new weapon of unknowable effects which may bring us victory
quickly but which will sow the seeds of hate more widely than
ever. . . ."[9]

In 1956 a Joint U.S. Commission for the Investigation of the
Effects of the Atomic Bomb in Japan issued a six-volume medical
research report with its statistical findings and their bearing on
continuing studies of the effects of damaging radiation on living
organisms.   These volumes include a report on the anatomical
findings, histological notes, case histories, and laboratory examinations of patients by autopsy.   Included also are studies of the
effect of blast, heat, and ionizing radiation, as well as of the
factors influencing the catastrophe, density and distribution of
populations, and the effects of follow-up medical care and facilities, for example, in pregnancy termination studies. The ultimate
purpose of these studies, it was stated, was to obtain more
information on the potential effects of atomic weapons so as to
provide some of the facts necessary for planning sound national
defense.   The work of this commission, which has been carried
out jointly by United States and Japanese scientists for the past
fifteen years, has been financed by the Atomic Energy Commission.   By 1960 about 160,000 persons in Hiroshima and
Nagasaki were still registered with the government as "survivors"
eligible for free medical care, should any radiation effects develop.

PSYCHOLOGICAL DEVASTATION

In Chapter 4 we shall discuss both the pathological and the
more subtle long-range genetic effects of radiation which accompany the use of nuclear weapons.   There is another type of
reaction which was experienced by the Japanese in 1945.   This
has to do with the emotional impact of the atomic bomb.   Studies
of the aftermath of atomic disaster were carried out in consider-

[9]H. W. Baldwin, *New York Times,* Aug. 7, 1945.

able detail in morale surveys in Hiroshima and Nagasaki. The various reactions of fear, aggression, neurosis, disorganized action, and demoralization which were evoked in these atomic catastrophes have proved to have some important implications for the student of general behavioral theory, especially as related to the basic processes of adjustment which operate under conditions of dire emotional tension.[10]   One of the most common reactions expressed by atomic survivors, for example, was that of direct personal involvement.   This was in marked contrast to all other types of conventional bombings where many people had the feeling, after it was all over, of having been relatively detached bystanders who merely observed what was happening to the rest of their fellow men.   In atomic blasts, by contrast, there has always been an experience of intense personal involvement.

Apart from the shock of an absolutely complete surprise explosion with no warning, the most damaging psychological experience to the survivors of Hiroshima and Nagasaki was that of trying to leave the bombed area.   Whereas the initial reactions were most frequently those of complete personal involvement, most survivors suffered additional intense emotional trauma during the process of trying to flee the area when they discovered that they were passing severely burned, dead, and maimed bodies everywhere.   The would-be escapee then, supposing that he was walking into the central area of the blast, would frequently turn completely around and flee the other way only to experience the same horrid sights.   In the aftermath, reactions of fear persisted and were frequently accompanied by exaggerated efforts to ward off all minor novel types of suspected danger. Anxiety-laden rumors circulated.   Sustained reactions of depression were common.   Psychologists who have studied these atomic bomb experiences have expressed the opinion that the psychological impact of nuclear attacks in the future may well be as great or greater for man than the physical devastation.

Some attempt has also been made to study the equally important social impacts and repercussions upon the total urban populations and the industry of Hiroshima and Nagasaki.   F. C. Iklé, for example, has subjected the total behavioral pattern of popu-

[10]See Irving L. Janis, *Air War and Emotional Stress, psychological studies of bombing and civilian defense* (New York, 1951).

lation groups in the bombed cities to an objective demographic study.[11]   Iklé was mainly concerned with the adaptive processes of a society which has suffered from nuclear bombing, and with the rehabilitation of destroyed cities in the months and years following the disaster rather than in the first few hours after an attack.

Talk about Keeping "The Secret"

Truman's announcement in 1945 carried to the world the news of such a revolutionary weapon that experts in military strategy declared almost immediately that it would no longer suffice to out-produce the enemy in numbers of weapons.   It was said that 500 bombs would be better than 100, but that 50,000 would not be much better than 5,000, since 5,000 could destroy all important targets in any country.   The implication was obvious.   Even a relatively poor nation might in future cripple a large nation by attacking first.

If we have already asserted elsewhere that no atomic bomb was possible before 1939, we should hasten to add here that after 1939 any government which could afford the "luxury" of an army or navy could also afford to manufacture and to deliver atomic bombs.   Since that included most governments, it definitely presented a serious threat to the one nation which had hoped somehow to be able to hang on to the new knowledge and to monopolize it indefinitely.   Could it be that the knowledge of atomic energy would ever become common property in the rest of the world?   Then it would not lie outside of the range of possibility that some day the fury of atomic bombs could rain down upon the cities of the nation which had perfected them.   Therefore, to prevent such an occurrence it was obligatory to positively keep the atomic bomb a guarded secret so that no other nation, large or small, might attain the position of military advantage of an arsenal of atomic bombs.

Even before Japan had surrendered, President Truman announced on August 10 that the secret of the bomb had to be kept.   He stated in his address: "The atomic bomb is too dangerous to be loose in a lawless world.   That is why Great Britain and the United States, who have the secret of its produc-

---

[11]F. C. Iklé, *The Social Impact of Bomb Destruction* (Norman, Okla., 1958).

tion, do not intend to reveal the secret until means have been found to control the bomb so as to protect ourselves and the rest of the world from the danger of total destruction."[12]   As prime minister of the United Kingdom, Clement Attlee pledged his support.

The Russian newspaper *Izvestia* minimized the importance of the atomic bomb in winning the war.   Before long, the Russian *New Times* urged the pooling of knowledge regarding atomic energy and assailed the American press for advocating world control through the bomb.   Stimson assumed that the Russians would sooner or later develop the atomic bomb, and so he urged that the Russians be approached with some practical solution to the control of atomic energy which would not irretrievably embitter her.   He recognized the vital political importance of the bomb and felt that moves such as exchange of information were worth the risk involved.   In his September 11, 1945, Memorandum for the President, Stimson wrote:

If we fail to approach them [the Russians] now and merely continue to negotiate with them, having this weapon rather ostentatiously on our hip, their suspicions and their distrust of our purposes and motives will increase.   It will inspire them to greater efforts in an all-out effort to solve the problem.   If the solution is achieved in that spirit, it is much less likely that we will ever get the kind of covenant we may desperately need in the future.   The risk is, I believe, greater than the other, inasmuch as our objective must be to get the best kind of international bargain we can—one that has some chance of being kept and saving civilization not for five or twenty years, but forever.[13]

The confusion of late 1945, however, did not permit that kind of a political approach, for to share knowledge concerning atomic energy was synonymous then with sharing the most cherished of military secrets.   There was much talk about the "absolute weapon," the obsolete character of conventional armies and weapons, and world government as the only alternative to destruction.   In a press conference late in 1945, Truman stated the opinion that only the United States had the industrial capacity and resources necessary to produce the bomb.   He also made it clear that the United States would not give any nation the engineering "know-how" to produce atomic bombs.

[12]*New York Times,* Aug. 10, 1945.
[13]Stimson, *On Active Service,* p. 644.

THE PROPHETS WERE WRONG

Among atomic scientists who had been on the Manhattan project, the most common reaction was that atomic science would not remain secret for long, and that our country's atomic leadership would therefore be only temporary. Scientists were worried lest an understandable but misguided zeal in protecting our atomic monopoly would only retard further American discoveries and some day leave our country hugging an obsolete weapon. It was feared that Congress would fail to understand that a more liberal policy of divulging atomic information would help our country even more than Russia.

Professor Thorfin Hogness, who had been the director of the chemical laboratory of the pultonium project, wrote in October 1945:

> The atomic bomb has opened Pandora's box and instead of returning to the good old days, as we had hoped, we shall be forced to live in a period of anxiety and fear. . . . From everywhere we hear, "Let us keep the secret to ourselves and thus secure our own position" . . . It has been repeatedly stated that there is no secret to be kept, but to a social scientist, an economist, a lawyer, a statesman, a lawmaker, to the layman, that statement does not make sense because the secret was so well kept during the war period. . . . By withholding . . . basic scientific information we shall force other countries to inaugurate such extensive research programs that they may easily surpass us in a relatively few years. Since our own scientific advance demands free exchange of information and ideas we cannot lose by releasing pure scientific information. . . . Can we bring about international accord by keeping scientific facts secret, temporarily assuming the leading position through fear, and aggravating those with whom we must eventually come to a common understanding? . . . The first step should be that of releasing the basic scientific nuclear information we possess. Through science which has always been international, we can make our initial gesture of good will, thereby contributing to the security of future generations of Americans. The only defense against the atomic bomb is not secrecy, but the creation of international good will and faithful agreement that there shall be no more wars. We who now own the bomb must take the lead.[14]

Before the end of 1945, sixty-four members of the University of Chicago faculty petitioned President Truman to renounce secrecy and to formulate statesmanlike plans regarding the bomb. Sir Henry Maitland Wilson stated brashly that under almost any conditions the Soviet Union would have the secret of the

[14]Thorfin R. Hogness, "Science cannot be secret," *The University of Chicago Magazine,* Oct. 1945, pp. 3-6.

atomic bomb within five years. General Groves insisted that it would take any other nation the equivalent of ten to twenty years to try and duplicate the work which had been accomplished by the Manhattan project under the exigencies of a war. Some politicians stated that they could see no possibility of an industrially backward Russia becoming an atomic power within the foreseeable future. Had the atomic bomb not reduced Russia to a second-rate military power overnight? Atomic scientists boldly stated that the atomic bomb might be developed by the Soviets at least by 1952. Scientists in Chicago and Oak Ridge banded together to proclaim that, since the United States would have no enduring monopoly, world control of atomic energy should be urged.

Almost all the prophets were wrong, and everybody was caught off guard, including many nuclear experts, when the Soviets exploded nuclear bombs in Russia in less than four years after the first American bomb and three years before the first British bomb. So the "big secret" was no longer a secret by 1949. Then in 1953 it was announced, and the Atomic Energy Commission confirmed it, that a thermonuclear weapon, namely an H-bomb, had been detonated somewhere in the Soviet Union. The United States and Russia had produced H-bombs within less than one year of each other. Twelve years after Hiroshima, the Russians put their first Sputnik into outer space, and thereby demonstrated the advanced state of their technology in aeronautics and rocketry. Thereafter, there was virtually no more talk about the Soviet Union being a second-rate and backward industrial nation. These events established Russia as a leading atomic and military power.

SCIENTISTS DETEST SECRECY

A few final critical remarks are in order concerning the overall achievement of the Manhattan project with the military while under the cloak of wartime secrecy. Our first point has to do with the well-known fact that there were a good number of scientists who came out of their wartime experience with a strong anti-military bias and with the resolution to steer clear of future government projects placed under military control. Much of this attitude can be traced back to the individual scientist's distaste for a degree of secrecy to which they were totally unaccustomed in their normal work. The release of the Smyth

Report of 1945 temporarily pacified the majority of scientists, even though there were subsequent military and congressional objections to its having been published.

It would be unrealistic to deny that certain vital types of information concerning weapons and counter measures ought to be kept secret in wartime in the interest of national security. But the basic principles and laws of science from which specific applications are drawn can hardly be expected to remain unknown very long. At some point, which it would be difficult to define, the military advantages of freely shared information between scientists will outweigh the dangers of information leaking out to an enemy. During the war it took two and a half years of daily suspicion and double talk on the part of an organized Counter-intelligence Corps to keep the atomic bomb from becoming prematurely famous. Certain penalties had to be paid for that secrecy. The long-kept total secret of the atomic bomb came upon the public as a surprise so suddenly and so dramatically with the end of hostilities that it was natural to conclude that no one else in the world had thought about problems in nuclear physics, let alone harnessing the atom for destruction. It was an American invention, no less.

What actually had been secret? Technological and production data mostly, but not a great deal of basic science. Even most graduate students in physics and chemistry had been exposed to the major advances in nuclear science before 1940, not only in America, but in Russia, Japan, India, and elsewhere. From the standpoint of our country's position in the eyes of the rest of the world, it does not seem in retrospect to have been very wise to act as if we were going to sit tight on the "secrets" of atomic energy, even if we were not in fact doing so.

The secrecy conditions under which scientists had chafed during the war developed into something much worse a number of years after the war. It was then that the notion of "the secret of the atomic bomb," after having been kicked around as a political football, came to be a rigidly accepted fact in the minds of the general public. There followed an ugly period of humiliation and public dissection of certain scientists for reasons allegedly connected with the question of security. It set a precedent for a new high in suspicion and distrust of scientists in the minds of the American public. This suspicion took the form of a common notion that well-meaning scientists would somewhere in loose talk give away the great secret of the atomic bomb. Or, what was even worse, that espionage agents would lay their hands on the vital atomic information and convey that information to foreign governments—even to Allies with whom we had but yesterday been linked together in a life and death struggle against the Nazi tyranny. It was the Soviet Union, no less, whose ultimate intentions against all capitalistic countries were becoming less trustworthy day by day. In that kind of an atmosphere, it seemed quite logical to believe that the secret of the atomic bomb had leaked out to the Russians especially when, in 1949, it became an established fact that atomic bombs had been detonated in the Soviet Union.

Scientists felt quite different about this. Shortly after the first atomic explosion in Russia, Professor Frederick Seitz of the University of Illinois and former Director of the Training Program at Oak Ridge, said, "If all of the knowledge which we possess today were relegated to the absolute 'security of the grave' so that it could not come to the eyes or ears of the prying Russian agent, the Russians would still come into possession of all of this knowledge in a relatively short time as a result of routine scientific and engineering investigation."[15]

We know that there were serious leaks of important atomic information through espionage agents operating in Canada and the United States. There were chiefly two British scientists, Klaus Fuchs (released from jail in the summer of 1959 and now deputy director of the East German nuclear research station near Dresden) and Alan Nunn May, the American David Greenglass, and Fermi's one-time colleague, the Italian Bruno Pontecorvo. These men had the requisite scientific background to operate with great advantage for the Soviet underground, especially since they had access to top-secret atomic bomb information. Nevertheless, even when all this is taken into account, it seems that the Soviet scientists possessed the capability of developing all important areas of atomic research on their own without any espionage information. It may well be that the most important information obtained by the Soviet scientists from the Manhattan project was the knowledge that certain processes and approaches and not others were feasible. According to the United States Joint Committee on Atomic Energy, the combined activity of spies

[15]Frederick Seitz, *Bulletin of Atomic Scientists,* Oct. 1949, p. 266.

advanced the Soviet atomic program by eighteen months at a
minimum.[16]   Scientists have generally judged that estimate to
be exaggerated and have pointed to the simple fact that the
mere announcement of the possibility of an atomic bomb was
the one most important piece of information for Soviet success.
In addition, we know that the official Smyth Report contained
a great deal of vital information concerning the various methods
of separating fissionable isotopes from uranium.

Security and secrecy are by no means always complementary
to one another even from the standpoint of military advantage.
We have learned that concealment does not necessarily insure
security, and that the short-term advantages of secrecy may often
be unimportant by comparison with the value of unhampered
and freely declassified information both from the standpoint of
accelerated scientific progress at home and because political
maturity at this level can set a precedent in international good
will and understanding.

We have also seen that our nation's technical superiority has
been seriously called into question by Russian peacetime thermonuclear reactor research, no less than by H-bombs and Sputniks.
Perhaps no modern nation can any longer hope to retain a
monopoly in scientific and technological achievement for any
great length of time.   That may be a good thing.   It may constitute man's greatest hope for a solution to the current mid-
century crisis, which was begun by the innocent investigations
of scientists in the 1930's.   As Louis J. Halle maintains: "It may
be better for new dilemmas to announce themselves by clattering
at the front door than to insinuate themselves slowly into the
premises and take possession while asleep."[17]

DISCOVERIES GREATER THAN ATOMIC ENERGY

Our second point deals with the question of the peculiar
circumstances under which atomic energy came to be developed.
When one reviews the phenomenal successes of the gigantic,
freely-financed and systematically organized research endeavors
of the Manhattan project, it is easy to arrive at the conclusion
that the discovery and development of atomic energy in the
twentieth century represents an achievement so unique that it

[16]*Soviet Atomic Espionage* (Washington, D. C., 1951).
[17]Louis J. Halle, *Choice for Survival* (New York, 1958), p. 15.

renders previous scientific accomplishments pale by comparison. To the historian of science this seems questionable. We have already mentioned that the initial and fundamental discoveries that led to atomic energy were made mostly by academic men with superb mental capacities and by working with rather simple equipment in an ingenious way. The motivations for doing these experiments could hardly have come from trying to satisfy any of the social or utilitarian needs of the communities in which the scientists were working. Enormous research funds by themselves would have been of little value. Without the fundamental research of countless investigators working mostly without utilitarian directives, there would have been small chance of the discoveries which led to the release of nuclear energy.

It is difficult, in fact, to see that the pioneers of atomic science were motivated by anything more than an intense scientific curiosity concerning the structure of matter or by the passionate compulsion to investigate the physical and chemical properties of the heaviest elements known to man. The really basic discoveries in nuclear physics were made in the 1890's, in 1905, the 1920's, and 1939. The wartime project was mostly a frantic and ruthless exploitation of what was known prior to 1940. It is conceivable that the means of releasing atomic energy would not have been developed in our day if the political, social, and cultural atmosphere had not been conducive to it. Perhaps our whole modern scientific technology is the more basic factor rather than any one product of that development such as the atomic bomb.

The important point is that the discovery and development of atomic energy as a science came about by conditions essentially no different from many discoveries of previous centuries. The discovery of the energy of the atom was as inevitable in the course of man's history as the discovery of microscopic organisms in a drop of rain water, or, of moons revolving about the planet Jupiter. Inevitable—but not without the intellectual and instrumental equipment of modern science.

Beyond the question of the extent to which the discovery of nuclear science was speeded up by the exigencies of the wartime effort, we might also raise the question whether the discovery itself will be more unique in the future annals of science than other discoveries which have been completely taken for granted by the twentieth century. The unleashing of atomic energy and man's leap into outer space are such spectacular events that they have overshadowed quieter revolutions which are taking place daily in the world of science. But to every age the events new to it are so distorted as to seem larger than the events of the past. Modern man is presumably no less myopic concerning things close at hand than the man of the past, and it is too much to demand of him an objectivity which can rid itself of all bias in the writing of events which are still taking place and concerning which he is both awed and frightened.

There is no objective standard by which to compare the significance of the steam engine with the airplane, and it would be difficult to compare the long range importance of the release of atomic energy with, say, modern synthetic organic chemistry. Revolutionary importance was not attached to the use of gunpowder in Europe until some centuries after its invention. In the fifteenth century no one was quite aware of the revolution which would one day come through the widespread use of the then-known invention of movable type. To use a modern example, we might suggest that future generations may judge that the discovery of a method to trap solar energy for power was vastly more important to man that the controlled release of nuclear energy by the processes of fusion and fission combined.

After all that has been said about the tremendous amounts of energy released by atomic fission and fusion, we must still recognize that the amount of solar energy reaching the earth daily is vastly greater than the total amounts of energy released in all of the atomic bombs which have ever been detonated. We need only be reminded here that the earth receives from the sun, in only three days, as much energy as could be obtained by burning all our reserves of fossil fuel. For that matter, the magnitude of energies connected with natural phenomena such as tornadoes and earthquakes is also much greater than that of atomic bombs, even though the latter have been known to significantly cut down radio reception, cause bright artificial aurora, and temporarily change the earth's magnetic field.

Our century has seen basic research investigations in physical science not only into atomic structure and nuclear and solar power, but into electromagnetism in terms of radio and television, aerodynamics and supersonic aircraft, properties of crystals and transistors, semiconductors, heat transfer, electronics, photosynthesis, and electronic machines which solve problems of staggering complexity.   In the crowded modern technological scene that presents itself to man's vision today, there is no certain way of knowing what discoveries will be of greatest significance for the future.   Who knows but that some scientific discovery which now escapes our observation may eventually overshadow in importance the release of atomic energy.

TEAM RESEARCH TAKES THE LEAD

One final point.   If we have stressed the importance of the work of individual scientists in the initial phases of the history of atomic energy, we should, nevertheless, realize that the character of twentieth-century science is changing rapidly at mid-century. We see that government, the military, and industry are coming to be ever more closely connected with virtually every phase of the atomic-energy program in this country and elsewhere.   Team research has taken the lead.   The late John von Neumann has said, "In modern science the era of the primitive church is passing, and the era of the Bishop is upon us.   Indeed the heads of great laboratories are very much like Bishops, with their association with the powerful in all walks of life, and the dangers they incur of the carnal sins of pride and lust for power."[18]

What does this kind of scientific professionalism have to do with our traditional image of the scientist—

Darwin in his cramped cabin on the 'Beagle,' or resting deep in thought on a couch in his country home; Newton isolated in the country by the plague, or hearing the clocks chime out over Trinity Court; Pasteur struggling with rabid dogs; Green, the miller; Lavoisier, the tax farmer; Dalton, the schoolmaster?   These men were not paid to do research. They were great scientists because their minds were on fire, because they could not help themselves, any more than Francis of Assisi could avoid being a Saint or the Brontes avoid writing novels.[19]

Research and development programs in atomic energy now have at their command the most impressive type of analytical equipment and instrumentation in the history of science.   While we must not be so dogmatic as to say that there will be no more fundamental "simple" discoveries in the physical sciences, it is becoming increasingly more difficult to come up with fundamental breakthroughs without rather special high-powered equip-

[18]Quoted by John Ziman, *The Listener,* April 7, 1960, p. 599.
[19]John Ziman, *Ibid.,* p. 599.

ment. Research now demands fantastically expensive equipment. Giant electronic computers, which work a thousand times as fast as man, process the co-ordinates of nuclear particles recorded at regular intervals and punched on tapes.

We recall, by contrast, the carefree days of Rutherford's Cavendish Laboratory at Cambridge, when apparatus contrived from tin cans and cigar boxes and connected with string and sealing wax opened up whole new worlds of science; when world-shaking discoveries depended upon skill in glass-blowing and fundamental particles were detected by peering at scintillations through a microscope. Since then, advances in the field and the change in instrumental methods of research have been accompanied by a shift away from individuals engaged in private research projects and toward the group and team research of highly specialized individuals each contributing only a fraction to the final outcome in a given investigation.

Gone are the days, says Hans Bethe, when

physicists in all countries knew each other well and were friends . . . [when] the life at the centers of the development of quantum theory, [in] Copenhagen and Göttingen, was idyllic and leisurely, in spite of the enormous amount of work accomplished. . . . How it has all changed! There are now enormous accelerators, with large groups of scientists working on each; a wealth of detailed material is published in highly specialized journals every week so that it has become impossible to keep up with the literature even in a narrow part of nuclear physics; announcements of important discoveries appear first in the *New York Times*. We fly many times a year across the Atlantic to hold mammoth conferences in which it is difficult to find our friends. The life of physicists has changed completely, even of those who are not involved in politics or in technological projects like atomic energy. The pace is hectic. Yet the progress of fundamental discovery is no faster, and perhaps slower, than in the thirties.[20]

Whether we like it or not we find that government-sponsored atomic research in the university and in industry are closely connected with almost every phase of a military defense program aimed at maintaining super atomic weapons as a deterrent to war, along with a wide variety of tactical atomic weapons to replace the now obsolete conventional tools of warfare. These newest tools have not yet been used in warfare, but they have been tested ever since 1945. We shall discuss those tests and then direct our attention later to the reactions which they have elicited from various individuals and groups in our society.

[20]Hans Bethe, *Bulletin of Atomic Scientists,* Dec. 1948, p. 426.

chapter 3

DEVELOPMENT AND TESTING OF
NUCLEAR WEAPONS SINCE 1945

In July 1946, while inspection and control were being proposed for an international United Nations authority, 42,000 United States civilians and servicemen were engaged in "Operation Crossroads" in the Pacific. Test "Able," an aerial bomb to test various types of naval vessels, was first exploded at Bikini Atoll. This test closely simulated the Hiroshima and Nagasaki blasts. It was reported by the navy that 90 per cent of the gamma radiation had penetrated eighteen inches of steel armor plate. Test "Baker" followed fourteen days later and was a shallow underwater explosion sixty feet below the surface of the ocean. The tower of water that was hurled up during the test was about one-half mile in diameter at its base and something less than two miles high. Both tests were designed to obtain information of future military value. Test "Charlie," the planned deep-water test of an atomic bomb, was called off in 1947.

By November 1947 Russian Minister of Foreign Affairs Vyacheslav Molotov declared that the secret of the atomic bomb was already long nonexistent. While the United States tightened up on its resolution to hold on to the most valuable military secret in history, and while atomic scientists became increasingly more vocal about their conviction that the atomic bomb could not remain secret much longer, the public became more and more confused about the truth.

Two years after the Bikini tests, in May 1948, President Truman announced that new atomic bombs were being tested at Eniwetok Atoll in the Pacific. There were three A-bomb tests in "Operation Standhouse" that year. Toward the end of 1948, after the United States had disengaged itself from England's wartime collaboration and veto over the military use of atomic bombs, and after the March Key West conference in

which the Joint Chiefs of Staff had deliberated over the question
of which military service should control atomic weapons, the
strategic decision was made, though it was never clearly stated,
that American defense and foreign policy should be committed
anew to atomic weapons. The new position, designed for long-
range strategic planning with atomic weapons, though arrived at
gradually, was a complete about-face with respect to the position
held three years earlier, when the United States had attempted
to outlaw the use of atomic weapons in international affairs.
Walter Millis, in a summary of recent developments of the relation between the military and civil factors which enter into
national policy-making, has suggested that in the early planning
for NATO it was probable that atomic bombs were meant to
represent the principal American contribution to the defense of
Western Europe.[1]

Renewed Atomic Weapons Race

On September 22, 1949, Truman shocked the nation with
the announcement that the Russians had detonated their own
atomic bomb somewhere within the Soviet Union in August of
that year. The United States had suddenly lost the military
advantage of its monopoly of nuclear weapons as a major
deterrent to aggression, and so the most important consideration
was to devise means to retrieve it. It was clear that in future
the advantages to be derived from nuclear weapons would
depend chiefly on maintaining a quantitative lead. That was
the common attitude until it was recognized that perhaps a
super nuclear weapon would provide a unique advantage even
over ordinary atomic bombs in quantity. A vigorous debate
over military and foreign policy followed—but only in secret at
high levels of government.

These debates centered in the question of how the United
States might regain its strategic position with respect to atomic
weapons. The most obvious solution was to proceed with an
accelerated program on the theoretically feasible but as yet
practically undeveloped H-bomb. Los Alamos scientists had
envisaged the possibility of a thermonuclear weapon in 1945
even before the nuclear bomb had been set off. In 1950 some
of these same scientists, led by Edward Teller and E. O.

[1]Walter Millis, *Arms and the State* (New York, 1958).

Lawrence, gave their full support to the initiation of an all-out thermonuclear crash program. After much discussion among the members of the Atomic Energy Commission (AEC), the military, and the National Security Council, the General Advisory Committee of the AEC under the leadership of Robert Oppenheimer unanimously decided not to support the H-bomb crash program for both technical and moral reasons. Nevertheless, Truman announced on February 1, 1950:

> It is part of my responsibility as Commander-in-Chief of the Armed Forces to see to it that our country is able to defend itself against any possible aggressor. Accordingly I have directed the Atomic Energy Commission to continue its work on all forms of atomic weapons, including the so-called hydrogen or super-bomb. Like all other work in the field of atomic weapons, it is being and will be carried forward on a basis consistent with the overall objectives of our program for peace and security. This we shall continue to do until a satisfactory plan for international control of atomic energy is achieved.[2]

In spite of basic disagreements as to specific allocations among the various military services, 1950 saw the beginning of an entirely new thrust into the area of atomic energy for military purposes. Ever since then the United States has been engaged in developing a wide variety of atomic weapons designed to meet every conceivable wartime emergency. We have heard it proclaimed that the ideal was directed toward the day when almost as complete a variety of atomic weapons would be available as were formerly used in conventional warfare. In part this was represented as an economy move and was motivated by the contention that a nuclear arsenal of full scale and smaller tactical atomic weapons would be cheaper per unit of energy release than conventional weapons. The United States Army, for example, by 1960 had developed the "Davy Crockett," a bazooka-like weapon capable of firing a small nuclear warhead. The army calls this a "tactical" nuclear weapon. It has a small enough yield to be limited to military targets in a military zone, the war zone, as distinguished from large bombs or missile warheads designed for use against strategic targets.

It should be mentioned here that since the end of the war, all of the special nuclear devices for warfare have been explored without in the least neglecting to stock the arsenal of the conventional tools of war. There have been phenomenal new advances

[2]Harry Truman, *Memoirs,* Vol. 2 (New York, 1956) p. 309.

in mobile guns, tanks, antitank weapons, army transport, use of radar and television, aircraft carriers, vessels with guided weapons, submarine and antisubmarine weapons, bombers, fighters, supersonic fighter techniques, transport aircraft, guided missiles, rocket propulsion, bombs to destroy bombs, interceptor bombs, incendiary and biological weapons, and poison gas. These new weapon developments have by no means been limited to the great powers. Belgium has produced a much improved rifle. France has developed a new machine gun and high grade supersonic aircraft and missiles. Canada has produced an antitank weapon to fire a projectile which generates sufficient heat to burn its way through heavy armor. Noel-Baker claims that there never has been a period of years, in either peacetime or wartime, that can compare with the advances in conventional weapons since 1945.[3] The United States military service budget for the fiscal year beginning July 1, 1959, was just short of 41 billion dollars. This was more than half of the total government budget of 77 billion for the same period.

President Truman's 1950 directive to the AEC brought quick results. Other nations followed suit. In 1951 there were sixteen United States A-bomb tests: twelve in Nevada and four in "Operation Greenhouse" at Eniwetok. The first American hydrogen device was set off in September 1952. There were two known tests in the U.S.S.R. in 1951. In 1952 there were eight A-bomb tests in Nevada. In addition, in November of that year there were two thermonuclear or H-bomb tests at Eniwetok— called "Operation Ivy." One of these tests was a full-scale thermonuclear bomb 250 times as powerful as the Hiroshima A-bomb. It completely obliterated a milewide island and left a crater in the ocean a mile across and 175 feet deep. The same year saw Britain's first atomic explosion at the Monte Bello Islands close to Australia. Sir Winston Churchill revealed three weeks after the test that the 1,450-ton frigate H.M.S. Plym had been vaporized by the blast.

The sudden bursts of activity in 1951 and 1952 were admittedly designed to develop new varieties of atomic weapons, and in this regard the changeover to the Republican administration of Eisenhower in 1952 did not greatly alter the over-all plans. In January 1953 President Eisenhower announced in his State

[3]Philip Noel-Baker, *The Arms Race, a programme for world disarmament* (London, 1958).

of the Union Message: "Recently in the thermonuclear tests at Eniwetok we have entered another stage in the world-shaking developments of atomic energy. From now on man moves into a new era of destructive power, capable of creating explosions of a new order of magnitude, dwarfing the mushroom clouds of Hiroshima and Nagasaki."

During the same year the AEC confirmed Russian reports that a thermonuclear explosion (H-bomb) had taken place in August 1953 in the Soviet Union. The Russians had again caught up with the United States. The Soviet announcement of an H-bomb set off a flurry of disputes over the classification of atomic matters in both scientific and nonscientific circles in the United States. Ralph Lapp, former executive officer of the Research and Development Board of the AEC, asserted that the problem of making H-bombs was no secret since it merely involved devising the means of securing deuterium and tritium. He furthermore challenged anyone to prove that atomic secrecy had ever done the United States any good. When it was suggested that espionage agents had given the H-bomb secrets to the Russians, Lapp countered by attributing such claims to American egotism in weapon development. Men like Oppenheimer and Gordon Dean of the AEC urged that the American people be given more facts about nuclear weapons and about Russia's atomic threat; AEC Commissioner Zuckert opposed such notions and went on record as being against greater exchange of atomic information to potential enemies and allies alike.

THE UNFORTUNATE LUCKY DRAGON

The first recorded major casualties of a nuclear test bomb were inflicted upon a crew of twenty-three Japanese fishermen when their tuna trawler, the *Fukuryu-Maru* (the Lucky Dragon), was caught in the downwind draft of the Bikini H-bomb "Bravo" test on the first of March 1954. The next day the following announcement was released in Washington, D. C.: "Lewis L. Strauss, Chairman of the United States AEC, announced today that Joint Task Force Seven has detonated an atomic device at the AEC's Proving Ground in the Marshall Islands. The detonation was the first in a series of tests." President Eisenhower created considerable public alarm after the test when he said that it had been "much more powerful than was expected." It was a fission-fusion-fission bomb of a type capable of combining tremendous explosive power and the contamination of from 5,000 to 10,000 square miles in a single detonation. It has been estimated that the bomb was between 750 and 1,000 times more powerful than the A-bomb of Hiroshima. Still, it was known to have been small enough to be carried by B-36 aircraft.

Dr. Ralph E. Lapp has given us the accurate and detailed factual circumstances of the incident as well as the personal and human story of these unfortunate fishermen's lives.[4] His account is based on personal interviews with the tuna fishermen three years after the incident, as well as on much other information, including research publications by the Japan Society for the Promotion of Science on the effects and influences of nuclear test explosions.

The fishermen, in search of better fishing, were 120 miles southeast of Tokyo, roaming somewhat beyond their usual range when, according to their description, shortly before breakfast the sun seemed to rise in the west. At the time, they were 85 miles from the center of detonation in the Bikini Atolls, where no nuclear tests had been staged since 1946. This was 300 miles from Eniwetok Atoll where nuclear tests had been held since 1946. The fishing vessel was twenty miles outside of the farthest zone of restriction which had been established by the AEC and announced to that effect to the Japanese Maritime Safety Board. While knowing about and abiding by the shipping regulations for this danger area, these fishermen were hardly aware of the existence of atomic dangers and certainly could have known nothing about the nuclear tests. Indeed, they came totally unannounced. Dr. Lapp could find no evidence of a broadcast warning of any kind to boats which were in this vicinity immediately prior to March 1. Nor were there any attempts to broadcast decontamination directions after the test, in spite of the fact that within an hour after the test the AEC and the Defense Department knew from United States naval rendezvous vessels in the area that something had gone wrong. Prompted by the Japanese, the United States government almost immediately increased the danger zone to include roughly eighty times the previously designated area. It was not, however, until almost a year later that the AEC released to the American people some of

[4]Ralph E. Lapp, *The Voyage of the Lucky Dragon* (New York, 1957).

the facts concerning the radioactive fallout. Some scientists in the United States suspected from the start that something had gone wrong. Lapp eventually was able to break the whole story for the American press.

Several hours after the test, the fishing vessel was covered with dangerous radioactive ashes as fine as talc. Its crew, blistered, nauseated, sick, and puzzled, eventually returned to port in Yaizu, Japan, on March 14, not knowing with certainty exactly what had happened to them. Most, but not all, of the contaminated tuna in the ship's cargo were buried before they had been distributed to consumer markets. All summer long, prices in the fish markets dropped throughout Japan as tuna catches continued to show contamination. Japanese records show that about 683 tuna boats had contaminated fish, and about 457 tons had to be discarded between March and December. Japanese fishermen claim that tuna can travel about 35 miles an hour, and this accounts for the fact that radioactive tuna continued to be caught at enormous distances from the Bikini Atolls. A Japanese research team in May 1954 studied the problem of radioactivity in marine organisms in the Pacific. They found radioactive fish over an area of about one million square miles and discovered that some of the smaller marine organisms had radioactive contents up to ten thousand times the activity of their aquatic surroundings.

It is difficult to understand what was gained by the strict security regulations which prohibited the announcement of this test and which prevailed after the test while the fishermen were being treated. Lapp says: "Much of the controversy could have been avoided had the United States Government adopted a straightforward approach to the problem. However, personalities in United States atomic circles, the dictates of atomic secrecy, the desire to avoid legal responsibility for the accident and a lack of understanding of the Oriental mind all played a part in confusing a rather involved situation. While the rift between the United States and Japan widened, the eyes of the Japanese focused upon the two hospitals in Tokyo in which the radiation-affected fishermen had been transferred for the best medical treatment."[5] Some two million dollars in monetary reparations were eventually distributed to the people and industries affected

[5]Lapp, *loc. cit.*, p. 135.

by the test.   Only one man died as a definite result of the
radiation, but all of the men were affected seriously and have
been the subject of careful scientific studies since then.

The manner in which this unexpectedly superexplosive bomb
of 1954 was explained to the world by the Japanese scientists
provides an exciting commentary on the history of security regulations.   We are again relying for our information on Dr. Lapp's
report.

Back in 1938 the Japanese radiochemist Kimura and some of
his colleagues first produced U-237 by the bombardment of
uranium in a cyclotron.   In 1954 Kimura and others detected
U-237 in the fallout ashes collected from the deck of the Lucky
Dragon.   Knowing that the U-237 was not a constituent of
ordinary A-bombs of U-235 or Pu-239, nor of the H-bomb type,
the Japanese scientists concluded that the bomb had been an
entirely new type of fission-fusion-fission bomb in which the
fissioning of an ordinary A-bomb had triggered an H-bomb
whose fusion in turn had initiated the fissioning of a surrounding
blanket of U-238, i.e., ordinary uranium.   U-237, which had
been discovered by Kimura in 1938, was therefore detected by
Kimura in 1954 as a "tell-tale product" in the radioactive fallout
of this bomb;   this indicated that U-238 had been employed in
the bomb.   The fact that this bomb had been vastly more powerful than any United States officials had expected was sufficient
evidence to indicate further that the cheaper and more abundant
U-238 had for the first time been induced at high temperatures
to fission in an atomic bomb. It was recognized, furthermore, that
a U-238 bomb produced large quantities of frightfully dangerous
radioactive fallout.   Thus, a whole string of connected secrets
had been "found out" by the analyses of the "ashes of death," as
they were called by the Japanese.

According to reports, the U-238 was responsible for most of
the bomb's explosive power and for nearly all of its fallout.
Calculations have shown that the fishermen had been exposed
to dosages over a period of fourteen days which have generally
been regarded high enough to produce death in 50 per cent of
a population.   AEC officials under Commissioner Strauss made
every effort to suppress the facts of fallout, which in this case
occurred on a very large scale. The United States government did
not even send out an advance warning for the second 1954 test
at Bikini on March 26.   There were more tests during the year:

April 6, April 26, and May 12. On February 15, 1955, the United States AEC published some information on the effects of high-yield nuclear explosions, including the heat, blast, and radioactivity effects of thermonuclear explosions. Still there was no explanation for the superexplosiveness of the March 1954 test. Perhaps, as Lapp suggests, it was this test which led the officials to begin to extol the virtues of "the humanitarian bomb" and later the "clean" bomb.[6]

"The Worse Things Get, the Better"

In January 1955 the United States launched an atomic-powered submarine, the navy's USS *Nautilus,* which boasted of almost unlimited cruising range; it was the first case of an atom-propelled means of transportation. On the same day, Russia announced that it would share its nuclear materials and technical knowledge with its European satellites and with Communist China. The following month the British government announced its decision to manufacture the H-bomb. It took twenty-seven months before their first H-bomb test was made.[7]

In 1955 Churchill said, "After a certain point has been passed, it may be said, the worse things get the better. . . . Then it shall be that we shall, by a process of sublime irony, have reached a stage in this story where safety will be the sturdy child of terror, and survival the twin brother of annihilation."[8]

In 1956 with Khrushchev and Bulganin in charge of the main direction of Russian affairs, East-West tensions relaxed somewhat and negotiations seemed to improve. That was the year in which the Soviet Union announced a drastic cut in their military manpower, in order, as they claimed, to free their youth for "more creative work." In the United States, 1956 was a presidential campaign year; the banning of H-bombs was a major issue in Adlai Stevenson's platform. On the international scene there were renewed efforts at atomic disarmament, but they all bogged down on a system of inspection to which the United States and Russia could agree. With the growing knowledge of the nature of harmful radioactive fallout from nuclear

[6]Lapp, *loc. cit.,* p. 197.
[7]For an analysis of the British decision to manufacture the H-bomb and thus duplicate American defense efforts, see Leon Epstein, "Britain and the H-Bomb, 1955-1958," *Review of Politics,* August 1959, pp. 511-529.
[8]*New York Times,* March 21, 1955.

tests, scientists began to speak up more firmly for a ban on further nuclear tests. While Pope Pius XII and the Soviet Union both proposed a ban on H-bomb tests, the United States and Great Britain continued to hold to the policy that the tests, as carried out, were not a health hazard.

By May 1957, when the British made their first two thermonuclear bomb tests at Christmas Island in mid-Pacific, three world powers had demonstrated their possession of megaton weapons, i.e., weapons equivalent to millions of tons of TNT. By that time the "testing" of nuclear weapons had become the subject of an acute world-wide controversy. In August 1957 the U.S.S.R. announced the accomplishment of an intercontinental ballistic missile. Two months later they successfully placed the first artificial earth satellite into orbit. Although of uncertain military importance, this major breakthrough produced an even greater impression of the capabilities of Soviet technology than the earlier detonation of nuclear bombs. The new attitude of respect for the scientific accomplishments of the Soviet Union were dramatized by many reactions and statements in the press.

It was not long thereafter that NATO countries voted for an enlarged Atlantic effort in scientific research and development to meet the challenge of the Sputniks. Thus, in December 1957 the North Atlantic Council decided that, in view of Russia's attitude, it would be necessary to establish stocks of nuclear warheads which would be available for the defense of the alliance in case of need. It was concluded that ballistic missiles with an intercontinental range would be placed at the disposal of the Supreme Allied Commander of NATO, General Lauris Norstad of the United States Air Force.

The Atomic Energy Act of 1954 was accordingly amended so that the United States would be able to share American atomic defense information with NATO allies. The Western powers then forged ahead to build the defense posture of the NATO group around the tactical atomic weapon and the short-range atomic missile. This was accomplished by introducing these weapons into the defenses of the continent wherever this was possible. Matador (650-mile range) launching bases were set up in West Germany; Jupiter (1,500-mile range) bases in Italy. By the end of 1959 the West German armed forces were extensively integrated with the NATO forces.

The French government, by contrast, refused to allow nuclear stockpiles for NATO on French soil as long as they were solely in custody of the Americans. The United States, anxious to prevent the spread of nuclear arms to other countries, offered to provide the French forces with atomic weapons under dual French-American control. General de Gaulle felt that France should have the same control over use of nuclear weapons that Britain had over strategic bombers stationed in the United Kingdom. France obviously was anxious to have an equal voice with the United States and United Kingdom on problems of global strategy involving nuclear weapons, viz., to be able to negotiate from a position of strength with the Russians. The French, it was seen, were going to insist on nuclear parity even if they had to develop their own nuclear weapons.

During 1958 the United States was the first to test a ballistic missile with a nuclear warhead in a shot over Johnston Island. The navy in that year also set off an atomic depth charge against a "moth ball" fleet—three destroyers, a submarine, and a transport. In addition, there were several tests from balloons at the Nevada Test Site and many small underground blasts. Some of the tests were power-rated at less than one hundred tons of TNT and presumably represented an advanced phase of development into tactical atomic weapons which can be released on the ground by a one-man device.

The United States Calls for Test Suspension

On August 22, 1958, Eisenhower announced that the United States would suspend all nuclear weapons tests for one year effective October 31, on two conditions: that the Soviet Union agree under United Nations auspices to begin political discussions on setting up a world-wide network of nuclear explosion detectors; and that the Soviet Union refrain from resuming its own nuclear tests which it had unilaterally suspended in March. It was stated, furthermore, that the United States would be interested in renewing the ban on a year by year basis if negotiations could be worked out with Britain and the Soviet Union. On the face of things it appeared that the United States ban proposal had been well timed with its earlier stepped-up United States testing program—to the advantage of the West. The Soviet Union was quick to take advantage of the situation. They felt that it would be only fair for Russia to postpone her own test ban until she had exploded as many bombs as the United States and the United Kingdom had done in the months just preceding the United States proposal. And so the Soviet tests continued, the last one (the 199th) being detonated in Siberia on November 3, 1958.

Let us take a look at the nature of the United States nuclear tests which were completed just before the October 31 suspension. It was disclosed in March of 1959 that in August and September of 1958 the United States under "Project Argus" had employed nine naval vessels in the South Atlantic Ocean near Antarctica to launch three guided missiles with atomic bombs. The bombs, said to be of kiloton size, exploded 300 miles above the earth, creating a temporary "shield" of electrons in the atmosphere. After each explosion, a thin shell of radiation spread around the globe. It has been suggested that man-made radiation belts set up by such bombs might be used in future to detonate incoming enemy nuclear bombs before they reach the lower atmosphere.

Test Blanca on October 30 was the last United States atomic detonation in a series of tests which had been started hurriedly September 19 after the date for the Geneva test ban discussion had been set for October 31. It was a Hiroshima-size underground blast equivalent to twenty thousand tons of TNT. It moved seven million tons of a mountain in Nevada and was recorded on instruments in New York, California, and Alaska. This test released virtually no atmospheric fallout and was hailed as a milestone in the accomplishment of a large-scale nuclear blast unaccompanied by radiation hazards. Officials were quick to point out its value for peacetime projects requiring the expenditure of very large amounts of energy: the dislodging of mountains, building of canals, heat for electric power, and underground blasting for squeezing oil out of shale. Underground ten kiloton atomic blastings were subsequently offered to the American petroleum industries by the AEC and the Bureau of Mines. The government offered to pay about half the cost as an inducement to re-explore the commercial aspects of vast amounts of oil trapped in the shale beds of Colorado, Utah, and Wyoming. This would fall under AEC's "Plowshare" program on the peaceful uses of nuclear explosions.

Eight "dirty" nuclear blasts (i.e., bombs containing very large amounts of high-level radioactivity) were detonated off an Arctic island by Russia between September 30 and October 24,

1958. This caused a disturbance in Stockholm where the radioactivity seven miles over Sweden registered five times that of normal. Helsinki reported that the radioactivity in rain water was approaching the danger limit. In Los Angeles on October 30, officials found the city air to be twenty per cent above the accepted safe level for long-term human exposure; they attributed the rise to United States and Soviet tests. The Russian tests were halted two days after Scandinavian newspapers reported the incidents. The Swedes called for a detailed report from its Defense Research Institute. In all, the Russians set off fourteen nuclear bombs in October of 1958—more than they had tested during all of 1957. The Soviet October tests, like the four detonated by Britain in the same month, were large-yield nuclear weapons of both fusion and fission type. In that month, four atomic blasts were set off in a single day—three in the United States and one in Russia.

In general, it has been claimed by United States experts on the subject that, although the Soviet total yield detonation has been less than half that of the United States and United Kingdom, the Soviet tests have contributed a highly disproportionate amount of radioactive fallout, i.e., for the most part the Soviet bombs have been particularly "dirty."

By way of summary, let us take a glance at the record of all atomic tests to date. Until the end of 1957 the United States had staged ninety tests; the U.S.S.R., thirty tests; and the United Kingdom, sixteen tests. For 1958, up to the time of the test ban, the United States had staged an additional thirty-five tests; the U.S.S.R., twenty-three tests; the United Kingdom, five tests. The total world-wide recorded atomic blasts by November 3, 1958, was therefore 199, of which over thirty per cent had been made during the last eleven months of that period.

Meanwhile, France had begun to produce atomic devices and was making plans for tests in the Sahara desert—test ban or no. Sweden, Switzerland, West Germany, and Red China began to show an interest in planning for atomic arsenals. Although England had staged no nuclear tests after the proposed ban, she was also making some plans to step up her own nuclear potential. In February 1959, Britain's elder statesman, Sir Winston Churchill, and Britain's leading atomic scientist, Sir John Cockcroft, director of the British Atomic Energy Authority, joined forces to challenge the Russians in the scientific race by establishing a new school at Cambridge University to train an elite corps of scientists and engineers.

FRANCE JOINS THE ATOMIC WEAPONS "CLUB"

France became the fourth nation to join the atomic weapons "club" when she set off an atomic explosion (equivalent to about 70,000 tons of TNT) on February 13, 1960, in the Sahara desert. This was the first explosion, so far as is known, since the Russians detonated a nuclear device in Siberia on November 3, 1958. The French press echoed President Charles de Gaulle's reaction: "Hurrah for France. She is stronger and prouder than before." The Big Three expressed mixed feelings of resignation and regret. Morocco called home her ambassador to Paris. Ghana seized French assets. Afro-Asian nations asked the United Nations to censure France. Germany called the explosion "an atomic crime." Red China, Japan, and India all condemned the test. With the Big Three, France's new status as a junior member of the "nuclear club" added a new note of uncertainty to atom test talks and muddled an already complex atomic situation. Nevertheless, de Gaulle voiced the hope that the explosion would place France in a better position with respect to agreements leading to nuclear disarmament.

Officials suggested that de Gaulle's real intention was probably not to build a full-scale atomic arsenal but to use the explosion to reinforce his demand for full partnership with the Big Three. The French accomplishment was obviously also a prestige gesture which brought a sigh of relief from many who had felt that the United States and Great Britain had cut France out of a fair share of the nuclear secrets of the wartime development to which her own scientists had made substantial contributions in the early stages of nuclear research.

Despite foreign criticisms of France for exploding an atomic device, de Gaulle laid plans to equip France with a nuclear striking force. As long as certain countries possess enough bombs to destroy the world, de Gaulle has said, France needs bombs too. But he has added that France would abandon atomic weapons "with profound joy" if other countries did the same.

On April 1, 1960, the second French atomic bomb was detonated at Reggan, Southwest Algeria. During the same month the French ambassador in Washington informally sounded out the

United States on the question of France's admission as a full-fledged member to the "atomic club." State Department officials felt that France would first have to come to terms with the United States by withdrawing her decision to prevent the stock-piling of atomic weapons on her territory in conformity with moves to strengthen NATO. It was also known that the Joint Congressional Committee had taken a rather jaundiced view of the reliability of French security in view of the strength of the Communist party in France.

Experts agreed that it would be a number of years before France would be able to provide an effective nuclear deterrent of her own. Meantime, other nations would have the A-bomb, too. In effect, the French had proved that a medium-sized industrial country, without access to many wartime secrets, could achieve an atomic explosion entirely on its own.

In February a number of scientists submitted a report to the National Planning Association in which they concluded that besides France, eleven nations had the scientists, money, and technology to begin a nuclear weapons program soon: West Germany, East Germany, Japan, Italy, India, Sweden, Switzer-land, Canada, Belgium, China, and Czechoslovakia. In addi-tion, eight countries — Yugoslavia, Poland, Hungary, Finland, Austria, Australia, Denmark, and the Netherlands — had the money and the technology but limited sources of top scientific manpower. Six countries — Argentina, Brazil, Mexico, Norway, Spain, and the Union of South Africa — were only economically capable. Conclusion: Scientists had reasons to fear that twenty-five other nations would sooner or later start to develop their own atomic bombs or else join the atomic weapons "club" by obtaining weapons from other members.

Intelligence experts in Hong Kong have agreed that Com-munist China will probably be one of the first countries to fire an atomic device late in 1961 or early in 1962. This is approxi-mately six years ahead of the timetable the Chinese originally set themselves in 1950 when they started from scratch. With Soviet help, the Chinese have been engaged since 1955 in an intensive drive to catch up with the West in science. By June 1958 China's first atomic reactor went into operation outside of Peiping. The success of even a crude atomic explosion in Communist China would radically shift the balance of power in Asia. With extensive territories, large population, and good natural resources, China nevertheless still lacks the industrial potential and the technological capacity to become a world power. Her mastery of the requisite nuclear techniques and membership in the nuclear "club" would go a long way toward achieving that goal.

SOLUTION UNSATISFACTORY

Before we leave the general question of nuclear weapons testing, we want to summarize some of the most important tentative conclusions which have been reached on the basis of nuclear bomb experience to date.

1. A-bombs and H-bombs are so highly destructive that almost any major city in the world could be obliterated in a single attack lasting several minutes. In 1939 the most powerful aerial weapon was the one-half-ton high-explosive TNT bomb. By 1943 we heard of ten and twenty-ton blockbusters. The Hiroshima bomb in 1945 was equivalent to about 20,000 tons of TNT. By 1955 the twenty-megaton (million-ton) H-bomb was announced — a bomb which possessed fifteen times the destructive power of all the high explosives dumped over Germany during World War II. Thus we see that the H-bomb exceeds the explosive power of the A-bomb by as much as the A-bomb exceeds the explosive power of the twenty-ton TNT blockbuster. In fact, there seems to be no theoretical upper limit to the size of an H-bomb. Undoubtedly, we and the Russians now possess enough power to kill everyone on earth several times over.

2. It is probably correct to assume that H-bombs could be deliberately rigged so as to render them dangerously radioactive —to give "dirty" bombs. Presumably a super super H-bomb, if rigged with the right materials, could on detonation render the materials so highly radioactive as to dangerously contaminate the world's entire population. Nuclear weapons are not, however, the only ones capable of all-out annihilation. According to reports of chemists at the American Chemical Society in Cleveland in April 1960, a single bomber loaded with newly discovered nerve gases and biological warfare agents could in a matter of minutes deliver death to more people than an H-bomb. For those who would survive any of these all-out attacks, one might expect that the values which had once seemed most precious—

including those on behalf of which a war was undertaken— would likely become relatively insignificant.

3. It might be conjectured that the H-bomb is not the most ideal and practical weapon. Its advantage over A-bombs has been seriously questioned even by military men. This point has to do with the fact that the radius of any blast damage increases at a much smaller rate than the power of the explosion. To increase the power of a bomb by a factor of 1000 increases the radius of damage by only ten (cube root of 1000). Bigger H-bombs dig deeper holes and dissipate themselves upward along the line of least resistance into the stratosphere. In other words, the law of diminishing returns, in terms of destruction, operates as the bombs get larger. In order to overcome the disadvantages of large weapons when smaller ones will do, there has been the recent development of smaller so-called tactical nuclear weapons to replace many of the conventional tools of war.

4. No completely effective defense system has yet been advanced against nuclear devastation. The bombs can be dropped from planes, delivered by rockets or intercontinental ballistic missiles, or planted secretly by mines or time bombs. Dispersal of cities is the only defense idea so far advanced which is even temporarily practical. One plan for redistributing the United States population has been estimated to cost 300 billion dollars.

5. No big secret protects the bombs. Only the major powers now know all the details of certain engineering procedures, but even small nations can be expected to master them within a few years. Talk of "keeping the secret" merely breeds suspicion in other countries. It also breeds false complacency in one's own country.

6. The cost of producing atomic bombs is not prohibitive, and any nation which can afford an army or navy can afford atomic or H-bombs. The raw materials for the H-bomb are extremely abundant: the waters of the ocean. There is no reason, then, to believe that cost, materials, or shortage of man-power would place any serious limitations on the number of hydrogen bombs which could be produced. By comparison, uranium, though fairly widely scattered about the earth, is by no means abundant.

7. Bomb stockpiles increase the probability of war by creating an atmosphere of mutual suspicion among nations. Atomic bombs provide incentive to aggression by increasing the advan-

tage of surprise, and by rendering possible attacks in which the aggressor need not reveal his identity. The surprise attack by the Japanese on Pearl Harbor, even with conventional explosives, came as a crippling blow without warning. If we were attacked tomorrow, we might be quite sure that it would be the Soviet Union. But twenty years hence India, China, Africa, South America, and the Soviet Union might all have bomb stockpiles. What if they were all our enemies? It would be difficult to be sure where to retaliate if a nation were attacked anonymously. In that case, fear of reprisal could not be counted on to prevent the other party from using atomic weapons in an attack.

8. The extent to which man's future will be altered by modern nuclear weapons cannot yet be predicted. Many sentiments about the effects of nuclear bombs have been expressed by groups primarily motivated by the moral and humanitarian issues. Equally, or perhaps more important in the long run, will be the objective studies of the physical, medical, psychological, political, military, and social consequences and the effects on international relations.

9. After everything has been said concerning the magnitude of the physical effect of nuclear bombs based on calculations and experimental test explosions (New Mexico, Nevada desert, Marshall Islands, Western Australia, Antarctica, and Siberia), the fact remains that the only empirical evidence of the effects on society has come from the experience of bombing cities—Hiroshima and Nagasaki.[9]

A look at the over-all situation which we face for the not too distant future reveals a world of governments, first-class and second-class, all possessing atomic weapons. The situation will be comparable to one described by Anson McDonald in his science fiction story entitled "Solution Unsatisfactory": "Once the secret is out—and it will be out if we ever use the stuff— the world will be comparable to a room full of men, each armed with a loaded .45. They can't get out of the room, and each

---

[9]See *The Effects of Atomic Weapons,* prepared for and in co-operation with the U.S. Department of Defense and the U.S. Atomic Energy Commission (Washington, D. C., 1950); and *The Effects of the Atomic Bombs at Hiroshima and Nagasaki,* Report of the British Mission to Japan (London, 1946). The National Research Council of Japan has also published a *Medical Report on Atomic Bomb Tests* (Tokyo, 1953).

one is dependent upon the good will of every other one to stay alive. All offense and no defense."[10]

It is just within the realm of possibility that the means of destruction with atomic weapons will make men so conscious of their mutual dependence on one another that they will unite from common necessity to free the world from the fear of war. While the fear keeps mounting, the possibility of escaping from it is strengthened by the very fact of its dimensions. Still the actions of fearful men are not predictable and hardly trustworthy when the "strategy of war" potentially includes such things as the threat of force, deterrence, nuclear blackmail, limited and accidental conflicts, and arms agreements.

Some authorities have voiced the opinion that the prospect of the terrible catastrophic destruction of nuclear war will tend to make rational statesmen less inclined to regard warfare as a useful instrument of settling international problems. Vernon Van Dyke has said: "If nuclear weapons make war less likely, this does not mean that they are leading to an abatement of the power struggle among states; the reasons for the struggle persist. Rather, it means that states pursuing contradictory objectives are likely to emphasize methods other than violence for obtaining what they want. They are likely to prefer cold war to hot war, stressing economic manipulations, organized subversion, and propaganda."[11]

[10]Anson McDonald, *Astounding Science Fiction,* May 1941.
[11]Vernon Van Dyke, *International Politics* (New York, 1957), pp. 224, 225.

chapter 4

RADIATION AND ITS EFFECTS ON MAN

The discovery of X rays by Röntgen in 1895 and of penetrating emanations from naturally occurring substances by Becquerel in 1896 opened up a new and exciting, if somewhat hazardous, area of medical research at the beginning of this century. In his Nobel prize address of 1905, Pierre Curie first mentioned the danger which would confront humanity if the powers of radioactivity were to fall into the hands of individuals to which he referred as *les grands criminels*.

In the first decade of the twentieth century, radium and other radioactive substances such as polonium, actinium, and thorium, began to be used in the treatment of cancer and tumors. X rays were used to look into the human body. Radiologists and roentgenologists eventually learned that peculiar biological effects frequently showed up in their patients as well as in themselves: minor skin irritations, loss of hair, and the formation of warts which developed into running sores and cancer.

In the late 1920's the dangers of radiation to humans were partly appreciated, and precautions were usually taken to avoid overexposure. In 1928, at the Second International Congress of Radiology in Stockholm, the International X ray and Radium Protection Commission was established.

It was not learned, however, until a number of decades ago, that an abnormally high incidence of bone cancer was to be found among factory girls who had been employed, between 1914 and 1924, to paint watch dials with luminous radium paints. It was recognized, furthermore, that Joachimsthal miners working close to high pitchblende (uranium mineral) concentrations, and who had been dying of an obscure disease called *Bergkrankheit*, were actually victims of lung cancer caused by atomic radiations. Eye cataracts were later found to be common among scientists who were operating neutron-producing cyclotrons. In 1936 a memorial was erected in Hamburg to the "roentgenologists and radiologists of all nations who have given their lives in the struggle against the diseases of mankind."

In 1959 the Radioactivity Center at Massachusetts Institute of Technology began a manhunt to track down some two thousand individuals who survived the radium poisoning of the 1920's. This included persons who had been exposed to radium while doing research or while making and applying radium products, as well as those who had taken radium compound injections for arthritis, gout, hypertension, and schizophrenia. The object of these studies was to learn how radioactive deposits in man affect such things as life span, susceptibility to disease, bone formations, and tumors.

It is perhaps not generally appreciated that an extensive scientific literature on the biological effects of radiation already existed several decades ago. In the earlier literature we find a good deal of attention devoted to the physiological and biological effects of radiant energy in studies dealing with embryonic development, cell metabolism, tissue changes in the brains of cats and monkeys, induced lethal mutations in the honeybee and the fruit fly, etc.

Before the second world war, scientists were conscious of only certain forms of radiation danger. During the early stages of the Manhattan project, scientists were aware, in a general way, of the health hazards which the project might create, but no exact information was available. Health groups were soon formed to enlist the best industrial hygiene specialists and to initiate a broad research program through the National Bureau of Standards and the National Health Institute. The general awareness of radiation hazards called for great caution on the part of administrators responsible for the protection of personnel. Liberal factors of safety were established in all the major atomic installations. The result was that in most cases actual exposures were far below the established permissible limits.

By 1944, radiation pocket meters were common, clinical examinations of urine and excrements of laboratory personnel were routine, and systematic checks were made on the atmospheres from the installations and affluent waters from the atomic projects. The over-all safety and health record of the Manhattan project to date is a very impressive one, the total number of accidents and health hazards being far below that of the average industrial and research laboratory.

Since the war and the advent of large scale release of atomic energy in bomb testing, the sinister effects of radiation have given rise to a renewed and more exhaustive scientific investigation of radiation phenomena and their effects on life. The object of these investigations is to assess the immediate and long-range pathological and somatic effects as well as the potential long-range genetic effects of radioactivity as related to fallout, medical therapeutics and diagnosis employing radioactive materials, and the handling of radioactive sources in scientific research, industry and agriculture.

In 1950, when the rapidly expanding field of radiation protection acquired a new urgency, the International X ray and Radium Protection Commission adopted its present name— The International Commission of Radiological Protection.

By March 1955 there had been sufficient public discussion of the question of radioactive fallout for President Eisenhower to request a special appropriation of 12½ million dollars to develop plans for studying fallout hazards as a part of civil defense. In the 201 nuclear test explosions since the war's end, the greatest precautions have been taken to effectively shield the bomb testing personnel from all near effects of radiation. Nevertheless, in most of these tests very large quantities of radioactive materials have been strewn into the atmosphere where they have remained to exert long-term effects on all areas of the globe.

In the upper atmosphere, where the winds prevail eastwardly, the radioactive particles are carried around the earth's globe in about six weeks. The particles may then fall to earth as radioactive fallout over days, months, and years. The intensity of radiation depends on the distance from the zero point of the blast, where and how and at what height above or depth below the earth's or sea's surface the detonation occurred, and the general meteorological conditions such as wind direction and strength, atmospheric moisture and dust conditions, and whether or not follow-up rains or snowfalls carry the radioactive debris to earth before it has dissipated its strength.

It was estimated in 1960 that most of the radioactive debris from atomic bombs detonated between 1945 and 1958 would be down by 1962-1963, assuming that there would be no more tests in the meantime. By 1960 the predicted ground concentration of radioactivity was twice that of 1958. As far as man is concerned, the main culprits from the radioactive fallout were seen to be the slowly decaying elements strontium-90, cesium-137, and carbon-14. These can affect man directly, or else, as in the case of strontium compounds which are insoluble and replace calcium in the body, they concentrate in vegetables, meat products, and milk. From such foods they can be selectively incorporated into the bones, especially of children in the growing stage. The strontium, for example, may settle in the bones and continue to emit beta rays for a number of years.

The Source and Nature of Radiation

It was already known at the beginning of this century that atomic or so-called "ionizing" radiation is a by-product of the nuclear disintegration of radioactive atoms. Some elements found in nature, like radium and uranium, decay spontaneously. Other elements can be rendered radioactive artificially in the cyclotron or atomic pile. Radioactive atoms of all kinds emit radiant energy called gamma rays (similar to X rays) traveling at the speed of light. They also emit high-energy subatomic particles like alpha rays, beta rays (electrons), and neutrons. All of these rays have one thing in common. They carry energy from one point to another and as a consequence are able to knock out electrons from the atoms of the materials through which they pass. This process is called ionization.

Let us note, in the first place, that the extent of radiation damage from these rays does not depend on the particular source of the rays but on their nature and energy, i.e., equally dangerous radiation might be emitted from atomic and thermonuclear bombs and reactors, or from any matter rendered radioactive by bombs or reactors. This would include atomic power plants, isotopic tracers used in research, radioactive materials for the treatment of cancer, radioactive fallout from bombs, etc. Even the X rays used by dentists and doctors are potentially dangerous sources of radiation if administered improperly. The extent of biological damage from exposure to radiation for man is conventionally expressed in units of "roentgen," where one roentgen is that quantity of "x" or "gamma" radiation which will produce a certain amount of ionization in a standard medium.

Mankind has been subjected to radiation from natural sources since the beginning of his existence. This "background radiation," as it is called, comprises the radiation from naturally occurring radioactive materials existing in the human body and cosmic rays which are everlastingly showering down upon all of us from outer space. It has been estimated that the average person receives per year about 0.05 roentgens from the soil and rock, 0.025 roentgens from radioactive chemicals in the body, and 0.025 roentgens from cosmic rays, i.e., about 0.1 roentgens per year from the average total natural background radiation.

It has been pointed out repeatedly that the radiation received as natural background can vary in intensity from place to place due to the earth's composition; that differences in altitude account for a significantly greater background cosmic radiation for populations at higher than at lower altitudes; that there are perhaps populations now living at altitudes where the natural radiation is twice that at sea level. It has also been said that there might be significant long-range radiation differences for two families living in the same locale, if one family's house is built against the side of a mountain and the other family's house stands out in the open. It has even been suggested that our ancestors of 200 or more years ago were subject to more natural background radiation than we are today. The reason is that until fairly recently sanitary conditions were such that people did not bathe or wash their clothes as frequently as we do today, thus carrying around with them more radioactivity in the form of granules of soot, dust, and accumulated dirt.

In the case of nuclear bombs, whether they are dropped on military or test targets, we know that fantastic amounts of very intense radiation are released immediately at the time of the explosion. In the March 1, 1954, Pacific test at Bikini Atoll, the radiation fallout at a distance ten miles downwind from the explosion was estimated at 5000 roentgens for the first thirty-six hours. Serious contamination covered about 7000 square miles. This type of radiation arises from the release of penetrating neutrons and gamma radiation, from the fission fragments of the constituent materials of the bomb, and from any materials which are rendered radioactive by the neutrons produced in the process of fission.

The immediate and near effects of such explosions are due to a combination of heat, blast, and radiation. They are well known and have been mentioned in Chapters 2 and 3. In 1946 a comprehensive long-term study of the potential delayed effects of exposure to atomic bombs in Hiroshima and Nagasaki was sponsored by the Atomic Bomb Casualty Commission in Japan under contract with the United States AEC. Their report on the effect of atomic weapons was published in 1950. The National Research Council of Japan in Tokyo in 1953 also published a medical report on the atomic bomb test.

DIRECT EFFECTS OF RADIATION ON LIFE

The detrimental changes which occur in man as a result of all types of radiation are complicated, but essentially depend on the degree of penetration into living tissue and the extent to which the radiation produces ionization of the molecules through which it passes. Ionized molecules in the tissue can initiate chemical changes within living cells which are at cross purposes with normally operating cells.

Basically there are three effects of radiation exposure: genetic effects, induction of abnormally behaving tissues such as cancer and leukemia, and the shortening of life span as an end result of the damage which is incurred. With very large amounts of radiation the cells are completely destroyed, as for example, with the intentional irradiation of cancer, where the object is to cause the death of abnormal or malignant cells. We should recognize that the same biochemical factors are at work during the intentional radiation for cancer as in the unintentional radiation received during an atomic bomb detonation.

The problem of estimating the cumulative damage to man of small amounts of radiation over long periods of time is an extremely difficult one. This is because there is still very little clinical and experimental radiation information on man. The intentional radiation of animals gives some information which can be used to make reasonable estimates for effects on man, but there is always a wide margin of interpretation possible. This is why scientists have been so very reluctant to make quantitative estimates of the cumulative effects of radiation on humans.

In the case of large-dose radiation of animals and man, considerably more information is available. Studies of bomb survivors and cancer patients indicate that the lethal dose for man is about 500 roentgens when the whole body is irradiated. Over small parts of the body, larger doses can be tolerated. A dose of 25 roentgens over a short time will produce temporary changes in the blood; 100 roentgens will occasion nausea and other symptoms of "radiation sickness." Bone marrow and related tissues associated with blood cell formation are peculiarly sensitive to radiation and are therefore very susceptible to cellular disorders such as leukemia. Any decrease in the normal quantity of white blood cells, for example, decreases the over-all bodily function of these cells to combat infection. The result is that the body no longer can ward off even minor infectious diseases. In other cases, radiation results in leukemia when the bone marrow wildly produces many more white blood cells than is normal.

Some of the secondary manifestations of radiation overdose, as evidenced from clinical studies of bomb survivors, are loss of hair, hemorrhages into the skin, ulceration of mouth and throat, uncontrolled production of malignant cells (cancer) including cancer from irradiated bone matter emitting alpha particles, lung cancer from the inhalation of radioactive gases and dusts, induction of eye cataracts from high-energy neutron exposure, sterility, abnormal menstruation difficulties, fetal-loss during pregnancy, and leukemia and mental retardation in the newly born. It is important to mention that most of these effects could have been confidently predicted from laboratory investigations in experimental pathology carried out long before the atomic bomb was conceived.[1]

Some of the radiation effects are thought to be cumulative in the sense that the permanent damage is proportional to the total exposure during a lifetime. One over-all effect is the shortening of the average normal life span. The question which has not yet been satisfactorily answered is whether there is or is not a dose below which these effects will exert no damage at all to the body. The figures for permissible body dose are still very hypothetical and will vary with the individual, his age, and his history.

POTENTIAL GENETIC DANGERS

In addition to all of these pathological or somatic effects of radiation, which more or less involve the outright death of cells and initiate malignancies or leukemia, there is the much more subtle question of the long-delayed radiation damage which, though it may not influence the life of the irradiated patient directly, will influence the health of the offspring several genera-

[1]For a history of clinical radiology in the 20th century see Hans R. Schinz, *Sechzig Jahre medizinische Radiologie* (Stuttgart, 1959).

tions removed.   These effects take place in the nucleus of the cell where the genes are located on chromosomes.

The genes are responsible for determining man's individual characteristics such as eye or hair color, disease tendency, intelligence.   Early experimental support for the genetic theory of heredity came primarily from controlled experiments in breeding new strains of plants and animals.   It was once believed that the genes of each strain and species of plant and animal life were permanent and unvarying.   But this view failed to explain how different strains and species arose in the first place.   Biological variation in plants and animals was first made plausible by assuming that there was an occasional alteration in the gene itself.   The permanent alteration of a gene was called mutation.

In 1927 the American Herman J. Muller (Nobel prize winner, 1946) announced his discovery that X rays markedly increased the rate of mutation in the fruit fly, *drosophila*, viz., that fruit flies whose ancestors had been exposed to radiation showed an increased number of hereditary abnormalities.   Later he reached similar results with neutron-induced mutations in dividing cells; and he showed that the higher the dose of radiation, the greater the frequency of induced mutations.   In effect, Muller's discovery provided geneticists with a tool to tinker with the gene on a wholesale basis.[2]

Today it is a well established fact that many types of ionizing radiation produce mutations.   The induction of genetic mutations is also thought to be initiated by certain chemical products —such as food additives, drugs, hormones, and cosmetics.   In fact, recent studies have suggested that all radiation may actually operate through the formation of certain chemical products.

There are "beneficial" as well as "harmful" mutations, but the majority, perhaps 99 per cent, are "harmful."   A "beneficial" mutation is defined here as one which increases the ability of an organism to cope with its environment.   A "harmful" mutation is one which shows up in some form of genetic abnormality.

Mutations can occur in all cells of the body, but only those mutations which occur in the cells of the reproductive system

[2]For an optimistic discussion of the prospects of future genetic progress in man see H. J. Muller, "The Prospects of Genetic Change," *American Scientist,* Dec. 1959, pp. 551-561.

lead to inherited changes. Thus, the entire biological ancestry of man is controlled by the genes in the male and female reproductive cells which are located in the testes and the ovaries of the parents. Mutations in these genes alter the functional character of the species, since altered (mutated) cells which survive will produce by normal cell division other altered cells exactly like themselves. Mutations of germ cells in persons who will no longer have children can, of course, cause no future genetic damage.

A mutated gene can either die, and thus be eliminated, or else cause an alteration in the physical characteristics of the offspring. If it survives, a mutated gene is just as stable as the old gene. Minor mutations are not unimportant, because over a long period of time they can bring about an accumulation of changes in a population. Every population automatically carries a store of undesirable genes which have resulted from mutations due to natural background radiation. Geneticists estimate that it takes about thirty to fifty generations for one half of the mutational damage at any one time to show up in the descendants. We emphasize that fallout as well as exposure to any other source of artificial radiation will only add to the total stock of undesirable genes.

The number of mutations is believed to be directly proportional to the amount of radiation reaching the reproductive cells. There is no minimum or threshold which can be accepted as a harmless or safe dose below which the potential genetic danger is unimportant. All that matters is the total cumulative amount of exposure. The effects of the mutations are permanent in the descendants; there is no recovery. Every mutant has to be eliminated from the population eventually through the failure to reproduce, i.e., death. An individual exposed to a radiation which is equivalent to a total risk of death can be compared with 100 individuals exposed to one one-hundredth the risk of death, if all future generations are taken into account. The quantitative information on the number of mutants which will result from a given amount of radiation is known for the fruit fly and the mouse, but not for man.

While geneticists are certain, therefore, that radioactive fallout from bomb tests will produce harmful genetic effects on life, there is not yet sufficient experimental information to make a precise quantitative estimate of the extent of the long-range damage of radiation to humans. Great difficulties are associated with designing experiments so as to give information which will be applicable to the long time intervals between successive human generations. In addition, experimental test matings are not feasible for man.

A vigorous experimental program on irradiation is being carried on at the present time, using the lower forms of animals which reproduce rapidly. The same is true for growing plants where the production of seedling mutants is particularly simple. By carefully watching the offspring of an irradiated animal or plant and choosing for further reproduction only those which are superior or improved, according to certain desired characteristics, it is possible to develop new strains. While artificial breeders, for example, are thus able to alter and even improve their animal strains by eliminating harmful or unwanted mutations, namely by careful choice of animals with certain desired characteristics, this is not possible for man without a careful regulation of the right of all individuals to reproduce.

We can well imagine that the question of the long-range genetic effects on the human race is the most perplexing aspect of the whole atomic energy problem. We understand why the scientists as well as the general public have been uneasy and somewhat jittery about the genetic outcome of the recent large-scale testing programs which have been taking place in various parts of the world.

Radioactive Fallout Estimated

Scientists are by no means agreed on where to set the "safe limits" of radiation if there is such a thing, or to assert what constitutes a maximum "tolerance dose." By "tolerance dose" is meant the level of radiation to which an individual can be subjected indefinitely without any harmful effects. This is usually expressed in an amount allowable for an average lifetime. If one estimates that in a thirty-year period (the average length of the reproductive period in man) the natural background radiation exposure to the reproductive cells amounts to three roentgens (30 years at 0.1 roentgens per year), and if one assumes that the aveage person receives an additional two to five roentgens for the same period from medical and dental radiations of a diagnostic and therapeutic nature, then the total

radiation for the thirty-year period amounts to a dose of about
five roentgens as a lower limit.   This is to be compared with an
estimated thirty-year dose from fallout at the present rate which
amounts to 0.03 to 0.15 roentgens.   This is less than five per
cent of the total non-fallout radiation.

In 1956 the National Academy of Sciences—National Research Council published a summary of scientific information
of the effects and potential effects of atomic radiation on man
and his progeny, and on the race as a whole.[3]   The summary,
which reported the findings of some 140 scientists, contained a
statement on the study of genetics, pathology, meteorology, oceanography and fisheries, agriculture and food supplies, and the
disposal and dispersal of radioactive wastes.   Over and above
the inevitable background radiation from natural causes, the
report set the maximum reproductive lifetime dose at ten roentgens of man-made radiation to the reproductive cells.   We
already are exposed to 3 to 4 roentgens for medical X rays,
and this is approximately, according to this summary, equal to
the average natural background radiation dosage.

According to W. F. Libby of the AEC, who reported for
"Project Sunshine," the cumulative fallout in 1957 in the United
States due to global bomb testings contributed the equivalent
of 0.001 to 0.005 roentgens per person per year—or less than 5
per cent of the natural background radiation, which we estimated above at 0.1 roentgen per year.   It was recognized that
these effects of fallout would statistically increase the amount of
radiation to which man was subject.   If natural radiation is
harmful, then fallout radiation adds something like 5 per cent
more damage to what existed before the advent of atomic bombs.

Geneticist James F. Crow of the University of Wisconsin in
1957 calculated that even this amount of radiation from fallout,
if distributed over the world's population of 2.5 billion persons,
would lead in the next generation to the birth of some 8,000
children with gross physical or mental defects, and a total of
80,000 in the long-time future; plus an estimate of 40,000 embryonic and infant deaths in the next generation, or a total of
700,000 for the long-range future.   These calculations were
made by Dr. Crow on the assumption that the human radiation-
induced rate of mutation is the same as in the mouse.   On this

[3]National Academy of Sciences, *The Biological Effects of Atomic
Radiation* (Washington, D. C., 1956).

basis, says Crow: "The fraction is tiny, but the numbers are enormous."[4]   Similarly, with respect to the somatic hazards of fallout, tens of thousands of cases of leukemia and bone cancer were estimated by Crow.

In May 1957, Albert Schweitzer, in a letter issued to the Norwegian Nobel Committee, appealed to the nations to end their nuclear tests. The announcement of this letter came just after a Soviet nuclear explosion had produced a heavy radioactive rain over Norway. Schweitzer's message, which initiated a heated controversy, included the following statements:

From official and unofficial sources we have been assured, time and time again, that the increase in radioactivity of the air does not exceed the amount which the human body can tolerate without any harmful effects. This is just evading the problem.

Even if not directly affected by the radioactive material in the air, we are indirectly affected through that which has fallen down, is falling down, and will fall down. . . .

We are forced to regard every increase in the existing danger through further creation of radioactive elements by atom bomb explosions as a catastrophe for the human race, a catastrophe that must be prevented under every circumstance. . . .

When public opinion has been created in the countries concerned . . . then the statesmen may reach an agreement to stop the experiments.

A public opinion of this kind stands in no need of plebiscites or forming of committees to express itself. It works through just being there.

The end of further experiments with atom bombs would be like the early sun's rays of hope which suffering humanity is longing for.[5]

Willard F. Libby, member of the United States AEC (1954-1959) responded to Schweitzer with an eight-page letter expressing respect for the motives behind his appeal, but questioning whether he had access to the most recent information on fallout. Libby contended that the risk from nuclear test radiation was "extremely small compared with other risks which persons everywhere take as a normal part of their lives." He urged Schweitzer to weigh this risk against what he believed would be the "far greater risk, to freedom-loving people everywhere in the world, of not maintaining our defenses against the totalitarian forces." He maintained, furthermore, that fallout radiation was far less

[4]James F. Crow, *Effects of Radiation and Fallout* (New York, 1957), p. 19. See also Crow's "Radiation and Future Generations," Chap. 6 in *Fallout*, ed. by J. M. Fowler (New York, 1960).

[5]Albert Schweitzer, *Bulletin of Atomic Scientists*, June 1957, pp. 204, 205.

than the natural radiation to which all peoples of the world
were exposed and asserted that a person could get a heavier
dose of radiation by moving from the beach to a hilltop or from
a wooden house to a brick house than he would from test
fallout.[6]

In answer to the statement that freedom-loving peoples had
to defend themselves against totalitarian forces, chemist O. T.
Benfey wrote: "We are told that the 'risks' of radiation damage
must be weighed against the risks of exposure to Communist
domination. If these are in effect the only alternatives, the West
is morally doomed. If the high ideals of democracy can only
be defended through the indiscriminate spreading of leukemia,
then it may be asked whether democracy is worth the price."[7]
California Institute of Technology's geochemist Harrison Brown
wrote: "We would not dream of lining thousands of people
against a wall and shooting them down in order to test a new
machine gun. But this, in effect, is what the United States, the
U.S.S.R., and the United Kingdom do when they test these fantastic new weapons. We do not know *who* the people are who
are afflicted, but we know that with little question many people
are killed as a result of these actions."[8]

DISAGREEMENT ON FALLOUT

Probably the single American scientist who most forcefully
advocated moral and ethical complaints to the weapons testing
program was California Institute of Technology's Nobel prize-
winning chemist, Linus Pauling. He has frequently been described in the press as being left-of-center. During the war, while
working for the Office of Scientific Research and Development,
his house was plastered with signs reading "Jap Lover." He
had hired a Japanese gardener. In 1952, at the same time that
the Department of State was refusing to grant him a passport
on the grounds of his "pro-Russian" sympathies, Russia was condemning his theory of molecular bonds on the basis of its in-
compatability with Soviet ideology.

In the February 1958 issue of the pacifist magazine *Liberation*,
Pauling took Libby to task for "immoral" implications of some

[6]Willard F. Libby, *Ibid.*, pp. 206, 207.
[7]O. T. Benfey, *SSRS Newsletter*, April 1957.
[8]Harrison Brown, *Ibid.*

of his rationalizations in favor of continued nuclear weapon tests. Libby had made some comparisons of the bomb-test damage with the 40,000 deaths per year from automobile accidents. To this Pauling replied:

The suggestion that is made . . . is that it would be all right to carry on bomb tests so long as the number of Americans killed by bomb tests is less than the number killed by automobiles, 40,000 per year. I consider this suggestion to be highly immoral. Dr. Libby has also compared the chance that a person takes of dying from leukemia or bone cancer or other disease caused by fallout radioactivity from the bomb tests with the chance that he takes of drowning if he goes swimming in the ocean. I believe that it is immoral also to make this comparison, and I am shocked that Dr. Libby should have made it. We believe in freedom of the individual human being, freedom to decide for himself to take the chance of drowning if he wants to go swimming. It is an entirely different matter for a few national leaders in Washington, Moscow and London to decide to subject everyone of the two and one half billion people in the world to the action of radioactive poisons that can cause leukemia, bone cancer, and other diseases.[9]

In a letter to the *New York Times,* Linus Pauling also took up the controversy of the H-bomb tests, contending that the by-product of hydrogen fusion, the carbon-14 released in the so-called "clean" H-bomb, was more harmful than strontium-90. Pauling calculated that the genetic effect of the 10 per cent atmospheric increase of carbon-14 resulting from H-bomb tests to that time would cause millions of genetically defective children in the next 300 generations (5,000 to 10,000 years). He also predicted that there would be millions of cases of bone cancer, leukemia, and other bodily damage. According to his total estimate, the carbon-14 damage would amount to more than the strontium-90 effect—perhaps 200 times the effect.[10]

Columbia University scientists challenged Pauling's calculation on the basis of what they called erroneous premises. They claimed that his figures were fifty times too high; that he had neglected to take into account the removal of carbon dioxide by plants and by solution in the oceans of the world. The Columbia scientists ended with a personal criticism of Pauling when they said: "Exaggerated statements by respected scientists only add to the public's confusion and do not contribute to the solution of this problem."[11]

[9]Linus Pauling, "Every test kills," *Liberation,* Feb. 1958, p. 9.
[10]*New York Times,* April 29, 1958.
[11]*New York Times,* May 2, 1958.

Pauling replied almost immediately with a statement giving his calculations and his basic assumptions. The net result of his figures showed again that the total bomb testing experiments until then would ultimately produce about one million defective children and about two million embryonic and neonatal deaths because of carbon-14, and a somewhat smaller number as a result of the radiation from fission products such as strontium-90. Pauling's letter ended as follows: "As other people have pointed out, these numbers will represent a minute fraction of the total number of seriously defective children and of embryonic and neonatal deaths during coming centuries. But I feel that each human being is important, and that it is well worthwhile to calculate the numbers of individual human beings who will be caused to suffer or to die because of the bomb tests, rather than talk about 'negligible effects,' 'undetectable increase,' 'extremely small fraction.' "[12]

Pauling continued to challenge an imposing array of scientists. In speeches made throughout the country and abroad and through appearances on television and radio he seemed to hold his own very well, although he often was accused by his opponents of being motivated more by humanitarian and emotional concerns than was proper for a scientist bent on examining the problems in an empirical way.

Arguments in favor of continuing nuclear tests were brought together by Edward Teller and his associate Albert Latter in a book published early in 1958.[13] Teller, professor of physics and until 1960 director of the University of California's Radiation Laboratory at Livermore, was one of the few top-flight atomic scientists who continued to give his complete support to a military directed atomic research program after the end of the war.

Most of the Teller and Latter book was devoted to an elementary exposition of the dangers and opportunities connected with the exploitation of atomic energy. In general, the hazards of bomb fallout were minimized in comparison with the amount of background and medical radiation to which societies have been subjected in the past. As to the bomb testing program, the book stressed the view that radioactive fallout "gives rise to a danger which is much smaller than many risks which we take in our

[12]*New York Times,* May 8, 1958.
[13]Edward Teller and Albert Latter, *Our Nuclear Future* (New York, 1958).

stride without worry." In any case, the problem of the potential
danger of radioactive fallout was looked upon as a technical
one connected with accomplishing the production of "clean"
thermonuclear bombs. We read: "By placing only certain
materials near the thermonuclear explosion one may obtain a
weapon in which the radioactivity is harmless. Thus the possibility of clean nuclear explosions lies before us."[14]

The imminent potential danger which these authors stress
is rather the nuclear attack of a tyrannical and opportunistic
Soviet power. Thus, it is argued that America must forestall
a surprise attack and possible annihilation by being prepared to
the hilt with all-out "nuclear firepower" which can be delivered
quickly and efficiently in small, mobile, inconspicuous units
hidden on land and sea and in the air. "What effect the existence of nuclear weapons will have upon the coexistence of nations," we read, "is a question less understood and less explored
than any other affecting our future. Most people turn away
from it with a feeling of terror. It is not easy to look at the
question with calm reason and little emotion."[15]

The work ends with the following optimistic proposal:

The general direction in which we should go is not to consider atomic
explosions and radioactivity as the inventions of the devil. On the
contrary, we must more fully explore all the consequences and possibilities that lie in nature, even when these possibilities seem frightening
at first. It may sound unusually optimistic in the atomic age, but we
believe that the human race is tough and in the long run the human
race is reasonable.[16]

In a review of this book, Jay Orear of the Department of
Physics at Columbia says:

It would seem to me to be more fair to compare fallout with something that is more familiar and generally recognized as a serious hazard—such as all-out war. If Teller and Latter had done this they would
have found that the loss of American life due to the past tests will be
twice that of the Korean War and 40 percent greater than American
life lost in battle in World War I! Teller and Latter estimate the shortening of life due to past tests (including the latest Russian tests) to
be about two days per world person or four days per American. The
total American loss of life due to past tests will be, then, four days mul-
tiplied by the projected population of the United States one mean life
span from now. This comes to three billion man-years, while the World

[14]Teller and Latter, loc. cit., pp. 171, 172.
[15]Ibid., pp. 169, 170.
[16]Ibid., p. 173.

War I battle deaths contributed a loss of 2.2 million man-years. Another revealing way of looking at the fallout hazard is the loss of life per megaton test. Using the Teller and Latter estimate of 1.5 day shortening of life due to testing 50 megatons of fission, this gives 3×10^5 man-years lost per megaton. Thus the testing of one megaton dirty bomb would be the same as killing 10,000 people of average age, while in warfare the same bomb would be expected to kill about 200,000. Thus, the difference between war and peace using Teller's own estimate is only a factor of 20![17]

Teller continued to emphasize the importance of more atomic tests for the sake of United States security, even if this would require additional research on the development of "clean bombs" with less radioactive fallout. Pauling argued that only the abolition of wars would prevent the world from plunging itself into a nuclear war; that no one should hope to expect that a nuclear war would be fought with "clean bombs." Teller insisted that it was senseless to end tests when atomic explosions could be hidden by powers which were not to be trusted. In any case, said Teller, fallout presented no health hazards significant enough to stop nuclear weapons testing. World-wide fallout, he remarked, was as dangerous as being one ounce overweight.

Late in 1958 Pauling published a book[18] which may be looked upon as an alternative to Teller's analysis. In this work, Pauling outlined his proposal for a gigantic "research for peace" program. To this end he recommended the establishment of an organization of some 10,000 scientists operating within the United Nations to study the problem of how to prevent the outbreak of a nuclear war either by design or by accident. He suggested that the organization would cost less than one-tenth of one per cent of the military expenditures; that this would be a cheap insurance policy.

Much of the expert literature on radiation and fallout was also reviewed by Pauling in his book along with calculations of his own. A single super nuclear test, he estimated, could cause the death of 10,000 people from leukemia and bone cancer and possibly 90,000 more by other diseases. This is to be compared with the estimate of Atomic Energy Commissioner Libby who said that by the beginning of 1955, radiation fallout was such that it could be increased 15,000 times without hazard from somatic (immediate corporeal) effects. In 1957 Libby still

[17]Jay Orear, *Bulletin of Atomic Scientists,* June 1958, pp. 235, 236.
[18]Linus Pauling, *No More War* (New York, 1958).

maintained that exposures from fallout were very much smaller than those required to produce observable effects in the world's total population.

To Pauling the danger of fallout from the cold-war testing of nuclear weapons is far greater than the actual amount of radioactivity released thus far. Fallout is a symbol of the real threat of war itself. The fallout from test bombs thus serves to remind men of the enormous stockpiles of nuclear weapons which, if ever used in a war, could make millions of square miles of land uninhabitable.

The above discussion concerning the potential dangers of radioactivity is a representative sampling of the earlier views which have appeared in the press on the subject. It undoubtedly overemphasizes the disagreements which now exist among scientists, and I think it would only be fair to add that, among experts, the differences of opinion are not so much in the facts as in the interpretation of the facts. We might say that, to some small extent, the lack of precise knowledge lies at the root of the debates on fallout. But the disagreement between scientists has not been quite so great as most people have been led to believe. In part, misunderstandings among the public have arisen out of the complexity of a subject which does not easily adapt itself to routine newspaper reporting. In addition, it is simply inevitable that a subject fraught with so many political and moral implications will become distorted to suit individual sentiments.

Specifically, we find that there is still no agreement on what constitutes a "permissible dose." The seemingly violent differences of opinion in the fallout debate result, in all likelihood, largely from the form in which the scientific conclusions are expressed. For example, the scientist who thinks predominantly in terms of risk of fallout to individuals may judge that a one-in-a-millon probability of fallout injury presents a "negligible" hazard to man's welfare. On the other hand, when applied to a population of three billion people, injury to one-in-a-million means that three thousand people will be affected. The figures which give the total extent of damage to humans are expressed in small fractions, but even small fractions when applied to the world's total population and to future generations give large numbers.

We see that much will depend on the interpretation of what

constitutes a "permissible dose." There is no disagreement about
the facts in the example given here. The seemingly different
conclusions are really quite compatible. But a complete exploration of any debate over such facts should go further and include
an analysis of the political and moral questions connected with
the technology of nuclear armaments and potential warfare.

In any case, it must be recognized that sincere scientists, whose
intellectual honesty is beyond reproach, are aligned on both
sides of the fallout debate. Much will depend on how these
scientists interpret the facts in terms of the over-all damage to
human populations when compared with a host of other potential dangers which now threaten and in future may threaten
man's survival and welfare. Policy decisions in this area involve
largely moral and economic factors rather than scientific information. For the layman it is confusing indeed to see that different "authorities" can, in good conscience, disagree so violently
when examining the same facts.

In general, it appears from our discussion here that influential
nuclear scientists who were supporting atomic weapons work for
the government or who were emotionally attached to such work
have minimized the dangers of fallout now and for the future.
They have argued that bomb fallout has contributed essentially
negligible quantities of radiation beyond the natural background
radiation. They have maintained that the potential risks of
fallout, whatever they may be, have seemed rather minimal compared to the potential threat of the Soviet Union to the stability
of the world; that modern life is so beset with risks of which the
long-range outcomes are quite unknown that the risks of radiation fallout are unimportant when placed alongside the many
other hazards of our technologically-oriented twentieth century.
It has also been argued that those who advocate the banning of
nuclear tests are motivated more strongly by idealism than by
sound scientific reasoning; that they are unwittingly playing into
the hands of the Communists who would like to see the United
States lose its military supremacy in the area of nuclear weapons.

On the other hand, numerous scientists have advocated a ban
on nuclear tests both from the standpoint of their humanitarian-
ism and in accordance with the belief that it is unwise and fool-
hardy to continue testing in the absence of sufficient information
to calculate the long-range risks for mankind.

It has been said many times that the public is constantly

being subjected to numerous real dangers connected with many phases of modern living. Experimental scientists, in particular, have frequently exposed themselves to unknown risks in the laboratory. The Curies did so in their work on polonium and radium. Robert Bunsen lost an eye while working on the cacodyls. Yet the argument based on the dangers of man's involvement in modern society are not very sound when applied to the question of fallout. Radiation dangers from fallout involve not only those who make the tests, but also the individuals who are innocent bystanders. The latter are the involuntary victims of the disaster even without knowing it.

In Chapter 8 we shall have much more to say about the organized concerns and appeals of scientists, but for the moment the account given thus far will suffice as background to our discussion which follows.

The Search for a "Permissible Dose"

While the public had been utterly confused by the lack of agreement among top-level scientists on the question of radioactive fallout, many people were hoping that the United Nations Scientific Committee on the Effects of Atomic Radiation would release its report and resolve the controversy. A United Nations report, an excellent factual statement, was released in August 1958 by a fifteen-nation committee in a 228-page document which took two years to compile. According to the report: a) low doses of radiation might produce *no* somatic effect; b) *if* low doses do induce leukemia, then the prolonged continuation of tests might cause 5,000 to 60,000 cases per year. According to the report: "Any present attempt to evaluate the effects of sources of radiation to which the world population is exposed can produce only tentative estimates with margins of uncertainty." For prolonged bomb testing the United Nations report projected the figure of 500 to 40,000 major genetic defects per year. The report further stated: "Even a slow rise in the environmental radioactivity in the world, whether from weapon tests or any other sources, might eventually cause appreciable damage to large populations before it could be definitely identified as due to radiation. As is the case with every technological advance, man must learn to live with new risks even as he accepts new benefits conferred upon him." The majority of the members of the committee took the view that the problem of controlling or banning nuclear tests and all other sources of radiation lay outside the scope of their task.[19]

The International Commission on Radiological Protection at about the same time defined the "permissible dose" as "a dose of ionizing radiation that, in the light of present knowledge, is not expected to cause appreciable bodily injury to a person at any time during his lifetime." This commission adopted a maximum permissible genetic dose for population exposure which reads as follows:

It is suggested that the genetic dose to the whole population from all sources additional to the natural background should not exceed 5 rems [roentgens] plus the lowest practicable contribution from medical exposure. The background is excluded from the suggested value because it varies considerably from country to country. The contribution from medical exposure is considered separately for the same reason and also because the subject is being studied for the purpose of limiting exposure to the minimum value consistent with medical requirements. No specific recommendations were made at this time as to the maximum permissible "somatically" relevant dose to the population, except that, for individuals, total doses to particular tissues in the body were given for exposure of the gonads, the blood-forming organs, lenses of the eye, etc.[20]

So a definite answer to the question of radioactive fallout still partly hung in the balance even after the two reports of 1958. Nevertheless, these reports certainly focused a great deal of attention on the urgent need for a more thorough long-range study of the effects of radiation on man. One outgrowth of the reports was that a national United States committee studying radiation recommended a broad twenty-year study program of the effects of radiation on man. This was to include close scrutiny of two million people for many years. Plans were made, for example, to compare the natural radioactivity in two widely differing geographic areas such as the high background activity of the Colorado plateau and the low background activity of the Pacific Coast. Included also would be the effects of bomb fallout and X rays.

[19]*Report of the United Nations Scientific Committee on the Effects of Atomic Radiation* (New York, 1958).

[20]International Commission on Radiological Protection, *Radiation Protection* (New York, 1959).

Expert and Sober Analyses: 1959-1960

During the year of 1959, a new round of fallout controversies in the United States was initiated by a number of conflicting reports. It was touched off in February by the release of a letter to Atomic Energy Commissioner Libby, from H. P. Loper, Assistant Secretary of Defense, and Clinton P. Anderson, Chairman of the Joint Committee on Atomic Energy. The letter contained a brief status report and the outline of a program for analyzing and evaluating the radiation hazards resulting from atomic detonations. The letter concluded: "The risk of damage resulting from the testing of weapons is . . . extremely small and much less than other common occurrences such as X rays, automobiles, chemical contaminants, household cleaners, etc. However, the probable casualties attributable to radioisotopes from weapon testing when summed over the populations of thousands of years create a moral issue that could be of considerable propaganda importance."[21]

L. S. Taylor, chief of the atomic and radiation division of the National Bureau of Standards, remarked that modern man would simply have to learn to accept radiation risks "philosophically," just as he has learned to accept the hazards of auto travel. The establishment of permissible levels of radiation exposure, he said, was basically not a scientific problem, but a problem of designing a philosophy of risk.

In March 1959 the government reported that the concentration of strontium-90 on the surface of the United States was greater than in any other area of the world. Fallout from airborne bombs was obviously much faster than had been expected.

In April the National Committee on Radiation Protection and Measurement, the nation's highest advisory committee on radiation protection, issued a new handbook on the maximum permissible concentration of radioactive materials in the human body and in air and water. The committee substantially increased its estimate of the maximum permissible concentration which had been arrived at by the International Committee on Radiation Protection the previous year.

By May 1959 a total of 255 reports on radiation sources, effects, measurements, and related problems had been submitted to the United Nations Scientific Committee on the Effects of

[21]*Science,* April 3, 1959, p. 884.

Atomic Radiation since it first began work three years earlier. The reports had come from thirty governments on all continents, from four specialized agencies of the United Nations, and from two non-governmental scientific bodies.

It was not until May 1959 that the United States fallout hearings before the Radiation Subcommittee brought about some measure of factual agreement among experts in areas where disagreement, dissension, and even distrust were common in 1957. Scientists reported steady progress in understanding the long-term man-made fallout patterns around the world. They found that bomb test debris did not uniformly circulate in the atmosphere. The greatest concentration of strontium-90 fallout was found to lie between latitudes 40 and 50 degrees north—a band covering the northern United States, most of Western Europe, and part of Central Russia. A pattern of maximum stratospheric concentration in two specific bands of latitude had been predicted in 1957 by Lester Machta, meteorologist of the United States Weather Bureau, but Atomic Energy Commissioner Libby had rejected the idea at the time.

By mid-1959 the wave of fallout and contamination scares reached a high point across the nation and elsewhere. The increase in concentration of bomb-produced radiocarbon in Denmark was several per cent higher than the average increase for the hemisphere. This additional increase was probably a carbon-14 equivalent to the spring peaks in strontium-90 fallout in the North Temperate Zone. It suggested latitudinal variations in carbon-14 contamination. Residents in the Dakotas learned that a major share of the fallout from the 1957 low-level tests in Nevada was settling on them. There were stories suggesting that people flying by jet were exposed to high radiation from fallout debris picked up by jet aircraft at high-flying altitudes. In Connecticut and Texas people were up in arms over disposal of radioactive wastes from hospitals using radioactive isotopes. More and more individuals worried about increasing food contamination, in bread, wheat, and milk.

A panel of experts allayed the fears of congressmen to some extent by telling them that, although the peak burden of strontium-90 fallout from past nuclear tests would come between 1962 and 1965, this would produce an average level of strontium-90 of not more than one-twelfth the "safe" limit which had been indicated in 1956 by the National Academy of Sciences.

It was estimated that when the debris from all bombs tested thus far would have reached the ground the radiation level of the soil would be only 10 per cent of the maximum permissible level set by the International Radiation Committee.

The 1959 analysis of data on total fission yield since 1945 indicated that the United States and United Kingdom had contributed three times as much to the world's radioactive fallout as had the Russians. Fallout was found to be greatest in the spring, lowest in the fall, most of it being brought down by precipitation. The length of time that the debris stays in the stratosphere was found to be from one to five years. Earlier estimates in 1957 had been placed at ten or more years. In general, most of the fallout was coming down faster than had been expected. Nuclear tests at altitudes above 200 miles were judged to be safe with no fallout.

There was also some measure of agreement on how much fallout material, specifically strontium-90, accumulates in humans, but there was no general agreement on the effect this would produce either in people now living or on future generations. Total radiation from all weapons tests to date was estimated at 5 per cent of the average exposure to natural background radiation and less than 5 per cent of the average American's exposure to medical X rays.

In general, the dangers of fallout were therefore downgraded to some extent by nuclear experts by the end of 1959. The General Advisory Committee of the AEC reported:

Human beings have lived for many generations in parts of the world which have five times or more the background radiation normal to the United States, or more than 100 times the average amount of radiation from fallout in the United States . . . In regard to internal effects of strontium-90 due to ingestion, the amount of strontium-90 which has been found in food and water is less of a hazard than the amount of radium normally present in public drinking water supply in certain places in the United States, and in public use for many decades.[22]

In its August report the committee concluded that current fallout was not hazardous but warned against test resumption.[23]

In April 1960 at the American Chemical Society in Cleveland, Dr. W. H. Langham from Los Alamos, disclosed that the maximum fallout deposits of radioactive strontium-90 and cesium-137

[22]*Science,* May 22, 1959, p. 1413.
[23]*Science,* Sept. 11, 1959, pp. 612-614.

from past tests would occur in children in 1962-1965, i.e., among those who were then five or six years old. These were the children who would be in their greatest bone and muscle-building growth during the time of greatest fallout. It was calculated that the world average bone and marrow doses for those children would be 10 per cent of the natural background radiation for strontium-90, and 5 per cent of the natural background radiation for cesium-137. Langham estimated that about one third of the total weapons test fallout had reached the earth close to the test sites, another third had fallen to earth all over the world, and the other third was still up in the stratosphere but constantly leaking down to earth.

In May 1960 the National Academy of Sciences—National Research Council published its second report,[24] summarizing the findings of 140 scientists on the effects of high-energy radiation on living beings. The report covered four areas: effects on health, radioactivity in food, disposal of radioactive waste, and the incidence of fallout. The report was generally reassuring on the danger of present radiation hazards in these four areas but stressed the urgent need for research of radiation problems on a wide front. The report repeated the same maximum dosage recommendation for the general population which had appeared in the 1956 report, viz., that the average dose in the first thirty years of life should not exceed ten roentgens of man-made radiation, the average in 1960 being less than one half that amount.

The experts were also fairly well agreed that man-made radiation in a number of forms would constitute a permanent addition to the hazards of human existence and well-being for the future—deleterious changes in hereditary material, leukemia and skin cancer, and shortening of life. Still, on the question of the quantitative extent of the hazards there was not yet sufficient observational evidence, said the report, to permit more than tentative conclusions. A cautious theme ran throughout the findings: "Many questions about radiation hazards . . . are unanswerable with present data."

In May 1960 a number of biologists from the AEC Oak Ridge National Laboratory reported to the National Academy

[24]National Academy of Sciences, *The Biological Effects of Atomic Radiation* (Washington, D. C., 1960).

of Sciences that the irradiation of mice embryos during the first twenty-four hours of conception produced a high number of abnormal females. Preliminary results from studies of 40,000 mice indicated that a radiation dose as low as ten roentgens per week did give higher mutation rates than control mice receiving only the normal background radiation. In a preliminary way these experiments indicated that there is no so-called threshold dose of radiation below which no damage will be caused. The implication of this was that women who might be pregnant should avoid any unnecessary exposure to radiation, especially during the first hours after conception.

In May 1960 the Joint Congressional Atomic Energy Committee had its hearings on the touchy and difficult problems connected with the health hazards of atomic radiation. Despite some differences of opinion in emphasis, there seemed to be wide agreement that the risks involved at 1960 levels of exposure were quite small compared with the other hazards of daily modern living (e.g., cigarettes, air and water pollution, and automobile accidents) or with the benefits derived from the medical use of radiation. Much more was known, it was said, about the hazards of radiation than about any number of other sources of contamination produced by modern society. Much stricter steps were being taken to control the hazard.[25]

During 1959 and 1960 so many inconsistencies and contradictory statements about the status of fallout and its implications were in print that congressmen, labor leaders, state officials, scientists, and citizens in many organizations began to renew their criticisms of the United States AEC and to voice their concerns about the dangers from weapon testing, the faster rate of fallout, the rising radioactivity in milk and other foods, and the growing problems of industrial radiation and atomic waste disposal.

In spite of all the criticism, the government had certainly looked at radiation very carefully. During the fiscal year 1958-1959 the AEC had spent 19 million dollars in research associated with standards and protection, with an additional 2.6 million for sampling and analysis of national and world-wide fallout. It was expected that in 1960 the figures for radiation standards and protection would be increased to 20 million. Since 1946

[25]*Science,* June 3, 1960, pp. 1656, 1657; June 10, 1960, pp. 1721-1723.

the AEC has appropriated about 250 million for biomedical investigations on radiation.

We know that the magnitude of fallout hazard from test explosions has been the subject of lively political and scientific debates over the past four years. During this time, much confusion has resulted from contradictory information and arguments reported in the literature; but scientists in general by 1960 had begun to provide some sober, careful, and unemotional analyses of their findings in the areas of medicine, genetics, and meteorology.[26]

Hazards of Handling Radioactive Materials

We now turn our attention to radiation hazards other than those which are associated with bomb fallout. We know that even if nuclear bomb testing and fallout were to be banished from the world in the future, severe precautionary measures would nevertheless have to be taken to protect the members of society from the radiation of atomic power plants and the private, commercial, and industrial nuclear installations and practices which are assuming an ever increasing importance in modern society. It has been estimated by scientists at Los Alamos that by 1965 the fission products produced annually by the world's power reactors alone will equal the amount of radioactivity released from bombs over the past fifteen years.

In the next chapter we shall deal with many of the peacetime applications of atomic energy, but we want to say something here about the question of devising protective measures to avoid the inadvertent exposure of persons to radiation. We shall examine the potential radiation hazards associated with the handling of radioactive materials in scientific research, medicine, nuclear power production, and industry.

The problem of nuclear liability in the operation of atomic power facilities and other nuclear installations has been studied intensively by the International Atomic Energy Agency's (IAEA) panel of experts on Civil Liability and State Responsibility for Nuclear Hazards. In May 1959 the panel held its second series of meetings at its headquarters in Austria to pool information

[26]For an excellent and up-to-date composite account by many specialists over all these areas, see John M. Fowler (editor), *Fallout* (New York, 1960).

on the safety evaluation of nuclear installations, the possibility of catastrophic accidents, the medical nature of injuries resulting from such accidents, the possible risks involved in the transportation and storage of nuclear fuels and radioactive materials, and detailed rules concerning liability between private parties and the state. More recently the IAEA has suggested that emergency teams be held in readiness to cope with radiation accidents in countries lacking the skilled manpower and experience to control nuclear hazards.

In March 1959 the National Advisory Committee on Radiation for the Surgeon General of the United States Public Health Service published a report assessing the influence of various types of ionizing radiation on biological systems. It was pointed out that an important weakness in this nation's efforts to control radiation safety was due to the absence of a comprehensive program through which the health hazards of all sources of ionization may be brought under supervision to cope with the rapid, anticipated growth of the use of devices and products which produce ionizing radiation. The report mentioned the fact that there had been a steady downward revision over the past thirty years in the maximum permissible levels of ionizing radiation—as recommended by the National Committee on Radiation Protection and other authoritative groups. Great emphasis was placed on future radiation research to fill in the gaps which are necessary to establish radiation protection standards on a wholly satisfactory basis. The question of state versus federal control of radiation was discussed at some length.

We should also mention here that the American College of Radiology, a national association of physicians specializing in radiology, has done a great deal in this country to improve the distribution, quality, and availability of radiological service to the sick through careful study of radiologic practice, the improvement of standards and facilities, and to acquaint the medical profession and the public with achievements and developments in radiology. They have prepared a practical manual on the medical and dental uses of X rays with control of radiation hazards.

While there is as yet no wide agreement on radiation protection, the over-all control in this country is in the hands of various branches of the AEC. For example, the Division of Licensing and Regulation functions as an agency to set up the statutory provisions for the possession, use, and standards of protection for all radioactive by-products as defined by the Atomic Energy Act of 1954 in terms of materials produced and distributed by the AEC or by commercial suppliers.

The hazards in the medical uses of radiation are now quite well known, and methods of protection have been worked out fairly satisfactorily. For example, there are definite regulations and precautionary measures for hospital administrators using radioisotopes in medical therapeutics and diagnosis. This includes the keeping of accurate accounts of stored radiochemicals, systematic radiation exposure records for patients as well as hospital personnel, prevention of radiocontamination in cleansing and laundering of equipment and soiled materials, proper waste disposal of contaminated materials by incineration or discharge into the atmosphere and sewage, methods of handling patients who have received large doses of radioactivity for medical treatment, and precautionary methods in the handling of patients who have expired after receiving large internal doses of radiochemicals.

Protection against overexposure is achieved by proper physical shielding against radiation, by avoiding ingestion, inhalation and absorption, by adequate ventilation, radioactive dust control, and periodic inspection of installations. Individuals are monitored for the total amount of their exposure to radiation by means of pocket dosimeters or film badges which are worn while on the job. In most instances of government-regulated atomic reactor experimentation and in university and industry-sponsored isotopic tracer research, it is to be expected that experimentally proved shielding devices will effectively protect research men and plant operators from radiation.

In spite of every conceivable precautionary measure, there still are great potential hazards for the general public and especially for small-company employees who will come in contact in the future with industrial instruments and processes using radioactive materials. We can hardly expect that a rapidly expanding civilian atomic energy business will be free from those radioactive dangers which arise from both negligence and ignorance.

A number of state governments are seriously trying to set up nuclear energy control regulations for themselves; but, in most cases so far, the attempts have bogged down for not knowing what to do and for not being able to find out where the AEC stops and where the state should begin taking over. Legislation passed in the closing days of Congress in 1959 led to some definitive steps toward settling the long controversy over responsibility for developing and enforcing standards for radiation safety. Greater federal state co-operation was urged.

The American Standards Association's Nuclear Standards Board has been advocating a uniform system of keeping records for industrial radiation exposure in order to prevent overexposure for personnel transferring from one job to another. Precautions are then taken to see that the individual's radiation exposure is kept below a designated maximum. Also being studied are safety measures to protect persons employed by producers and users of fissionable material against routine hazards, reactor accidents and runaways, waste disposal, nuclear fuel recovery, packaging, and the handling and transportation of radioactive materials. The Harvard Law School is currently engaged in research on how best to provide financial protection and multilateral agreements to cover the risk of accidents and overexposures in atomic plants.

The disposal of large quantities of radioactive wastes from nuclear reactors and power plants and from industrial usage poses a very special problem. Ideally, these wastes should be stored in inaccessible places until their radioactivity has died away. This is not a simple problem because it takes some radioactive elements an extraordinarily long time to lose all of their radioactivity—in some cases, thousands of years. Without adequate controls, radioactive wastes could become a serious public hazard if there were atomic reactors operating throughout the world. Presumably, it would also be difficult for individual governments to maintain a completely rigorous check on the over-all disposal of radioactive wastes, especially when being handled by private, medical, industrial, and research establishments whose more immediate financial objectives might outweigh any concern for the very long-range effects which small amounts of radiation would have upon the distant offspring of the members of a community. The problem is all the more aggravating in that the experts do not yet quite know what the long-range cumulative effects of different types of radiation may be.

A moment's reflection will convince us that these radioactive wastes cannot simply be drained into rivers or pumped into the atmosphere. One might expect that the oceans would be the ideal dumping ground for radioactive wastes due to the tremendous dilution effects of the great volumes of water. Actually, the dilution effect is not nearly so effective as one might expect because fish and other aquatic animals tend to preferentially accumulate certain heavy elements in their bones. Since these sea animals form a substantial part of the food economy of many maritime countries, the ocean dumping suggestions are not very feasible. Nevertheless, sea-dumping has been used, for example, as a normal procedure by the British Royal Fleet Auxiliaries which several times a year journey out a hundred or so miles to sea to dump concrete-covered metal canisters filled with radioactive disposal. The British have also been experimenting with the dumping of liquid wastes into the Irish Sea and in the Atlantic and Pacific Oceans. Some marine biologists are opposed to putting any radioactive waste in the oceans. The AEC now allows only the dumping of low-level radioactive wastes in ocean areas off the continental shelf where the water is at least 6,000 feet deep. To date, close to a hundred million gallons of high-level waste (mostly from spent nuclear reactor fuels) have been stored in underground tanks in the United States. The AEC has suggested the locking up of radioactive wastes in deep abandoned oil wells.

Studies have also been made to see whether radioactive wastes could be dumped into the Marianas trench in the Pacific where the ocean bottom is almost seven miles below the surface. Russian oceanographers at an IGY meeting in 1958 voiced a complaint to that proposal. Their own studies had shown, they said, that the ocean waters circulate at a much more rapid rate from these depths than had been supposed.

The suggestion has been made that the only remaining safe method would be to periodically send rockets with radioactive wastes to the moon. That idea met with tremendous opposition from scientists all over the world who have pointed out that the contamination of the moon's surface would wreck any future plans to reserve the very special physical and biological conditions now existing on the surface of the moon for making scientific studies which could never be carried out on our contaminated earth.

In May 1958, at the Hague, the International Council of Scientific Unions responded to the National Academy of Sciences' request to establish a Committee on Contamination by Extra-terrestrial Exploration—known since as CETEX. Since its for-mation, this committee has set up some general principles gov-erning space research on the moon and planets, including safe-guards and steps to prevent contamination which would render certain future experiments impossible. In December 1959 the United Nations General Assembly approved the establishment of a permanent Committee for International Co-operation in the Peaceful Uses of Outer Space.

Public apprehension as to the safe disposal of radioactive wastes will probably continue for a long time. This problem, like atomic test explosions and their accompanying fallout dan-gers, will sooner or later have to receive more international attention. This was the feeling expressed by United States AEC Commissioner Floberg at the Vienna IAEA meeting in September 1959. Proposals for immediate action included the setting up of regional or international burial grounds for sea disposal operations, study of the fate of radioactive materials that find their way into international rivers, basic criteria and design for radioisotope laboratories, and a study of the inter-national nature of the waste disposal problem.

The increased use of radioactive materials in industrial assem-bly and packaging techniques has also created a special problem in connection with the radioactive contamination of foods. In a government study made by the Food and Drug Administration, the radioactivity of foods taken from grocery shelves were com-pared with foods canned and processed before the first atomic bomb in 1945. The results, released in October 1958, revealed that notable increases in radioactivity had occurred in tea, dairy products, and some sea foods. Samples of tea harvested in 1956-1957 showed radioactivity averaging thirty times greater than samples harvested before 1945. Some samples were 135 times as radioactive. The amounts according to the Secretary of the Department of Health, Education, and Welfare, were still within "safe" limits. It was assumed that the increase was due to post-1945 fallout and contamination from nuclear power plants and other applications. Vegetables, fruit, meat, wheat, and sugar were all at the same pre-1945 level in radioactivity. Dried fruits have been suspect because they are cured in a manner that could result in exposure.

The 1960 National Academy of Sciences report, which was

mentioned above, was directly concerned with the potential hazards accompanying the consumption of plant and animal products which have accumulated radioactive fission products from soil or vegetation. The apparent disagreement between scientists, the report said, merely reflected a basic lack of essential information. The report further stated that "although the present levels in foodstuffs are low, it is the cumulative and retained isotope burden in man that must be considered." There was also some concern over the uneven distribution fallout in agricultural areas, especially "in view of our current inability to monitor all foods or food ingredients."

The Public Health Service has been devoting special attention to the testing of milk. Strontium-90 in milk is one of the best known means of tracking radioactivity in man, since milk is important in the diet of large numbers of people of all ages. By the end of 1960, samples of all the nation's milk were being tested for radioactive contamination in sixty sampling stations throughout the nation. The Food and Drug Administration simultaneously expanded its program of monitoring foods to detect and evaluate radioactivity due to fallout. It was discovered, for example, that washing spinach reduced its beta radioactivity content by 60 per cent. Comprehensive radioactive water pollution studies were also undertaken, and air and precipitation stations were examining air, rain, and snow for their radioactive count. It was hoped that eventually all of this information could be compiled into a statistical map of the environmental radioactivity in all areas of the United States.

chapter 5

ATOMIC ENERGY FOR PEACE

Thus far we have dealt rather exclusively with the military applications of atomic energy. It would be unfortunate if we were to be left with the impression that research in atomic energy has been devoted solely to the production of weapons of destruction. Some remarks are, therefore, in order concerning the far-flung constructive accomplishments in atomic energy for pure science, engineering, industry, medicine, and agriculture. We shall contrast the peacetime benefits of atomic energy with the military developments as we go along, since the two have evolved side by side since 1945.

Much as it has been said that wars hinder the development of science and technology, it is possible to present a fairly strong case for the opposite thesis, viz., that wars have frequently been a positive stimulus for the development of science and technology. We may point out, for example, that atomic power, electronic devices, and many special types of automation are being used on a considerable scale today as a result of technical progress made during World War II. Similarly the interwar years saw the widespread application of the internal combustion engine to transportation and agriculture, great strides in aircraft construction and wireless communication, and the widespread introduction of the conveyor-belt system. These changes were likewise due largely to progress that had been made during World War I. It could be argued that such advances are far removed from pure, basic, or fundamental scientific activity. Nevertheless, it is certain that a great deal of high-powered engineering equipment and analytical instrumentation is quite indispensable to large areas of even the purest non-utilitarian scientific endeavors. It would be difficult to deny that World War II saw tremendous progress in analytical instrumentation and in a wide variety of scientifically important sensing devices.[1]

[1]See the argument at the end of Chapter 2.

PURE RESEARCH — A BARGAIN FOR AMERICA

Most scientists have felt that a onesided preoccupation with the immediate and practical results of science does not in the long run insure scientific advance. Governments in the past have been criticized repeatedly for shortsightedness in their piecemeal allocation of research funds to scientific projects which seem to "pay off" in the more obvious kinds of positive end results. To the extent that scientific research is specifically designed so as to "pay off" quickly, it becomes the more difficult for an enterprising scientist to venture out into an uncharted area where failure is the rule, but where an occasional fundamental discovery of great importance awaits the investigator at the very frontiers of science.

Most scientists will agree that pure, basic, or fundamental research is a prerequisite for all other technological and engineering applications. Engineering research and development are as necessary for technological progress as pure science, but the task and the method of procedure are more clearly defined in that area. Although it is usually asserted that it is the advance of basic science which alters society, it is, of course, technology which is the carrier of the change, while basic science constitutes the foundation upon which technology can thrive.

What scientists mean by basic science is an activity motivated largely by a bold pioneering type of intellectual curiosity which is as admirable as the highest qualities of endeavor of which man is capable. This type of activity demands broad and far-reaching goals with indefinite deadlines. If new scientific ideas and discoveries are always somewhat unpredictable, then what we really are asking for here is that skilled scientists be allowed to gamble against large odds without the urgency of any "pay off." If a scientist strikes out in a direction of research which he knows in advance will almost certainly give him some positive results, the chances of his making genuine novel advances are probably limited. But the man whose ventures have proved to be obviously successful is the one who will be sought out and subsidized. The officers who are handing out research support do not always understand that basic progress in science ultimately thrives on judicious gambling by competent scientists. Two or three failures in a row may be the best indication that a scientist has set his goals very high. Someday he may hit the jackpot. It would not have to happen very frequently to be worthwhile.

A situation in which advancement in pure science would thrive according to this model is one in which the time and money would be freely allocated to a capable and promising scientist in order for him to do whatever he would like to do. One might wish that the person should work hard at whatever he was planning to do, but perhaps he ought also to know that even hard work would not be required of him if he could accomplish his plans in some other way. No one will deny that it would be very difficult for a governmental agency to finance that kind of research, but it would be the greatest bargain the American people ever received.

INDUSTRIAL AND GOVERNMENTAL LABORATORY RESEARCH

No one questions the importance of university and privately owned research establishments when it comes to basic research. We must also mention the tremendous contribution to basic science by both industrial and governmental laboratories and agencies. It could be argued rather convincingly that industry has been more keenly aware of the importance of subsidizing basic research in many areas than military and congressional bodies have been. At this moment the latter are under tremendous pressure to tag money for "hot" projects which will enable the United States to catch up with the Soviet "lead" in the development of high-powered rocket research, guided systems for continent-spanning weapons, and space control by artificial satellites and planets.

Satellites are not weapons yet, and informed officials do not look upon space as a major battlefield for the foreseeable future. But it is true that the ability to successfully launch rockets with a very high thrust—in which the Soviet Union excels—is related to the ability to effectively launch intercontinental ballistic missiles. Presumably space satellites do have some other potential military uses: communications, mapping, navigation, weather forecasting, spying on military installations on foreign soil, and providing early warning from possible attack. But still, the matter of *who* does *what* first in outer space is going to be very much a matter of national prestige.

While America may have lost face to the Russians in regard to some current "hot" projects, experts in this country more or less agree, and the Russian scientists have admitted as much, that the United States is still ahead in some branches of nuclear physics. As to the whole vast area of chemistry, Russia is hardly in the lead, especially with respect to industrial chemical equipment. The other major areas in which the Soviet Union is lagging are medicine and public health. The present position of the United States in these areas can hardly be attributed to military-oriented research. That belongs to American industry and its management which is not exclusively geared to a wartime economy.

At mid-century, management hardly needs to be sold on basic research. That happened about a generation ago when scientists were just starting to scale the campus walls in appreciable numbers in order to infiltrate industry. The prime responsibility of management toward research has been envisioned recently as one of seeing to it that a country's scientific potential is fulfilled. Twenty-five years ago the number of industrial research laboratories rose from 500 to 1,000. Today there are some 4,300, and the nation's annual expense for industrial research is something like seven billion dollars. It has been estimated that this country has spent more on research since World War II than it did between George Washington's inauguration and Pearl Harbor. Much of this upsurge is related to crash programs during World War II, accompanied by a burgeoning postwar consumer market, but we shall see that a large fraction of these expenditures is directly and indirectly tied up with an atomic energy program which is expanding at a fantastic pace. A major part of that program relates to the peacetime aspects of atomic energy.

New Frontiers in Nuclear Science

The manner in which basic and applied research grew out of the realization of atomic energy under the Manhattan project in this country demands our special attention. The prime objective of the far-flung scientific and engineering activities of this project, and of related postwar government research agencies, has been the utilization of atomic energy for military purposes. In striving for that goal there have been numerous developments which have had a much wider significance than application to war. To date, a tremendous volume of declassified technical information on atomic energy has been published in the areas sponsored by the AEC. These technical reports, which began to take form in the fall of 1944, describe all phases of the government-sponsored research which was set up under the Manhattan project for military purposes. They contain a wealth of basic atomic information which is of tremendous value to scientists in all areas of peacetime atomic research and development.

Immediately after the war the temper of the times was so strained that in some quarters there were serious proposals to put a ban on future investigations dealing with all applications of nuclear fission. It was suggested that only the most drastic restrictive measures would prevent man from blowing himself off this planet. Scientists were quick to point out a host of potential applications of atomic energy to pure research, agriculture, medicine, and industry. In fact, a somewhat bewildered and uncritical public hastily reversed its original fearful attitude toward atomic energy and then went overboard with enthusiasm for the new atomic millennium which was alleged to have in store for man unlimited resources of power, freedom from the irksomeness of daily toil, and cures for cancer, heart disease, and old age.

In spite of all the exaggerations, it is quite obvious that nuclear science has grown within fifty years from a harmless and relatively impractical scientific curiosity to a major determining factor in national welfare and survival. Atomic energy has entered big business. The budget of the United States AEC alone comes to about two billion annual dollars. This does not include the money spent by industry in its privately financed atomic energy programs, which is also considerable. By 1957 the government had an investment in atomic energy amounting to ten billion dollars, not counting the monetary value of the stockpiles of atomic bombs hidden in arsenals around the world. The magnitude of the investment in this country already in 1957 was such that every family on the average had paid for about 300 dollars' worth of government atomic energy business. By 1959 the AEC was exceeded only by the Department of Defense in the magnitude of its scientific activities. About two-thirds of the AEC's research and development program was conducted in government-owned facilities operated under contract with industry and institutions.

Some indication of the phenomenal growth of nuclear research and development in this country can be gained by examining the job offers appearing in current scientific journals. What factors are there to lure scientists into creative, new, and unusual careers in nuclear science? According to the advertisements, there are many: sophisticated assignments; challenging projects (theoretical, experimental, and engineering); professional advancement due to rapid expansion; freedom from routine, and maximum opportunities for original and creative research; special recognition on an individual merit basis for imaginative resourcefulness and for outstanding contributions on the frontiers of science; academic atmosphere and in-training education; top-level associates; environmental factors which encourage the creative process; advantageous geographical placement; attractive salaries, life insurance, sickness benefits, retirement plan, and generous vacations. How inviting for young atomic scientists of this generation to actually be paid well to probe the mysteries of the unknown and to unfold the secrets hitherto denied to twentieth century man. These are the challenges of the new frontier. There are almost limitless opportunities for success in a career in nuclear science—military and civilian—on land, sea, air, and outer space.

The peacetime uses of atomic energy, which have been proposed and in part undertaken by governments and enterprising private industries, both young and old, are simply incredible. We could hardly begin to mention the areas of pure and applied peacetime research in which the release of atomic energy is destined to play vitally important roles in the future. Let us consider some of them.

ELECTRIC POWER FROM ATOMIC REACTORS

Since 1800, when the world's production of energy from coal was negligible, there have been steadily increasing demands upon energy-yielding substances and processes. By 1800, energy from coal began to be supplemented with petroleum and hydroelectric power. At present, in the United States, a non-food energy equivalent of about ten tons of coal is consumed per capita per year. This is obviously much higher than for non-industrialized countries. It is about fifteen times greater than that required for a primitive agrarian existence and about nine times the world average.

The urgency of exploring new methods of obtaining energy will be appreciated in view of the fact that half of the coal which has been consumed by man throughout his history has been burned since 1920. It has been estimated that by 1975 the United States alone will be using energy at the rate of an equivalent of 2 billion tons of coal per year. This is about the energy consumption of the entire world at the present time. If present industrialization and population trends continue in Europe, Asia, Africa, and South and Central America, fossil fuels as sources of energy will have almost disappeared by the end of the next century.

Among the most important scientific achievements of the Manhattan project was the successful construction of an atomic reactor or "pile" in December 1942. This pile accomplished the sustained and controlled release of atomic energy from the fissioning of atomic fuels. This achievement came at a most crucial moment in history, just when the end of conventional sources of energy seemed to be in sight. The success of the atomic pile indicated that it would be theoretically feasible to construct atomic power plants to compete in the production of power with conventional fossil fuels such as coal, liquid petroleum, peat, lignite, natural gas, oil shale, and tar. Atomic fuels, it was seen, would offer the greatest immediate hope of meeting man's future energy needs. We will have some idea of the energy potential which is available from the atomic reactor if we note that three cubic feet of plutonium, weighing one and a half tons, has the energy equivalent of about five million tons of coal.

After the war, both government and private industry took up the challenge of mastering some of the technical difficulties involved in converting atomic energy into electricity. By 1955, it was learned at the first Geneva conference, that about eighty atomic reactors were in use or were being built in the United States, England, Russia, Canada, Australia, France, India, Norway, Spain, Sweden, Switzerland, and Belgium. Every one of these nuclear reactors is a potential electric power station, but most of the reactors in 1955 had been designed as research tools or as producers of fissionable fuels for bombs.

According to the Russians, the world's first atomic *power* station was constructed in the Soviet Union as a 5,000 kilowatt unit; it began operation in June 1954.[2] The power of the installation was generated by a turbogenerator operating on steam produced by the heat of uranium fission in an atomic pile. The energy was utilized to produce electric light, to operate machines at plants and factories, and to drive mechanisms at grain and

[2]P. Semenovsky, *Conquering the Atom* (Moscow, 1956), pp. 47-69.

cattle farms. Until the Geneva conference in August 1955, when Russia presented complete details of her plant, the existence of a Soviet atomic power plant had been questioned by the West. As a part of her sixth Five Years Plan, beginning in 1955, Russia laid plans to build atomic power plants to supply some 2.5 million kilowatts to the Urals and to the Moscow and Leningrad areas. While the central atomic power stations of Russia were rated at a somewhat higher total nuclear capacity than the stations in the United States in 1960, the American nuclear reactor program covered a greater variety of reactor types with greater over-all flexibility.

The Russians have an abundance of conventional fossil fuels, but since they have the economic problem of moving these fuels great distances, atomic power plants strategically placed within Russia would provide a more economical usage of the fossil fuels which they do have. Until recently, however, it did not appear from the Soviet technical literature that Russian engineers had come to any closer agreement on the over-all economic aspects of nuclear power than had their Western counterparts.

In February 1955 Britain announced its intention to proceed with the construction of a full-scale nuclear power station at Calder Hall. This station was built to provide industrial and domestic electricity in competition with conventional coal-burning installations. The reactor first supplied electrical power to Britain's national power system in February 1957. The reactor had been originally planned for the production of plutonium, but the by-product power obtained at its opening was used to serve a town of 100,000 people at about the same cost of electricity as that of a conventional coal power station. It was later expanded to four times its original size.

In March 1957 the British government authorized the construction of nineteen new nuclear plants designed to save eighteen million tons of coal. Today the British are pushing their nuclear power research to the limit. New atomic power stations are being built all over Great Britain. In January of 1960 the British were making plans to build the largest atomic plant in the world at Sizewell, Suffolk. Dwindling coal supplies, the lack of domestic petroleum, and ever-increasing energy demands, have given the British Isles the impetus to take the world's lead in the development of commercial atomic power reactors.

At first the new British nuclear power stations generated electricity at a cost slightly higher than the latest, most efficient coal-fired power stations. By 1962 the cost of electricity produced by nuclear and conventional power plants was predicted to be strictly competitive. The British now estimate that by 1965 twenty-five per cent of all their electrical energy will be supplied from atomic reactors. By 1982 the cost of electricity produced by atomic power is predicted to be half that of electricity from coal. It is worth emphasizing that all current figures for electricity generated from nuclear piles have been worked out on present reactor plans. Much intensive research into new types of reactors is in process in the laboratories of the United Kingdom Atomic Energy Authority and among the British industrial firms directly concerned with the construction of nuclear power plants. It is to be expected that more efficient and more economical reactor designs will produce still more favorable results in the future.

The United Kingdom Atomic Energy Authority, unlike the United States Atomic Energy Commission, is a large scientific organization in the public service, which has been separated from the civil service system in order to achieve great flexibility and speed in administration. A basic and major administrative policy of the authority is the delegation of a maximum responsibility for day-to-day administration to individual groups within the organization.[3]

France became the first country on the west European continent to produce electricity by atomic means. The atomic reactor at Marcoule, which had been primarily designed as a producer of plutonium, began, with the aid of specially constructed steam turbines, to produce sufficient heat in September 1956 to generate a foreseeable maximum of 5,000 kilowatts of electricity. On a commercial basis electricity in France was scheduled for 1959 in a plant in the Loire valley. Many smaller European countries such as Norway, Sweden, Holland, Germany, and Finland have also taken active steps to establish their own atomic power plants.[4]

In Canada the development of an atomic power plant was early placed into the hands of Atomic Energy of Canada, in collaboration with industry and the utility companies. During

[3]For a comparison of the use of scientific manpower in European countries see: Edward McCrensky, *The Scientific Manpower in Europe* (New York, 1958).

[4]Donald J. Hughes, *On Nuclear Energy* (Cambridge, Mass., 1957).

the war, Canada's atomic energy research was incorporated in an integral way into the successes of the Manhattan project. Since the war, Canada has been going her own way in the peacetime development of atomic energy. Unlike England, where natural uranium is scarce, Canada has large deposits of this crucially important metal. The most unusual feature of atomic energy research and development in Canada is that, like all of her other scientific activities, atomic energy does not fall under any governmental department. Her scientific system is therefore highly independent of any political pressure and operates at a consistently high level of competence.

In the United States, where ordinary fossil fuels are relatively cheap, the atomic power program took on a fairly slow time scale of construction while advanced types of experimental reactors took precedence over atomic power stations. As early as 1955, 10,000 kilowatts of electricity were drawn from at least one experimental reactor in West Milton, New York. The electricity was sold by the United States government to private industry.

By January 1959, more than eighty atomic reactors were either operating or under development in the United States. Of these, seven were civilian power reactors in operation, and twenty were civilian reactors in the construction or design stage. Only the Shippingport, Pennsylvania, reactor (60,000 kilowatts) was operating as a power-distribution plant. This plant was dedicated in May 1958 and marked the official advent of electricity from a full-scale civilian nuclear power station in the United States. It was built and operated by the Duquesne Light Company of Pittsburgh and was partly financed by the AEC; Westinghouse designed the reactor. In November of 1958 fifty utility companies had formed the High Temperature Reactor Development Associates to promote a special nuclear power plant to supply the Philadelphia Electric Company's utility system with 40,000 kilowatts.

United States industry by 1959 was also looking forward to a good share of the sales in all foreign markets for power reactors. As an example, we cite the case in which the United States government and General Dynamics were helping the South Koreans to build a one million dollar research reactor as a part of the Korean Atomic Energy Research Institute at Seoul. The United States share of it ($350,000) came from the seventeenth atoms-for-peace grant. For the fiscal year ending June 1959, private enterprise expenditures for the fabrication of power reactors was estimated at 70 million dollars. Total private and federal reactor commitments, civilian and military, were estimated at 400 million for the same one-year period.

By 1960 the United States Army had begun construction of a small atomic-powered town beneath the surface of the Greenland icecap. The nation's largest operating nuclear power reactor was performing "outstandingly well" during its test run in June 1960. The reactor formed the core of the Dresden Nuclear Power Station at San Jose, California. An AEC report in 1960 predicted that by 1970 nuclear power would be economically competitive with conventional power sources in high-cost fuel areas in the United States. It was also reported that before the end of 1960, five nuclear power plants would go into operation in the United States to generate a total of 557,000 kilowatts. Two more were scheduled for operation in 1961 and four more for 1962. As a part of its Plowshare Project the AEC had also undertaken studies to determine the practicability of producing power from underground explosions.

Ever since 1945 there has been considerable discussion in this country on the question of the civilian versus the military role in atomic power plant construction. There were early talks to decide whether or not private industry should be allowed to own patents which would protect atomic development programs and entitle them to profit by their ingenuity. Another question was whether the government would sell fissionable materials to industry at realistic costs, but not so high as to include all of the expensive military developments that had been achieved. To date the AEC has retained the exclusive rights on patents concerned with atomic energy matters under the monopoly set up by the Atomic Energy Act of 1946. The government in this country, therefore, still has complete control over all fissionable materials.

An advisory committee appointed in September 1958 by AEC Chairman McCone studied the over-all American civilian atomic power program and recommended that the government continue to take the lead for a number of years before turning the problem over to private industry. At the end of 1958 the Joint Committee on Atomic Energy proposed to Congress a five-year one-billion-dollar atomic-power program. Crash programs through industry without joint government and AEC leadership were not recommended. Some industry spokesmen were unhappy with the recommendation. The AEC Committee, however, felt that United States atomic power would hardly be able to compete with fossil fuels in less than ten years in some parts of the country and within twenty to thirty years in most parts of the country. Neither the government nor the AEC in 1959 seemed to be in the frame of mind to force the issue of commercial United States atomic power through private enterprise.

ATOMIC AND FOSSIL FUELS IN COMPETITION

Atomic reactors will undoubtedly someday provide heat and electricity for cities, drive steamships, submarines, locomotives, and aircraft, and launch satellites and rockets into outer space. Some of these uses are not absolutely indispensable as yet, and some are clearly exotic. Still, there are already very strong demands for concentrated power in this country. We might cite the heavy chemicals industry, and the cement, brick, glass, iron, and steel manufacturers. These industries are keenly aware of future atomic reactor possibilities and are actively engaged in planning for that day.

To date, atomic power in most countries is still more expensive than electric power produced by the cheapest diesel fuel. We, therefore, realize that atomic energy will have to compete on the economic front with all other sources of fossil fuel and that the initial money outlay for atomic reactor equipment will be very great. Nevertheless, it is estimated that atomic energy reactors could already compete economically with the existing power sources in some cities of the world. The generating costs for electrical power in this country, mostly derived from the burning of coal, vary between 0.3 and 0.8 cents per kilowatt hour. In Sao Paulo, Brazil, electricity is now being produced from generators with diesel oil at a cost of 1.5 cents per kilowatt hour. At the end of 1959 the AEC announced that nuclear power plants would soon be able to generate power for 0.7 to 0.85 cents per kilowatt hour. This would make these plants competitive with 25 per cent of existing United States utility systems.

In this country the goal set by General Electric for 1970 is atomic power at 0.6 cents per kilowatt hour. Whereas atomic power might even now be argued for underdeveloped countries like Tibet and remote parts of Africa where conventional power is expensive, it must be remembered that atomic reactors are feasible only where a constant high load of power is in demand. In the underdeveloped countries, consumer power demands in general are low. Still, Pakistan, Iraq, Brazil, and Argentina have recently shown a great deal of genuine interest in small atomic reactors.

The rate at which nuclear power will develop in the world in future will depend on the extent to which the nuclear industries in any particular area shall be able to compete with dwindling fossil fuel reserves. Present estimates of reserves are full of vagaries and pitfalls. Petroleum experts are predicting increased reserves from methods not now being exploited, as well as from the utilization of large amounts of gas now being wasted.[5] Comprehensive analyses of global energy resources and demands have been made by Norman Lansdell[6] and by Hans Thirring.[7]

These authors compare all of the new sources of energy—wind power, water power, fossil-fuel resources, solar energy, and electrochemical generation of electricity—with the world's foreseeable atomic energy resources. It is generally understood that the world's energy demands are increasing at such a fantastic rate that all known coal, wood, and oil reserves would not meet the foreseeable needs of the twenty-first century.

While much of the requisite knowledge concerning reactors is still in the experimental stage, it is not hard to imagine that an extensive new technology of power would have important effects upon economic activities in any country. We merely mention the changes in the location of economic activity which would be brought about with the establishment of atomic reactors far away from conventional supplies of fuel and natural power. The effect could well work itself out into a sequence of complicated repercussions of one economic sector of the world on another. If cheap atomic power plants could be constructed virtually anywhere, oil and coal fields and waterfalls would no longer be the dominant factors in the location of manufacturing plants. Cheap atomic power would mean cheap hydrogen gas

[5]Bruce C. Netschert, *The Future Supply of Oil and Gas* (Baltimore, 1958).

[6]Norman Lansdell, *The Atom and the Energy Revolution* (Middlesex, England, 1958).

[7]Hans Thirring, *Energy for Man, Windmills to Nuclear Power* (Bloomington, Indiana, 1958).

from electrolysis of water, and this in turn would lower the cost of manufacture of ammonia for fertilizers. It might alter the conventional metallurgical process for iron and steel. Nuclear power would also help to eliminate smog.

We must not paint too rosy a picture for the future, for even essentially free energy will not solve the serious problem of the world's future supply of carbon. Carbon, which is mostly available in the world's petroleum reserves, is the starting product for the synthetic organic chemicals industry—rubber, plastics, fiber, pharmaceuticals, etc. The question of reserves is aggravated by the brute fact that 75 per cent of the earth's petroleum reserves are in the Middle East. This obviously accounts for the stubbornness with which nations have tried to hold on to these areas in the past.

Students of economic geography have demonstrated that in the past a close correlation has usually existed between a country's willingness to declare war and its economic status with respect to the industrial power necessary to successfully back up and carry out a declaration of war. It is a well established fact that one of the most reliable indices of a nation's industrial and military potential is its available power. This will serve as a guide for its economic status, its military potential, and its standard of living. Available power has conventionally been reckoned mostly in terms of coal, oil, and water power. What is going to happen when the older political systems, based on the strength of conventional power, no longer are in possession of the necessary reserve to back up a declaration of war? Uranium is fairly widely distributed all over the world. What kind of power politics is going to operate when many small nations have their own atomic reactors to carry out basic research, or to supply heat and electricity to cities, or to convert uranium into plutonium for atomic bombs? It is a relatively simple matter to transform peacetime nuclear reactors and power plants into factories for converting ordinary uranium into plutonium for atomic bombs.

Atomic reactors may help to develop countries poor in natural resources and may for the first time in modern history provide a reasonably decent existence for peoples whose standard of living has been incredibly low. But atomic reactors also provide the means for nuclear warfare. What are the big powers going to do when men everywhere become conscious of the right to rule

themselves? And then, what if they acquire the power to demand that their right to rule themselves be put into effect? We
might suggest that in the twentieth century the nonwhite peoples
of the world will not rest content to see Western technology lay
them flat. They have felt that way for a long time, but atomic
reactors may provide them with the opportunity to do something
about it. Billy the Kid, who was once a helpless runt standing
beside a six-foot-two rustler from Oklahoma City, became a
major terror with the invention of the revolver. The analogy
applies to small nations with atomic weapons.

THERMONUCLEAR POWER

This is all we shall have to say here about the peacetime
production of atomic power by means of uranium reactors. But
we have not thereby exhausted our discussion of the potential
sources of atomic power. What about thermonuclear fusion?
In Chapter 1 we mentioned that the thermonuclear fusion of
lighter elements had been predicted to be theoretically feasible.
In Chapter 3 we discussed some of the military uses of thermonuclear bombs. The question which we must now raise is
whether there are any peacetime applications of thermonuclear
fusion. Various suggestions have been made for the use of H-
bombs: the leveling of mountains, the melting of Arctic ice-
caps, the bottoming-out of old harbors and the creation of new
ones, the dislodging of shale oil from sand, the production of
underground power reservoirs, and the dispersal of the energy
of hurricanes into the stratosphere.

A more challenging assignment confronting scientists today
is to devise means of controlling the thermonuclear fusion reaction in a manner which is analogous to the controlled atomic
fissioning of uranium which Fermi and his associates accomplished in 1942. One can calculate, for example, that the
conversion of one pound of hydrogen into helium would be
equivalent theoretically to the release of about 11 million kilowatts of electricity.

Mere reflection on the problem will reveal the enormous
difficulty of accomplishing a controlled thermonuclear fusion
reaction. For, given that one can discover how to *maintain* a
reaction at 10 to 100 million degrees, how is one to *contain* it?
This would be like asking the ancient alchemists in what kind
of a container they expected to store their much sought-after

"universal solvent," if they ever got it. How shall one house a reaction which requires the energy equivalent of millions of degrees to proceed, when even the most refractory alloys and ceramics will melt and vaporize at temperatures below ten thousand degrees? This, to thermonucleonics experts, is the current 64 million dollar question. If the solution to this specific problem seems inconceivable and impossible, it will not be the first time that scientists have tackled such problems—as the history of science will attest. Without going into the details of thus-far attempted solutions to the problem, we should mention that the reactions conceivably might be induced to take place without contacting the walls of the container.

The Institute of Atomic Energy of the U.S.S.R. Academy of Science was engaged in experimental and theoretical investigations into controlled thermonuclear fusion as early as 1951. In April 1956 the late director of this institute, Soviet Academician Igor Kurchatov, who helped develop the first Soviet atomic and hydrogen bombs, broke the classification barrier on this subject in a talk at Harwell, England, and spoke for the first time about the efforts of the U.S.S.R. Academy of Science to control thermonuclear reactions with heavy hydrogen. Temperatures of one million degrees were reported. The Russian accomplishments to date are contained in a four-volume publication which was published in English translation in 1959 in London.

British thermonuclear research has concentrated on the so-called Zeta experiment, designed at Harwell, England, under the United Kingdom Atomic Energy Research Establishment. In this experiment, heavy hydrogen is stripped of all of its electrons in a near-vacuum electric discharge tube constructed in the shape of a doughnut. The "temperature" of this "plasma" of heavy hydrogen, where all the atoms of the gas are present as stripped nuclei and electrons, is raised to several million degrees (energy equivalent), using electrical currents of 200,000 amperes. By means of a magnetic method of focusing, similar to the one used by the Russians, the electrons and nuclei in the plasma are constrained in closed circular curves. The magnetic field acts to constantly drive the plasma toward the center of the chamber where it is confined to a thin cord. It is thereby barred from approaching the walls. This magnetic restriction is called the "pinch effect," and the chamber is called the "magnetic bottle." The Zeta experiments have achieved the equiva-

lent of five million degrees of temperature.   In 1959 the British
Atomic Energy Authority announced plans to build a research
station exclusively devoted to thermonuclear power.

The United States, in its earliest phases of thermonuclear
research, was a little reluctant to announce the status of its
thermonuclear programs.   Toward the end of 1957, the British
press took the United States AEC to task for withholding vital
information which had been obtained by both the United States
and Britain on controlled thermonuclear reaction research.   Early
in 1958, then, the AEC revealed that temperature equivalents
of 5 to 6 million degrees had been achieved in Los Alamos; that
the reacting materials, the hot "plasma," had been held in the
reaction zone for small fractions of a second, using the "pinch
effect."   As the year progressed, all sorts of thermonuclear information cleared the hurdle of secrecy.

By the fall of 1958 the declassification of fusion research was
virtually complete.   The AEC then revealed that besides research
into the "pinch effect" at Los Alamos, the United States was
attacking the problem from three other approaches: Princeton's
magnetic Stellerator scheduled for completion late in 1960;   the
University of California's "mirror machine"; and the Oak Ridge
National Laboratory's "hot injection system."   Temperatures the
equivalent of 50 million degrees were anticipated.   Some idea
of the magnitude of United States effort directed toward thermonucleonics can be obtained from its 1959 fiscal budget of 39
million dollars.   A short nontechnical report of the United
States program on controlled fusion was published by the AEC
in 1958 in time for distribution to the official delegates of the
Second Geneva Conference on the Peaceful Uses of Atomic
Energy.[8]

At the time of this writing the control of thermonuclear fusion
has not yet been realized.   In spite of much brilliant theoretical,
experimental, and engineering work in France, West Germany,
the United Kingdom, Russia, and United States, no country has
yet succeeded in producing a true controlled thermonuclear
reaction.   By mid-1960, in a report to the Joint Committee on
Atomic Energy, scientists reported that after two years of intensive research, fusion looked a lot more promising as a potential
energy source than it did in 1958.   Scientists now are hopeful

[8]Amasa S. Bishop, *Project Sherwood* (Reading, Mass., 1958).

that concerted effort on the part of many scientists the world over will sooner or later bring positive results. In this area of research, international co-operation is very close, since the work has been freed from secrecy restrictions.

Curiously enough, there now seems to be some evidence that man-made satellites probing space within our solar system may turn up not only knowledge of how our galaxies have developed, but also information which would be useful to tame the H-bomb reaction and solve the problem of peacetime thermonuclear fusion as well. This has to do with discovering how electromagnetic fields originate in stars and space; how particles speed up so as to produce auroras and cosmic rays.

If it were to be discovered that the thermonuclear reaction could be put under control, as the uranium reaction has been, then it can be calculated that at the present rate of energy consumption the thermonuclear fuel supply in the seas would last almost indefinitely. It has been estimated, for example, that there is enough deuterium in sea water to produce power at one thousand times the current rate for a million years. At the present rate of consumption of energy, the world's easily obtainable fossil fuel reserves would by comparison be exhausted in something less than 100 years, and the nuclear fuels for fission in some 200 years.

Fusion reactions, if they could be achieved, would conceivably have the advantage over conventional uranium reactors of allowing the nuclear energy to be converted into electrical or magnetic energy without going through the stages from heat to steam, to turbine, to generator, to electricity—which is what now happens in the uranium power reactors. Another advantage would be the production of very much less unwanted radioactive waste product than in the conventional fission reactor.

One other important matter should be mentioned. We have already said that uranium reactors for peacetime power can be converted almost overnight into installations for producing the plutonium necessary for atomic bombs. Thermonuclear power reactors, by contrast, would be of no direct military value in the production of bombs. This is not to say dogmatically that present-day advances in peacetime thermonuclear research never will have any military applications. We can illustrate this with an example. We recall from Chapter 3 that three atomic bombs were exploded 300 miles above the South Atlantic in late August and early September 1958 to test the possibility of stopping an incoming missile by setting up a sheet of high-energy electrons. The idea for these shots resulted from research at the University of California's Radiation Laboratory while working on methods to control the fusion reaction of hydrogen for peaceful purposes —a program known as Project Sherwood. In the laboratory a device was proposed to produce a sheet of high-energy electrons, called the E-layer, to provide the magnetic confinement of the plasma and for heating it to thermonuclear temperatures. The Atlantic tests showed that the same kind of effect also worked to trap electrons in the earth's magnetic field.

Indirectly, thermonuclear reactors would also be of value in wartime, since any means of supplying almost limitless amounts of energy would be of obvious military value to a nation. Wartime economies present a terrific drain on all the available energy resources of a country.

ATOM-POWERED TRANSPORTATION

Finally, let us indicate some of the successful applications of atomic power to transportation. Politically and technically this has been a controversial subject in the United States as well as in the Soviet Union. All manned vehicles propelled by atomic energy require large bulky shielding devices to protect the personnel and the instruments from radiation. This presents difficult technical problems for units below a certain size.

The risks associated with the future use of nuclear-powered means of transportation center in devising special methods of radioactive waste disposal and of retaining the fission products of the reactors in case of fire, collision, crash, or engine failure due to corrosion. Any such catastrophe—for example, to a ship in port in a large city—would expose a very large number of people to lethal doses of radiation. This presumably was what the Danish officials were worried about in September 1958 when they denied entrance to a nuclear-powered United States submarine at the port of Copenhagen. On a number of occasions the Pentagon has dropped hints about American bombers which have crashed while carrying nuclear weapons. There have also been half a dozen instances of nuclear bombs dropped accidentally from planes in flight. None of these cases have resulted in an atomic explosion. A nuclear-powered society will presumably have to set up stringent rules and regulations for land, sea, and air travel. Radiation inspectors may someday become as commonplace as policemen and firemen. In spite of great obstacles, much progress has been made in atom-powered transportation.

The Russians' most advanced and most publicized nuclear propulsion project was the building of the world's first atomic-powered civilian ship, the icebreaker *Lenin,* now in regular operation. This surface vessel was launched in December 1957; in September 1959 it left Leningrad on its maiden voyage into the Baltic. The 44,000 horse power which was developed by the ship's three atomic reactors was said to be double that of the next biggest conventional icebreaker afloat, the American *Glacier.* It was reported that the *Lenin* could operate easily through six-foot ice. Ordinarily a ship of such size would require some 200 tons of oil daily. The *Lenin* will require refueling once every other year. This vessel was designed with the objective of widening the scope of scientific exploration in the central polar basin by opening up places in the Arctic hitherto inaccessible by aircraft, submarine, or ice-drifting station. The ship also served to extend shipping along the presently used channels of high-latitude Soviet sea routes along a 3,000-mile northern coast line. This coast line which is ice-bound for most of the year, stretches in the west from Murmansk on the Berents Sea in the Atlantic Ocean to the east through Bering Strait into the Pacific Ocean. There is no doubt but that strategic military advantage is also gained for the Russians by keeping supply routes open to theaters of military operation in the Far North from which the North American continent can be easily struck.

In 1959 the United States Navy launched its first nuclear-powered surface vessel, the guided-missile cruiser U.S.S. *Long Beach.* On the civilian scene, 1959 saw the launching of the world's first nuclear-powered passenger cargo vessel which was christened the N.S. (Nuclear Ship) *Savannah.* Estimated cost was about 40 million; fueling range was 300,000 miles on a charge of 132 pounds of enriched uranium oxide. It was hoped that the *Savannah* would demonstrate to the world the employ-ment of nuclear power in an instrument of peace in trade and commerce. In the words of President Eisenhower, "This new vessel will be a floating laboratory, providing indispensable infor-mation for the further application of atomic energy in the field

of ocean transportation."[9]   These events marked the beginning
of new methods of ocean-going transportation which may well be
as revolutionary as the changeover from wind-driven ships to
steamships which took place 150 years ago.

While the world's first atomic civilian surface ship, the icebreaker *Lenin,* was a Soviet accomplishment, the world's first
atomic submarine, the *Nautilus,* was launched by the Americans
in January of 1954.   A year later it was put to test in the sea.
During 1958 the United States completed a number of record-
breaking exploits in the area of nuclear submarines.   During
March the U.S.S. *Skate* crossed the Atlantic in 7.2 days.   The
Nautilus sailed across the top of the world under the Arctic
icecap.   The *Seawolf* submerged for 60 days without snorkeling,
distilling its own water, and purifying its own air by using power
from its nuclear reactor.

By June 1960 the navy had laid plans for a fleet of 45 Polaris
submarines costing 100 million dollars each and equipped to
launch 1,500-mile atomic warhead ballistic missiles.   This was
at a cost of about 15 dollars for every man, woman, and child
in the United States.   We recognize in these recent submarine
advances both the peacetime study of the fascinating world
under the Arctic icecap, but also the carrier of the deadliest of
missiles capable of destroying in one blow a city the size of
Washington, D. C.   There has been no definitive published
evidence that the Russians had nuclear submarines by the end
of 1959, although there is no reason why this should be technically beyond them.

Nuclear-propelled aircraft, manned and unmanned, are presumably still in the developmental stage in both the United
States and Russia.   Reports that the Russians have flown an
atomic plane have not been verified.   There are a number of
technically difficult problems associated with the successful operation of nuclear aircraft.   The most important of these is
connected with the heavy and bulky shielding necessary to protect the personnel and the instruments from the radiations of
the atomic reactor.   Feasible long distance air transportation
would probably be of greater significance to the Russians than
to the West because they have such tremendous internal distances to cover.   Besides, they do not possess the overseas air

[9]*Science,* May 1, 1959, p. 1213.

bases with which the United States Air Force has surrounded
Communist countries.

In 1960 the United States AEC revealed that it was engaged
in experiments to study the possibility of unmanned nuclear-
propelled satellites and space ships. A superrocket for space
research, with two of its five stages being atomic, was scheduled
for completion in 1964. These rockets, it was said, would do
the job of a forty-eight-million-dollar rocket at half price.

Nuclear Developments in the Communist Bloc

Throughout our discussion thus far we have attempted to
indicate the level of specific technological accomplishments for
Russia and the Western powers. To judge from end results,
one might suggest that Soviet nuclear efforts are roughly comparable to those of the United States. In general, it is perhaps
true, however, that the scientific and technological potential of
the Soviet Union has been somewhat underestimated in the
West. Soviet restrictions on the release of information have
had something to do with this underestimation. It is desirable
to emphasize here that the total economic and political framework of the West and Russia are different in so many ways
that simple comparisons of their respective technological achievements often fail utterly to provide us with a meaningful and
unbiased estimate of the true state of affairs.

Apart from all of the Soviet advances mentioned thus far,
we must point out that the entire Soviet bloc of states allied
to the Soviet Union and under Communist government will
ultimately have some part in both the military and industrial
aspects of the expanding nuclear potentials of the world.[10] (In
Soviet bloc we include here primarily the European satellite
states—Poland, Czechoslovakia, Romania, Hungary, Bulgaria,
Albania, and East Germany—and Communist China.) George
Modelski, who has analyzed atomic energy in the whole Communist bloc concludes that, "Although internal obstacles to
technological adaptation are great (bureaucratic inertia, a de-
pressed standard of living, the deadening demand for political
conformity and penalties on the unorthodox), the political system
may still provide the necessary impetus for change, and atomic

[10]An excellent source of information on the industrial developments of
the Communist part of the world is given by George A. Modelski, *Atomic
Energy of the Communist Bloc* (Melbourne University Press, 1959).

energy could carry the Communist economies to higher levels of industrial power."[11]

Following the end of World War II, while the United States and the United Kingdom issued comprehensive technical reports on many phases of the development of their atomic energy programs, Russia continued to withhold most of the information which historians would need in order to reconstruct the history of the atomic energy program inside the Soviet Union. As a matter of fact, there was practically a total blackout in Communist publications on Soviet atomic efforts between 1945 and 1955. Nuclear co-operation, even within the Soviet bloc, between Russia and her European satellites and China, was virtually nonexistent. This was the period during which the Russians manufactured atomic weapons. In the West, by contrast, the level of atomic research and development could be gauged to some extent after 1949 simply from the knowledge of demonstrated technological accomplishments. But in the Russian literature there was virtually no information.

On January 17, 1955, the Soviet Council of Ministers announced through their news agency *Tass* that peaceful atomic programs were being launched in China, Poland, Czechoslovakia, Romania, and East Germany. The Soviet government, it was stated, would share her own scientific and technical personnel and her equipment and data with these governments so that they could eventually set up their own atomic research establishments. The Soviet Union's liberal release of atomic information thus was accompanied by a push into the area of domestic peaceful atomic energy programs for the more advanced Russian-dominated states. It was also in 1955 that the West accelerated its world-wide distribution of industrial atomic programs, especially after scientists from all over the world convened in Geneva to discuss the peaceful uses of atomic energy.

Large-scale plans for nuclear expansion, therefore, started to unfold and take shape in Eastern Europe and in China in 1955. Each state was initially offered an isotope-producing experimental reactor and a cyclotron capable of accelerating alpha particles to 25 million electron volts, along with Soviet assistance in putting these machines into operation. Beyond this, the nations were given a chance to set up their own organizations for

[11]Modelski, *loc cit.*, pp. 214, 215.

building power stations and for handling problems pertaining to isotope production, instrumentation, radiation protection for personnel, measurement of fallout, etc.[12]

Until now, all the reactor programs have been under close Soviet supervision because, lacking the facilities, the uranium ore had to be sent to Russia for processing. The more advanced bloc nations like China, however, have indicated their desire to make their own domestic atomic programs autonomous as quickly as possible. Russia has kept in close contact with these nations by encouraging visits of their atomic scientists to the Joint Institute of Nuclear Research at Dubna in the Soviet Union. This is a co-operative research center but with policy clearly in the hands of the Soviet officials.

The increased flow of Soviet information with emphasis on the peaceful atomic energy matters after 1955 had obvious propaganda value. "It would be most unwise," says Modelski, "to conclude from the publicity accorded to the peaceful uses of atomic energy that at any time the military applications had anything less than full priority in Soviet planning."[13]

RADIOISOTOPES IN BIOLOGY AND MEDICINE

Atomic power, as we have discussed it, is only a small part of the over-all peacetime atomic energy program. We now want to move on to a consideration of the use of atomic reactors as producers of radioactive isotopes, sometimes called radio-isotopes or tracer isotopes. The examples which we shall cite were chosen at random from an enormous field. They can do no more than illustrate the growing importance of the use of isotopes.

Isotopes of one and the same element differ in certain physical properties, but mainly in their atomic weights and their radio-activity. The unique applicability of radioisotopes to scientific research derives from the fact that during the process of spontaneous disintegration these isotopes constantly emit radiations. These can be detected with simple electronic devices like ionization chambers, Geiger counters, and photo-emulsions. Radioisotopes, one might say, are "tagged" or "labeled" atoms which

[12]Anne M. Jonas, "Atomic Energy in Soviet Bloc Nations," *Bulletin of Atomic Scientists,* Nov. 1959, pp. 379-383.
[13]Modelski, *loc cit.,* p. 4.

cannot hide their identity in the presence of Geiger counters. Each radioisotope has its own characteristic spectra of radiation and its own disintegration rate. That is what distinguishes its atoms from those of all other isotopes. The technique of locating these radioisotopes is called the tracer technique.

Fortunately, radioisotopes of most elements can be obtained easily in almost any desired quantity by inserting specific chemical substances into an atomic reactor. It is there that the elements are altered and rendered radioactive by virtue of the high neutron density of the reactor system. Radioisotopes were produced with the aid of cyclotrons before the war, but nuclear reactors can now outproduce the cyclotrons in this respect by a billion times. Great Britain, we have mentioned, was the great pioneer in the design and construction of new types of atomic reactors, and it has also been by far the greatest producer and exporter of radioisotopes since the war.

The use of the radioisotope tracer technique has been extended to every conceivable area of the physical and biological sciences, as well as to earth sciences such as meteorology, geology, paleontology, and oceanography. Let us in first place cite a number of specific and representative examples of the manner in which the tracer technique has been adapted to research in the biological and medical sciences. To date, it has been possible to obtain radioisotopes for almost every biologically important element, the two notable exceptions being oxygen and nitrogen.

It is well known that iodine, when circulated through the blood stream, is taken up preferentially by certain glands in the body. By means of the salt of radioactive iodine-131 it is a relatively simple matter to find out exactly where and at what rate the iodine is absorbed. By holding a Geiger counter near different parts of the body, after injecting or ingesting the radioactive iodine salt, one can tell, from the local intensity of the radiation, where the iodine is being preferentially absorbed. In the Royal Marsden Hospital in England there is a completely automatic robot capable of drawing a map of the human body which indicates how a radioactive tracer has distributed itself in various organs of the body.

Since it is known that cancerous growths will absorb certain elements preferentially, radioactive atoms have also been used to locate the growths quickly. Thus the preferential absorption of iodine by brain tumors has been used to locate growths in

order to carry out skull surgery. Radioiodine has also been used
to calculate the total amount of blood in an individual or animal.
The experiment takes fifteen minutes. The calculation is simple
and merely requires the determination of the extent of dilution
of the radioiodine in the blood. Incidentally, the same isotopic
dilution technique can be applied, using radioactive carbon-14,
to determine the amount of natural gas in a large storage tank.

Another widely used tracer isotope is calcium-45. Very important investigations with radiocalcium have indicated the manner in which calcium from milk is distributed in the bones and
teeth of a growing child. In another instance, studies have
shown that chicken eggs contained some chemicals from food
eaten up to forty days before the egg was laid. On the other
hand, the calcium-rich shell was formed almost entirely from
food eaten within a day or two before the egg was laid.

In many cases it has been of value to study the physiological
fate of complex organic pharmaceuticals and drugs in the body.
Frequently the chemist is able to synthesize these substances and
incorporate radiocarbon into the molecules so that the physiolo-
gist can trace their course in the body. In a great many
instances, however, the physiologically interesting substances
(usually fairly complex chemically) have not yet been synthe-
sized by chemists, although they can be obtained from nature.
The trick is to discover a method of radioactively tagging these
materials which are available from natural sources. It is impossible to render such natural organic substances radioactive
by placing them directly into the atomic reactor, although that
is the way in which radioactive iron, for example, is obtained.

This problem has been solved in an ingenious way by supplying radioactive carbon dioxide to growing plants in a greenhouse, so that by the natural process of photosynthesis the radiocarbon ends up in the physiologically important material. The
radioactive material can then be extracted from the plant.
Radioactive carbon dioxide is easily obtained by burning radioactive carbon, which in turn is produced in the atomic pile by
irradiating nitrogen. In this manner it is possible, for example,
to obtain radioactive digitoxin, the vital heart drug from the
foxglove plant. By the tracer technique it is possible to determine how long the drug remains in the human body after having
been administered intravenously. It is possible to determine

how much of it reaches the brain.   Scientists had no method of attacking such problems fifteen years ago.

By the same greenhouse technique it would be possible to obtain ragweed pollen to study hayfever and seasonal asthma. The same can be done for belladonna, the source of atropine, or hellebore and meadow saffron used as a gout remedy and as a tumor inhibitor.   Or one might study marijuana physiologically, or morphine, or plant hormones and vitamins.   This method is a veritable bonanza for pharmacological research.

In one specific case, University of Chicago pharmacologist E. M. K. Geiling wanted to learn more about the physiological effects of an arrow poison used by West India tribesmen.   The poison comes from a creamy substance secreted in the glands high on the neck of the Jamaican toad.   Dr. Geiling wanted to study the preferential mode of action of this poison on the human heart.   He needed radioactive toad poison.   He solved his problem as follows.   He first grew radioactive lettuce in a special greenhouse supplied by radioactive carbon dioxide.   He fed the radioactive lettuce to snails, and then he fed the radioactive snails to Jamaican toads.   In time he collected the radioactive neck juice from the toads and used it for his research. In his studies the radioactive toad poison revealed its identity wherever it went, as its radioactive carbon atoms disintegrated. He could determine what happened to the drug as it entered the body, how long it stayed, in what tissues it was preferentially taken up, and at what rate the body ultimately disposed of the drug.

In another experiment, by the British National Institute of Medical Research, radioactive carbon dioxide was bubbled through green pondweed known as chlorella.   The chlorella was fed to a chicken which in due course laid an egg containing radioactive albumen.   The latter was crystallized and purified in order to study the attack of antibodies on albumen.   It eventually yielded valuable information on the human body's protective mechanisms against disease.

By similar methods it is possible to grow radioactive alfalfa in the atomic greenhouse and feed it to animals.   Later, radioactive materials from the pituitary, adrenal, and thyroid glands and cholesterol from the nerve tissue can be obtained from the slaughtered animal. Radioactively tagged, these biologically interesting substances are used to great advantage because the radiocarbon can be followed throughout the body: in the exhaled carbon dioxide of the breath, in the excrements, the urine, the blood, and the body sweat. Radiocarbon truly provides a most unique method of studying the complex metabolic functions of the human body. The radiotracer technique in general is certainly one of the most potent research tools ever to have been placed into the hands of medical researchers. Perhaps the value of the tracer technique will someday be compared to that of the compound microscope.

Apart from their use in medical research, the radioisotopes of sodium, iodine, phosphorous, cobalt, gold, strontium, sulfur, carbon, and bromine are being employed extensively in the clinical treatment of patients. Medical officials estimated already at the end of 1958 that radioactive isotopes were being used to diagnose or treat various ailments in seventeen hundred American hospitals. More than a quarter million Americans are now receiving radiocobalt treatment annually.

We have already mentioned the fact that some elements are absorbed preferentially in certain parts of the human body. Medical therapy takes advantage of this in the location and treatment of goiter, localized cancer, and brain tumors. This is accomplished by administering radioactive doses of elements which preferentially locate themselves in certain tissues. Once located in the cancerous or tumorous area, the radioisotopes destroy unhealthy malignant cells by radiation. In cases where surgery is particularly hazardous, these radioactive materials offer almost the only means of treating malignant cells without totally destroying the surrounding healthy tissue. Tumor therapy can be carried out by inserting radiocobalt needles into the diseased tissue or by locating atomic pellets at the site of the cancer.

All living cells will be damaged by radiation, but sensitivity to damage in cells is very greatly increased while the cell is in the process of division. Cells in malignant growths, i.e., those which divide and multiply (proliferate) at an abnormal rate, are damaged more than normal cells. Thus malignant growths are held in check. Where external radiation treatment was formerly accomplished with X-ray machines and radium, it is now possible to utilize cobalt-60 sources which are so powerful as to be equivalent to two pounds of radium. Still, the powerful rays from cobalt-60 can be pinpointed so accurately that the healthy tissue is not injured by side-scatter as much as with the former radium and X-ray treatments.

Research activities at the Mount Sinai Hospital in New York revealed in 1960 that small doses of radiation directed toward the heart appeared to be capable of providing the heart muscle with new blood supplies even after the normal pathway of blood to the heart became clogged.

RADIOISOTOPES IN AGRICULTURE AND INDUSTRY

Radioisotopes have also been applied successfully to agriculture. Biologists and agronomists are now able to use tagged atoms to study processes that take place below the surface of the soil. They can observe how plants assimilate nutrition and how metabolic reactions transpire in the plant cells.

Synthetic plant fertilizers containing phosphorus-32 can be traced through the entire cycle from the time of addition to the soil to the ultimate fruit or seed. In this way it is possible to determine how much of the phosphorus ends up in the leaves of a plant, how much in the root, say of the potato. When we recall that the United States now spends annually over a billion dollars on fertilizers, we can see that the information from radioactive fertilizer research would be important to the Department of Agriculture.

Tracer research has also been used to advantage in the study of the productivity of crops as correlated with the amounts of various trace elements that get into the growing plant. One totally unexpected result in this direction has been that plants absorb many trace elements more efficiently through the leaves on external spraying than they do through conventional fertilizers applied to the soil. It has also been discovered that nonroot feeding such as spraying, pollination, and curing have an important influence on improving harvests. Experiments are under way to determine what role trace quantities of cobalt, zinc, copper, strontium, and many other elements may play in increasing harvest yields and cattle productivity.

In addition to the medical and agricultural uses of radioisotopes we find that industry has simply gone hog-wild experimenting with radioactive materials. We will limit our remarks here to a general description of a few of the most common areas of application.

An extremely important application which could revolutionize the metals industry makes use of radioactive iron to study the rate of tool and engine wear. The conventional method of studying these factors has been to determine the time necessary to wear away a significant part of a tool or machine. Sometimes that took months, and with automobile engines it took much longer. Since 1953, when the Shell Oil Company demonstrated the new technique in London, the tool or piston of an automobile is placed into an atomic pile; then, after the machine's test performance, the crankcase oil or metallic chips are analyzed for radioactivity. A simple calculation permits the evaluation and extrapolation of the lifetime performance of the tool or machine. This can be accomplished without stopping or dismantling the machinery. The cost of these experiments is about two per cent of previous cost by conventional methods. This is important industrially for the lathe, drill press, and shaper business which amounts to ten billion dollars per year.

The same method can be applied to determining the rate of automobile tire wear. The life history of a tire can be measured by tracer techniques in a matter of minutes. Recurrent features in the wear on piston rings, pistons, bearings, gear wheels, and other aircraft and automobile parts are similarly determined.

A second area of industrial application has to do with the utilization of the effects of the radiation emitted by the radioactive wastes from atomic reactors. This application includes all of the new factory packaging and monitoring devices and the radioactive thickness gauges and calipers which operate on the basis of interrupted and intensity-monitored radiation beams in a production line. For example, by using radioactive wastes, the thickness of sticky flows of linoleum and hot rolled steel sheets are carefully regulated for thickness at great speeds, without any contact of the measuring device. According to one recent estimate, 90 per cent of all tire fabrics and 80 per cent of all tin cans are now subjected to radioactive thickness gauge tests.

Other applications are sterilization of fresh meats to keep them several months without refrigeration; extension of storage time for potatoes and vegetables; sterilization of city sewage for recovery of the proteins for animal feeds; the hastening of seed germination for early agricultural crops; the detection of leaks in oil pipelines, water supply lines, and sewage systems; tests for the efficiency of mixing processes; the spotting of blow holes, bubbles, fissures, and casting flaws in steel plate and other metal

items at substantial depths below the surface; the examination
of the refractory lining of blast furnaces during high-temperature operation, etc. By the end of 1958 more than 1,300
United States establishments were using atomic tools of some
sort or another. It was stated by AEC's W. F. Libby at Geneva
in 1958 that radioactive isotopes in 1957 had saved the American
economy 500 million dollars in the form of improved production
techniques.

A number of industries are already working toward atomic
energy applications which are far in advance of any foreseeable
customer demands. For example, a number of petroleum industries are actively engaged in the application of atomic radiation to the creation of new petroleum processes and products.
They are convinced that if they do not do the basic research
now, they will have little opportunity to take advantage of
atomic radiation advances in the future.

Atomic Energy in Fundamental Research

In our discussion thus far we have emphasized the utilitarian
exploitation of peacetime atomic energy. Scientists on the whole
welcome all of these aspects of atomic energy, but there is little
doubt that, for many individuals, science itself is just as much
of an end in itself as literature or the fine arts. Scientists are,
therefore, perhaps most excited about the application of all the
new nuclear tools and concepts to problems of a more fundamental nature.

These problems have to do with man's persistent attempts
to narrow down the area of ignorance concerning the underlying
structure of matter. Scientists would like to have a much better
understanding of the complex balance of many interdependent
factors operating in the inorganic world and in all forms of
animal life. What, for example, are the strange forces (neither
electrical nor gravitational) which hold the protons and neutrons
together in the nucleus? What function do the thirty or more
subnuclear particles play for the nucleus? How is matter transformed into radiation? What are cosmic rays, and what is
their origin? Most of the specific details of such problems are
beyond us here, but we may mention a few others of great
academic interest.

One of these is the attack on the problem of the action of
chlorophyll and the mechanism of photosynthesis by which car-

bon dioxide and water are combined in the growing plant through the agency of sunlight on green leaves. Radiocarbon has provided a unique tool for studying synthetic photosynthesis.

In another case, radiocarbon dating techniques grew out of the analyses of the methane content of Baltimore sewage which was begun by W. F. Libby and associates in 1949. The outcome was a method for dating archaeologically important materials involved in the growing life cycle of plants and animals which lived as long ago as 30,000 years. The method is based on the fact that the radiocarbon, which is formed in the earth's atmosphere under the influence of ever-present cosmic radiation, is assimilated by living plants in the form of carbon dioxide. Since all animals derive their nourishment from plants or from other animals which eat plants, a certain amount of radiocarbon finds its way into the bodies of all plants and animals. After the plant or animal dies, the radiocarbon intake is cut off. Thereafter it merely continues to decay at a steady rate. In order to determine the time when the plant or animal died, one needs to know the amount of radiocarbon which has remained. The technique of determining this quantity with precision is not simple. But it is amazing to discover that means have been devised to render this analysis accurate enough to permit calculation of the age of the wooden coffins and mummies of the Egyptian Pharaohs, of the Dead Sea Scrolls, and of samples of bones, charcoal, baskets, and rugs found in the caves of primitive man.

One of the most important fields of investigation today is the study of neutron-induced mutations in living germ cells which speed up the production of new strains of plant and animal life. Geneticists are excited about the new theoretical insights which may come from accelerated mutations in living organisms. The controversial questions about fallout and cancer, aging and mutation, have given a new impetus to biologists to tackle basic problems which have been avoided in the past. "It may well be," says Austin M. Brues, director of the Biological and Medical Research Division of the Argonne National Laboratory, "that some day we will look back and see that the greatest benefit of atomic energy to mankind was that it forced a solution of some of the mysteries of life."[14]

[14]Austin M. Brues, *Bulletin of Atomic Scientists*, Jan. 1958, p. 14.

So far, atomic energy has been used in three main areas: the construction of military instruments of destruction; the production of electric power; and the creation of a host of new substances useful in scientific research, industry, medicine, and agriculture. Of these the military uses of atomic energy are most genuinely revolutionary, because they have now made it possible to virtually annihilate life on earth and thus render the potential peaceful uses of the atom innocuous.

Many of the peacetime discoveries with atomic energy will significantly alter the physical conditions of modern life. Atomic energy will necessarily alter the relations of men to men. This is but a general characteristic of science. Science attacks and solves one problem after another. Each new solution, however, introduces greater unsolved technical problems. This enables the scientist to take a closer look at nature and to reconstruct the details with more finesse. And this simply means that he can ask more questions again. Unfortunately, greater scientific knowledge by itself does not always include the wisdom of how to use that new knowledge. And this means that the solution of scientific problems is accompanied by greater responsibilities for the use or misuse of new knowledge.

Separating the Concepts of War and Peace

We have seen from our discussion that the destructive and constructive aspects of atomic energy in some areas are so strongly intertwined that it is almost impossible to control one strictly without markedly altering the other. There are not many phases of the atomic energy effort which can be unambiguously categorized as being war or peace oriented. As to the former, we might cite research on the war-oriented methods of detonating bombs to gain weapon efficiency. As to the latter, we could mention the peace-oriented production of radioisotopes for the treatment of cancer. Still these are extremes, and most atomic energy research will fall somewhere in between.

We know that a very large part of the present government program is being used to produce fissionable materials like uranium-235 and plutonium for nuclear reactors. Research into the peaceful applications of atomic energy may help to develop its wartime uses. Atomic reactors can produce power and plutonium. Plutonium can be used in weapons or to produce more power. Presumably fissionable materials are somewhere placed in storage. These materials can be utilized for atomic warheads, submarine propulsion, construction of reactors for peacetime radioisotopes, electric power plants, etc.

Now who can say how much goes for each of these projects, or for example, what part of the individual's income tax dollar goes into cancer research? That depends on politics, world affairs, public opinion, and on a multitude of factors which can only be analyzed by historians in retrospect. Thus, in all of our efforts which are devoted to furthering the peacetime benefits of atomic energy over against its destructive potentialities, we must, in order to be quite realistic, keep in mind that any phase of the atomic energy program directed toward peaceful or toward military objectives will strongly affect all others.

This is what the free development of science implies, namely, that the outcome of scientific research is always surrounded by an aura of uncertainty. We never quite know whether its potentialities will be greater for good or for evil. But one thing is quite certain, as has already been implied. It is that new discoveries bring new moral responsibilities in terms of the uses to which the discoveries will be put.

If we have made it quite clear here that there is no telling whether the ultimate outcome of certain types of scientific research will contribute to weapons of destruction or to man's health and welfare, we have nowhere implied that the nuclear scientist need necessarily ally himself outright with war-oriented research. In fact, many scientists of our times have had the courage to boycott every nuclear research program which is war oriented. They have done so by limiting their services to assignments in which, to the best of their consciences, their professional skills were being utilized for constructive purposes. They may turn out to have been largely mistaken about the outcome, but they have exercised to the limit of their ability a measure of social responsibility in science.

We hope that by now the reader will appreciate the fact that a healthy attitude toward present-day atomic energy developments can only be achieved after a certain amount of serious study of the basic technical facts of nuclear energy. This is a great complex of problems. The prerequisites for understanding them fortunately have much more to do with mental effort than with technical competence in mathematics, physics, and chemistry.

We have presented this historical and technical background information because of the conviction that the knowledge of some basic facts is the minimum for any intelligent action on the part of individuals who feel that they have some personal or group responsibility to the current nuclear bomb-testing program and the question of radioactive fallout. We have tried to show that it will not do to simply banish all future nuclear energy investigations because of the tremendous potential peacetime benefits for all nations of the world. On the other hand, we have noted that the concepts of atomic energy for peace and atomic energy for war are abstract concepts which cannot be entirely separated in practice.

This should not keep us from taking positive action in favor of one and against the other. Life is full of daily compromises and calculated risks. I believe that we must support our government in every type of action and legislation which promotes the peacetime benefits of atomic energy for mankind, provided that it does not involve too great a risk in favor of the conversion of the peacetime atomic energy benefits into weapons of destruction. After all, it is not atomic energy we are against, but war and destruction.

part II

REACTIONS OF
GOVERNMENTS,
SCIENTISTS, AND
RELIGIOUS GROUPS

chapter 6

POLITICAL ATTITUDES TOWARD
NUCLEAR DISARMAMENT

We have seen that the discovery and utilization of atomic energy belong wholly to the twentieth century. Still, we recognize that the experimental and theoretical foundations of modern physical science reach back many centuries. While the bold exploitation of atomic energy is of very recent origin, we must, nevertheless, acknowledge the fact that man had already linked his future to modern science and technology long before the atomic age. Recent scientific achievements in many different areas have manifestly drawn widespread attention to the need for new political and social responsibilities to keep pace with the advances of science and technology. There is little reason for believing that the current feverish study of the atom will be any slower or less radical in the foreseeable future. Presumably, our basic understanding of nuclear science may someday level off, but even that would hardly put a halt to the invention of new industrial and engineering applications. Atomic energy, then, for better or for worse, will be a permanent part of man's environment.

It is common to say that the progressive conquest and understanding of the physical world by man is continuing at a pace unprecedented in history. In our discussion we have made the assumption that man can no longer reverse the present state of affairs by trying to get along *without* atomic energy. If this assumption is a valid one, we ought to seriously consider the question of how he is going to get along *with* atomic energy. Conquering the physical world in an atomic and space age, man has not yet conquered himself. How is he going to accomplish this? Among the answers to this question there is an incredible diversity of opinion.

Let us introduce this second part of our study on the impact of atomic energy by considering a number of the most commonly expressed general political attitudes toward the question of nuclear disarmament. Thereafter we will be in a better position to evaluate the group reactions and responses to other atomic energy issues which have come up since 1945.

A CLOSE LOOK AT DISARMAMENT

One of the questions to which we turn our attention here is to ask whether or not the powers of the world which are now engaged in a deadly arms race are capable in principle of settling their disputes by peaceful means; and, if so, whether there now are international institutions which can adequately cope with the mechanics of carrying out the necessary negotiations.

It has been argued that an arms race inevitably must lead to an overt military conflict. On the other hand, it has been said that there have been instances in the past where the failure to make adequate military preparations has led to aggression and war. It is said, for example, that Hitler might not have been tempted to move so boldly from military threats to open aggression if counter military threats and the capacity to carry out those threats had been placed as an obstacle in his way. Historically, this view is associated with the idea that whatever happens is more or less dictated by the balance of power.

It is in this light, for example, that K. W. Thompson views the present situation.[1] He says: "Since World War II we can discover straws in the wind that suggest the Soviet Union has been more amenable to reason and diplomacy when the West was strong and not weak. Similarly, the recent posture of jaunty self-confidence and bold expansiveness of Soviet leaders is probably a result of the relative decline of Western powers in recent years." Thompson argues that the armaments race is a symptom and not the cause of tensions; that disarmament cannot be the prelude *to* but the result *of* an easing of the East-West political struggles.

As to the other question—whether or not international institutions are, in principle, capable of handling the disputes—it has been maintained that this will depend on the extent to which the negotiating organizations have been designed to cope with specific problems such as nuclear disarmament. Others would

[1]Kenneth W. Thompson, *Christianity and Crisis,* Nov. 2, 1959, pp. 153, 154.

insist that the peaceful settlement of disputes and the reduction of nuclear armaments depend less on the negotiating organization and apparatus than on the will and national interests of the states and their peoples.   In the latter case, the substance of foreign policy goals and the analyses of diplomats, statesmen, and scientists, rather than the mere forum of the negotiations, assumes the greater importance.

Nuclear Disarmament at Any Price

Among the wide range of suggestions as to the direction toward which the nuclear policy of the Western world ought to move, in light of what appears to be a drift toward global nuclear warfare, we mention first a plan for the unilateral abolition of all nuclear weapons and testing programs in our country and the withdrawal of nuclear arsenals from military bases and installations outside the continental United States.   The logic of this view also demands that economic aid be denied to any other nation engaged in the testing and manufacture of nuclear weapons.   This view is equivalent to nuclear disarmament at any price, in the name of decency and sanity.   It appeals to large segments of the world which are anxious for new moral leadership during a time of unprecedented crisis—a crisis occasioned by what has been called an idiots' arms race between the United States and Russia.

According to Hanson W. Baldwin of the *New York Times,* an examination of the foreign policies of the two major powers and a comparison of their military efforts must reveal that they are both sufficiently bankrupt morally to be committed, if need be, to a doctrine of massive retaliation and mutual annihilation which is equivalent to nuclear suicide.[2]

Proponents of complete nuclear disarmament will argue that the differences between Communism and the Western democracies are less important than the survival of the human race. The evil of nuclear warfare, regardless of outcome, it is implied, would be worse than to belong to a Communist empire.   It is argued that a global holocaust could be set off by a single irresponsible or fanatic commander, perhaps by a technological failure, or merely by the loss of nerve of a bomber pilot or rocket commander in possession of tactical nuclear weapons.

[2]Hanson W. Baldwin, *The Great Arms Race* (New York, 1958).

To prevent such a catastrophe, it is said, there is only one choice which the West can make. The solution is to throw in the sponge on the nuclear arms race, negotiate with the Soviet Union, and get the best terms available, even if this turns out to be economically and politically disadvantageous to the West.

According to Philip Toynbee, son of the famous historian, who represents this view for the British: "It would be wicked and pointless to launch a nuclear attack on Russia *before* we have ourselves been attacked. Wicked for obvious reasons; pointless because we would immediately get back a great deal more than we were able to give. It would be wicked and pointless to launch a nuclear attack on Russia *after* we had ourselves been attacked. Wicked for obvious reasons; pointless because we would no longer have anything to gain by it."[3] In other words, Toynbee concludes that it would be both wicked and pointless to use nuclear weapons under any circumstances. Therefore, why own them?

At worst, it is argued, the outcome of negotiations with the Communists could not crush Western civilization. In the first place, because even Communist regimes are incapable of totally changing man's true and proper behavior; and secondly, because many democratic areas of the world would prove to be so indigestible for the Communists that they would be neither anxious nor able to completely take over even a defenseless Western world. In the end, it is said, dictatorships are self-destructive, and internal revolution, the lesser evil, could become the harbinger of some kind of new freedom.

At best, according to this view, the Russians would take seriously their own propaganda motto, which is to dominate the world not by force but by political and economic pressures. That would represent a state of political coexistence in which there could conceivably be some give and take on both sides, even if all negotiations were to proceed from a position of physical weakness for the West. If this is labeled Utopianism or Pacificism (restated in terms of modern weapons), the proponents of this view, nevertheless, insist that it is the only condition for human survival.

There is nothing wrong with an individual dying for the sake of his community, or for a community dying for the sake of the world, thinks Toynbee, but no community will choose to die for

[3]Philip Toynbee, *The Fearful Choice* (London, 1958), p. 14.

the sake of wholly uncertain results. His example runs as follows: "If you and another man are fighting on a cliff-edge and are about to fall over it together you would be well-advised to break off the fight on his terms if it seems certain that he will not do so on yours. Morally you *must* break off your fight if it so happens that you and your opponent are roped to many others who will be equally involved in your catastrophe. What happens afterwards must be met with courage and imagination. Nobody can accurately foresee it, but it is hard indeed to believe that it would be worse than what would happen if negotiations were a total failure."[4]   Indeed, Toynbee believes it illogical for a Christian to take the attitude that God would allow His redeemed creation—including the Communists—to be irredeemably evil. He says it would be more noble to die under Russian occupation by some deliberate act of refusal than to die uselessly by atomization; for the former would at least be dying to some purpose.

As to positive recommendations for a program of the most drastic kind of nuclear disarmament, we have the analysis of British Laborite Philip Noel-Baker. A lifelong campaign for total world disarmament brought him the Nobel Peace Prize in 1959. In an analysis of 1958 he assessed the dangers of the nuclear arms race and attempted to face the technical and political problems which will arise when governments begin the detailed multilateral consideration of how the present armaments are to be reduced. Noel-Baker believes that the disarmament problem is extremely complex, but not insoluble. It is his thesis that no disarmament treaty will be worthwhile which does not drastically deal with both conventional and nuclear weapons.[5] The foremost argument against this view is that disarmament cannot precede the settlement of international disputes, since disarmament can only be the consequence of improvement in international relations and never the cause of it.

In any case, the situation actually is such, Noel-Baker points out, that a complete deadlock has resulted from every attempt to reach any agreement on armament control. He believes that until May 1955 the Russians were overwhelmingly to blame for the deadlock on the question of nuclear disarmament, but that since then the record shows that "the Russians have made considerable efforts to reach agreement, including the acceptance,

[4]Toynbee, *loc. cit.*, p. 101.
[5]Philip Noel-Baker, *The Arms Race* (London, 1958).

in principle, of a large measure of international inspection and control; while the Western governments have withdrawn the reasonable 'comprehensive' proposal for a first-stage disarmament agreement which they had previously urged."[6]

In January 1960, Noel-Baker, speaking in New York, stated, on the basis of conversations with Premier Khrushchev and other high officials in Moscow, that the Soviet Union was genuinely prepared to disarm drastically and to accept strict nuclear controls if the Western nations would do likewise.[7] He said that the Russians "know that if the arms race goes on they cannot raise their national output of wealth per head of their population until it equals that of the United States; and that is their declared objective for 1970." In the second place, he said that the Russians know "that if the arms race goes on it will all too likely end in general nuclear war; and they know that not much would survive in Russia and certainly not the Communist system to which they have given their lives." Noel-Baker suggested that the West accept Khrushchev's sincerity and attempt a serious negotiation —the comprehensive drastic disarmament proposals which the Russians have suggested.

THE BALANCE OF TERROR

The drastic disarmament view stands in contrast to extremes from the other side which favor all-out superior nuclear preparedness as a deterrent to Soviet aggression. The late Secretary of State John Foster Dulles, for example, insisted that it was simply not practicable to consider the abolition of nuclear weapons. The advocates of superior and all-out military preparedness would maintain that it is better to run the risk of annihilation than to betray the freedom-loving nations of the world and sell out to the Communists by unconditional surrender, i.e., it is better to run the risk of accidental annihilation of most of the human race than to accept the certainty of racial slavery, or perhaps the mass murder of 200 million people, if that suited the Kremlin. It is argued that any negotiation taken from a position of military weakness would be so disadvantageous for the West as to put her in a position of complete impotence for any further action. And that kind of total surrender is worse

[6]Noel-Baker, loc. cit., p. 9.
[7]New York Times, Jan. 24, 1960.

than death. It has been mentioned that while the Soviet leaders really do subscribe to a policy aimed at extending their domination without the risk of a major war, they have not hesitated to use either force or the threat of force to achieve their objectives when necessary.

The conclusion reached is that if the United States is to stop Russia short of a showdown she must "keep the lead." Let Russia gain the lead and she would chance World War III in an attempt to reach her goal—world rule. Accordingly, the United States can keep its "lead" as long as she maintains a greater and more versatile stock of nuclear weapons and the ability to deliver them quickly and efficiently. This, according to expert military advice, would require the United States and its allies to surround the Soviet Union with a series of strategically placed aircraft and missile bases supplied with jet bombers of long and short-range striking power and capable of delivering a wide range of nuclear missiles. In addition, it would mean aircraft carriers, shipborne and battlefield missiles, high speed atomic-powered submarines with indefinite cruising range capable of launching atomic missiles, and a whole arsenal of specially tailored atomic weapons from superthermonuclear bombs to small battlefield-size tactical atomic weapons.

The main argument which is advanced here for keeping ahead of the Russians in every phase of the arms race is that this alone provides the advantage one needs in order to negotiate from strength rather than from weakness. This is what is called the balance of power, or the balance of terror in our day. It is pursued endlessly by both sides. It is calculated, in effect, to lead to a cold war of constant negotiation, with each side carefully calculating the risks of every potential move in terms of the ability to force the enemy to retreat. The situation, it is argued, is not quite so precarious as some would believe, because both sides possess weapons so terrible that each deters the other from making use of its ultimate nuclear potential. Thus, each side presents a deterrent to the other and the result is a nuclear stalemate. Still, the arms race is a race without any finish because it works by "keeping a lead."

EXPERT DIPLOMACY FOR LIMITED WARFARE

A careful and expert military analysis of the necessary balance between force and diplomacy in terms of modern military strategy with nuclear weapons has been made by Henry A. Kissinger[8] who is the associate director of the Center for International Affairs and lecturer in Government at Harvard University. In addition, he is a captain in the Military Intelligence Reserve, Counter Intelligence Corps, and consultant to the Operations Research Office and the Weapons System Evaluation Group of the Joint Chiefs of Staff. Kissinger subjects to close scrutiny the common assertion that nuclear war is no longer a conceivable instrument of policy to settle international disputes. The assertion implies that the diplomacy of honest compromise is now the only alternative. Kissinger's disagreement with this assertion and its implication is that the renunciation of force would be like handing the Russians a blank check. It would create a vacuum into which Russia and Communist China would "move with impunity." The only hope of diverting the Communists, he believes, resides in the cultivation of superior military preparedness, expert diplomacy not excluded.

What Kissinger means by superior military preparedness is spelled out in great detail and begins with the rejection of the concepts of total war and total peace. He severely criticizes American foreign policy based on a historically outmoded purist and abstract doctrine of aggression which is too preoccupied with surprise nuclear attacks and massive retaliations requiring a maximum assemblage of force. "By leaving no room between total war and stalemate," he says, "we [have] posed alternatives for ourselves which do not, in fact, exhaust our options."[9]

Kissinger finds the most disturbing aspects of the American situation to be, on the one hand, the intermilitary service wrangles and rivalries in connection with the development of nuclear weapons, and on the other hand, the absence of a well-defined doctrine to co-ordinate the military and political aspects of limited types of warfare which are short of outright declarations of war and total victory. Total war, with its emphasis on thermonuclear devastation as the only alternative to complete recapitulation, he says, is too risky and too unprofitable. While total war is something for which the West must be prepared, Kissinger maintains that it is unrealistic and dangerous to tie the country's military machinery so closely to an all-out doctrine

[8]Henry A. Kissinger, *Nuclear Weapons and Foreign Policy* (New York, 1958).
[9]Kissinger, *loc. cit.*, p. 38.

of warfare, especially since the potential threats which now face the West range all the way from minor disagreements on ambiguous political situations to an all-out showdown between the major powers. He points out, for example, that Russia and Communist China have been making steady, methodical, almost imperceptible advances, not by means of large threats, but by carefully calculated challenges which are all less than declarations of war. The Communists thus are able to achieve their over-all objectives by using small increments of military power coupled with political and psychological pressures which appear relatively harmless to the rest of the world. This puts the West into an infinitely vulnerable position and in the end, he says, the Communists will realize their intentions by nibbling the West to death without a major military encounter.

What Kissinger, therefore, advocates when he recommends superior military preparedness in terms of nuclear weapons is the ability to effectively deal with a complete spectrum of potential challenges with the aid of weapons ranging all the way from small tactical nuclear weapons, equivalent to, say, 20 thousand tons of TNT, to thermonuclear devices of the order of 20 million tons of TNT. The objectives must be based on a strategy aimed to avoid small defeats, rather than to achieve victory; they must include retaliatory measures capable of inflicting damage which Russia would consider unacceptable in terms of the risks involved. By this method, the nation which can always present its challenges in something less than an all-out form will gain the psychological advantage.

What Kissinger means by expert diplomacy is the ability to recognize and cope with aggressions which are just short of an outright declaration of war. It is to grasp the opportunities of limited warfare without posing absolute alternatives. This, he says, demands a military machine which is truly graduated. It means more specially trained divisions in every branch of the service, a greater spectrum of weapons, and an exhaustively complete system for the efficient and rapid execution of offensive and defensive warfare. Above all, it requires the closest cooperation between political and military personnel; the policies of limited warfare and political strategy must overlap extensively.

Now, since the Soviet leaders will be no less intent than the West upon perfecting every aspect of their own military and political strength, it will be difficult for any one major power to "keep the lead" indefinitely. The ultimate advantage of the West, says Kissinger, will have to depend "on leadership of a high order, personal initiative, and mechanical aptitude, qualities more prevalent in our society than in the Soviet bloc."[10]   The difficult assignment, as he sees it, is to devise techniques which in practice will make limited wars more attractive and slower-paced, and therefore render diplomatic settlement more favorable through bargaining.   Indeed, the ideal would be to educate the world to fight according to rules established well in advance of specific types of conflict.

Kissinger's position belongs to a whole pattern of thought that has been urged upon the nation by very influential minds in the Pentagon and the AEC.   The whole argument boils down to a confidence that future wars will and can be fought as limited nuclear wars.   In June 1960 Kissinger argued that Moscow had too big a propaganda edge for the United States to try and compete with the punch of sweeping new Soviet proposals for disarmament.   He objected, he said, to any total disarmament control plan and urged that the United States rather support an equilibrium between Soviet and Western retaliatory forces to stabilize the arms race.[11]

An analysis of modern war by the French sociologist, Raymond Aron, has much in common with Kissinger's view.[12]   Aron finds little value in world-government proposals, disarmament by international agreement, and all types of appeasement.   He rather places his hopes in the achievement of limited objectives by means of traditional diplomacy backed by limited war capabilities.   The single goal of the West, he believes, should be to remove the temptation of Russia to embark on a nuclear war. This would mean fewer references to massive retaliation and less brinksmanship on our side, and less atomic blackmail on the other.   It is dangerous, he says, to approach the problem with the intention of absolutely eliminating nuclear war.   Rather, the danger must be minimized.

INTERNATIONAL PROBLEM SOLVING

Between the two extreme positions (i.e., keeping the lead in various phases of potential nuclear warfare or immediate and

[10]Kissinger, *loc. cit.,* p. 162.
[11]*New York Times,* June 19, 1960.
[12]Raymond Aron, *On War* (New York, 1959).

complete nuclear disarmament—often equated with outright recapitulation to the Soviet Union) there arc a number of positions calculated to underline some specific aspect of international settlement which has not yet been mentioned here. Perhaps the most challenging of these ideas has to do with positive suggestions for creating international understanding among nations whose political and philosophical ideals are worlds apart. No one could argue convincingly that the peoples of the world have yet exhausted the means of achieving some measure of acceptable agreement by the methods of international diplomacy and bargaining. Certainly something by way of positive achievement has already resulted from meetings which have taken on the character of endless horse trading on technical issues pertaining to science, government, and politics. The success of such methods usually will depend on "holding one's own" for a while (perhaps with the backing of some military strength) while persuasion and understanding are at work in another sphere.

We also find that a good deal of emphasis has been placed on the pursuit of science and technology as a co-operative activity of the human race, in preferment to the exploitation of one political sector of the world by another. There have been pleas for diplomatic bargaining at summit meetings, the United Nations, Moscow, or wherever the Russian and Chinese Communists are willing to appear. There have been pleas for the interchange of university and high school students and teachers, ideas, scientific know-how, and the pooling of technological data through the agencies of International Congresses and co-operative programs similar to the International Geophysical Year which ended on December 31, 1958, with some 30,000 scientists and technicians from sixty-six countries participating. There have been pleas for world-wide united attacks on major problems: the correlation and integration of international scientific resources, health education, population studies, outer space exploration, long-range weather forecasting, world-wide studies of natural background radiation, and particularly the co-operative and exhaustive exploitation of the far-flung peacetime benefits of nuclear energy in scientific research and nuclear power developments. It is claimed, for example, by J. D. Bernal,[13] that it is now perfectly feasible with existing resources of men

[13] J. D. Bernal, *World Without War* (London, 1958).

and materials for the whole of mankind to advance within little more than a generation to the highest standard of living hitherto attained.

The arguments for more co-operation do not rest alone on the assumption that the peoples of the Soviet Union will change a little and that the Americans will change a little and thereby bring about understanding through compromise. There are other factors at work which have to do with the normal processes of history. It has been said that no nation on earth would have more to lose and less to gain from warfare than the Russians. They already have about as much land, population, and natural resources as they can manage. They now need time to develop what they possess in order to attain a higher standard of living. To achieve that end, a long period of peace would be to their advantage.

It has also been argued convincingly, for example, by J. B. Morton of the London *Daily Express*, that Soviet Marxism, since it has passed its peak, will never be capable of dominating the world. Russia has appealed to a perverted idea of justice for the poor which cannot endure beyond the time when its own peoples and those of the world will achieve a decent standard of living. Marxism as a system, it is said, is too much of an outrage to the dignity of man to last. Where the people and the government mutually fear each other, the government must depend upon armed force to keep its people in line; and, once that force is removed, the whole structure will topple.

THE SOVIET THREAT IS POLITICAL

George F. Kennan, of the School of Historical Studies at the Institute for Advanced Study in Princeton and former American Ambassador to Russia, has spelled out with great clarity and insight some of the conceivable political consequences, for the West, of atomic weapons in the hands of the Soviet Union.[14] He reviews the fantastic Soviet accomplishments in industrial and military production which have come about since the war. In face of all the handicaps which Russia faced at the end of a devastating war, with her peoples physically and spiritually exhausted, Kennan points to Russia's industrial accomplishments

[14]George F. Kennan, *Russia, the Atom and the West* (New York, 1958).

in fifteen years, which have brought her into the world's number two spot as far as industrial and military output production is concerned. Within a mere twelve years after Hiroshima, the Russians had placed their first Sputnik into outer space; they stood determined to outstrip the United States in all aspects of the art of peace and war based on modern technological developments.

If the Russians have surpassed anything which the economic and scientific experts thought possible, Kennan thinks that the Soviet society, like any society in the early stages of its industrialization, will enjoy its rapid growth and, nevertheless, level off as new and inevitable organizational and manpower problems show up. The present motive of the Russians to catch up and surpass, says Kennan, will then die down when the Russians discover "that the most serious problems in modern life only begin with the achievement of material plenty."[15] It is then that the Russians will run into some of the same problems which have thus far been baffling the Western industrialized nations, and for which Kennan supposes the Communists will have no better answers than any of the rest of us. Marx said to the Prussians: "You have swallowed Poland, but you will never digest her."

At the cost of poor standards of living and the neglect of consumer products manufacture and agriculture, the Russians, one could argue, have expended their greatest efforts in the field of military industrialization. Scientific and engineering careers have become the new channels of advancement to positions of influence in the Soviet system, so that the scientist today is riding a great wave of respect in Russia. Dr. John Turkevich of Princeton University, who acted as scientific attaché to Russia in the summer of 1960, remarked recently at a science writers seminar in New York that the Soviet citizen, the Soviet government, and Mr. Khrushchev all have more faith in science and technology than in Marxism. Mr. Turkevich told his audience that Soviet people do not tell visitors to their country that Russia will surpass the United States because of the Communist philosophy, but because of scientific advances. Russia's stated objective to surpass American science in diversity and in the quality and quantity of production has not been taken lightly in this country.

[15]Kennan, loc. cit., p. 10.

Knowing that at the present rate of industrialization she will catch up and outproduce the United States, the Communists have taken every conceivable opportunity to emphasize their rapid and competitive economic growth.

The Soviet propaganda line has so successfully proclaimed the notion that every scientific and economic achievement of their own is a loss for the West, that the West has almost automatically come to accept this thesis. To this Kennan says: "I cannot find it in my heart to begrudge the Russians this kind of success; nor can I see that we are in any way handicapped by it in our attack on our own problems."[16]

Wherein then lies our solution to the terrible immediate dangers of the atomic weapons race? Kennan's answer: Not in the continued multiplication of the destructiveness and speed of delivery of atomic weapons; not in keeping a tiny bit ahead as a deterrent with the balance of bargaining power on our side.

Asks Kennan: "Are we to flee like haunted creatures from one defensive device to another, each more costly and humiliating than the one before, cowering underground one day, breaking up our cities the next, attempting to surround ourselves with elaborate electronic shields on the third, concerned only to prolong the length of our lives while sacrificing all the values for which it might be worthwhile to live at all?" All of the available means of driving nations deeper and deeper into exertions oriented toward superior offensive and defensive devices, each more costly and more demanding technologically than the last, can only temporarily and expediently delay the settlement. "If I thought," says Kennan, "that this was the best the future held for us, I should be tempted to join those who say: Let us stake our safety on God's grace and our good consciences and on that measure of common sense and humanity which even our adversaries possess; but then let us at least walk like men, with our heads up, so long as we are permitted to walk at all."[17]

It is obviously too late for our nation to prevent another nation from acquiring the technological means to destroy us. The problem is to see to it that we decrease the other nation's incentive to destroy us. Many have said that this is the deterrent to nuclear annihilation which must be strengthened in place of

[16]Kennan, *loc. cit.*, p. 9.
[17]Kennan, *loc. cit.*, p. 54.

explosive nuclear arsenals and extravagant satellite projects. The Soviet threat is military and political, but it is more political than military.

The policies of the Russians fluctuate from hot to cold as the exigencies of their power politics demand; but as to their conviction about the outcome of international Communism they do not waver. They are engaged in a life and death struggle to gain the free world, and they are firmly convinced that they will win out in the end whether there is eventually a military showdown or not. They would be better off, they think, if there were no showdown.

Some economists consider that the Russians have come to a fork-in-the-road. They maintain that if Russia is to progress in the sectors of transportation and consumer goods, Khrushchev will soon have to find ways of making drastic cutbacks in the present staggering proportions of her military expenditures. They point out that Mr. Khrushchev has more than once assumed the role of a peacemaker, and it appears that more than anything else he would like to be looked upon as the master builder of a better life for the Russian people. He has also spoken often of the importance of increasing contacts between peoples of the world. But, of course, all this goes on without any sensible abatement in the flow of poisonous Soviet propaganda.

The game which the Russians would like to play, says Kennan, is to exploit every element of disunity and confusion and short-sightedness in our society and, with a characteristic carelessness about the truth, to cultivate falsehood as a deliberate weapon of policy in order to confuse the problem of negotiation with the West. This approach is what the Western diplomats cannot understand or trust, because of a tradition of legalistic dealings based on great moral commitments and official pronouncements by international organizations at high level or summit conferences, where great issues are decided and signed with the understanding that the nations involved will abide by those decisions.

We might suggest that all progress toward disarmament with the Russians has faltered because too much has been expected from summit meetings. Too little attention, by contrast, has been placed on the practicable details of working out the specific requirements for disarmament. The summit conferences, which in the past have been scheduled at the highest level between government heads, have generally yielded no tangible results.

The scheduling of these conferences have left many people with the impression that such grand discussions on global terms become possible only by pushing aside other people's problems—the people who are not represented at the conference. Thus the agreements which are accepted, if any, are accomplished at the expense of those who are absent, viz., those who might be capable of discussing the practical issues of complicated international misunderstandings. It is not that the meetings of the heads of governments need fail utterly to provide a chance for the friendly interchange of ideas, but is it not too much to expect that major problems can be settled by some kind of magic high-level diplomacy? We know that in the past there have been occasions when the foreign ministers of the Big Three have met without being able even to agree on how to proceed with the meeting.

What is needed much more than the summit conferences of presidents, secretaries of state, and senior diplomats, is a meeting ground, as we have already seen, for industrialists and scientists —at something less than the diplomatic level. The informal co-operative analysis of specific detailed problems would be the primary joint concern. The West would say to the Russians under this and that situation we would be prepared to do or not to do such and so. The discussions would be designed to avoid, or at least postpone to a later date, the great and sweeping global questions. They would concentrate on breaking down every main issue into individual and specific components capable of empirical solution.

It seems appropriate finally to suggest that the United States may be paying too much attention to Moscow and too little to the rest of the uncommitted world. The crucial battle between Communism and the free world may well be fought in the underdeveloped non-Communist areas of the world where revolutions are in process. Under such circumstances it seems unwise to let the Soviet challenge become the most exclusive preoccupation of American policy. Americans tend to believe that European nations would not willingly throw away the values of an open society such as ours for a Communist dictatorship. But can we be so certain that nations of non-Western tradition would express the same preference or have the inner consistency to make the same choice?

chapter 7

DOMESTIC AND INTERNATIONAL
EFFORTS TO ACHIEVE CONTROLS

It is well known that in the United States very strong support for civilian domestic control and for international co-operation on atomic energy has come from scientists, educational and religious organizations, as well as from industrial, farm, labor, and youth groups. In this chapter we want to treat the formal organization and political implications of atomic energy controls since 1945. The question of group motivations and reactions to atomic energy will be taken up in the last two chapters of the book.

On October 3, 1945, less than two months after the end of the war, while American policy on atomic matters was still largely uncrystallized, President Truman sent a special message to Congress, calling for legislation to fix a policy for the domestic control of atomic energy. Truman summarized the needs for domestic legislation as follows: (a) to establish a peacetime organization to take over the plants and facilities developed during the war; (b) to develop and direct further research on atomic fission; and (c) to secure control over the basic raw materials in this country. He also stated that he would soon initiate international discussions for the control of atomic energy and the outlawing of atomic weapons.

By the end of 1945 a number of organizations, such as the Federation of American Scientists and the Atomic Scientists of Chicago, had advocated legislation to insure civilian rather than military control of atomic energy. At the same time, many individuals sensed the need for consistency between domestic and international atomic policies. It was stated, for example, that it would not do to advocate an international policy designed to prevent the use of atomic weapons while simultaneously placing the development of United States domestic controls into the hands of the military. That would only lead in the long run to the distrust of our country's motives.

Three months before the atomic bombs were used at Hiroshima and Nagasaki, Secretary of War Stimson, in May 1945, had already formed a committee to consider the subject of atomic energy legislation. War Department officials realized full well that the means of producing the atomic bomb could not forever remain the exclusive property of the United States. Stimson was one of the first to recommend a policy of international control of atomic energy, with a view to outlawing its use for war. The legislation which Stimson's Interim Committee initiated was later introduced as the May-Johnson Bill.

This bill, subsequently termed the War Department Bill, was drafted and sponsored by civilians in order to reduce the military responsibility for atomic energy. It, nevertheless, would have placed the executive administration in the hands of two military officers as administrators and a nine-man commission to serve part time. A good deal of military secrecy, restriction, and regimentation was written into the bill, and the way was open for outright military control, should the President so choose. Many atomic scientists maintained that under such legislation they would not continue to work on atomic energy. This meant that the United States might soon be at the bottom of the scientific world in nuclear science rather than at the top. General Leslie R. Groves, wartime director of the Manhattan project, sought frantically to retain military control of atomic energy by trying to rush the May-Johnson bill through Congress. He was foiled in this by scientists. The bill eventually was dropped. According to E. U. Condon, Groves took his revenge through the House Committee on Un-American Activities in 1948 and 1949 by actions "which deprived this country of the services of so many brilliant young American scientists."[1]

THE UNITED STATES ATOMIC ENERGY COMMISSION

In December 1945 Senator Brian McMahon introduced a bill which tried to resolve some of the basic national issues on the question of military versus civilian domestic atomic energy. The record shows that McMahon had a clear understanding of the bomb's appalling destructiveness and of the possible short-lived

[1]*Science,* Dec. 4, 1959, pp. 1599, 1600.

monopoly over it by any nation.   He furthermore foresaw no real military defense against the bomb except in the prevention of war itself.   The "secrets" of atomic energy, he realized, were "matters of science and engineering which other nations can and will discover."   As to the great peacetime benefits of atomic energy, he remarked that plants which would produce power would also be capable of producing explosive material for bombs. Finally, he recommended complete civilian control of atomic energy with the armed services entitled to extensive participation in the military aspects of developments connected with atomic energy.

The McMahon Bill was endorsed with recommendations for minor amendments by President Truman and Secretaries Wallace, Ickes, and Patterson.   Scientists gave their overwhelming support to the bill.   General Groves opposed the bill, saying in testimony to a Senate Committee on February 27 that he would like to see a representative on the proposed Atomic Energy Commission "who is not going to forget for a minute that as long as this is the prime military weapon of the country, defense must come first and other things afterwards."   He added: "Until other nations are willing to join us in reciprocal agreements, we cannot afford to give any essential part of the information we have until such time as we are assured that it will not be used against us."   In short, it was advocated that the United States hold on to the "secret" of the bomb until other nations had demonstrated their "anxiety for peace."   Because scientists were abandoning the Manhattan project in large numbers, and research on atomic energy was being markedly slowed down, it did not seem appropriate to try and invest the real management of the whole atomic program exclusively in the hands of the military.

The United States Atomic Energy Bill, better known as the McMahon Bill, was adopted in the Senate in June 1946.   It provided for a five-man full-time all-civilian Atomic Energy Commission with an administrator chosen by the commission as executive agent but responsible to it.   It also provided for complete government monopoly over all fissionable materials, manufacturing, licensing, etc., but with opportunity for research and development through private industry and industrial research establishments.   After a time of wrangling on the Mc-Mahon Bill in the House, this piece of "socialistic but necessary legislation," as Clare Booth Luce called it, was signed by the President in August 1946. On October 28, 1946, President Truman appointed the five AEC members. Chairman David E. Lilienthal already then had the strong backing of many atomic scientists in the country. His reputation with them increased steadily during his administration. By 1959 the wartime Manhattan project had turned over the last of its contracts to the AEC.

Most scientists in 1946 were of the opinion that the McMahon Bill was a very successful piece of legislation for the control of domestic atomic energy, at least as a preliminary measure. But even before the bill had been passed, scientists voiced the opinion that Russia and other countries would soon put forth all of their efforts to mastering the techniques of nuclear weapons, unless the fabrication of atomic bombs was somehow made impossible by efficient international control.

On the international front, the battle over atomic energy control has been so complicated that even to this date no fundamental agreement among the big powers has ever been reached on the question of international limitation or control of nuclear weapons. Nevertheless, it is unfair to say that nothing has been accomplished through the attempts. The fact that an all-out shooting war has thus far been stayed is attributable at least in part to concessions on the part of all the major powers who have been willing to discuss international atomic energy problems even when there was no wide area of agreement.[2]

INTERNATIONAL CONTROL EFFORTS

Toward the end of 1945, when the American Association for the United Nations called for immediate organization to face the problems of atomic energy, the Council of Foreign Ministers at London ended in a stalemate. On November 15, 1945, the President of the United States and the Prime Ministers of Great Britain and Canada agreed on a declaration offering the atomic bomb to the United Nations on a reciprocal basis. In effect, the western powers, nevertheless, retained a monopoly on all atomic information. By December, in Moscow, Byrnes, Bevin,

[2]An authoritative month by month account of U. N. attempts to achieve international control of atomic energy to 1950 has been edited by Eugene Rabinowitch, *Minutes to Midnight, the international control of atomic energy* (Chicago, 1950).

and Molotov announced the agreement of the United States, Great Britain, and the Soviet Union to sponsor a resolution at the first meeting of the Assembly of the United Nations to set up an international atomic agency. On January 24, 1946, the United Nations Assembly approved the resolution and established the United Nations Atomic Energy Commission (U.N. AEC) made up of one representative from each of the eleven member-nations of the Security Council plus Canada.

In this country, definitive plans for international control of atomic energy began to take shape in January 1946 when the State Department released its first report. This report, which came to be known as the Acheson-Lilienthal plan, was a broad and eloquent proposal for a definite course of action for a United Nations Atomic Development Authority. It recommended a multiplicity of safeguards against misuse of atomic energy: complete monopoly and control by an international authority over the mining, refining, production, and separation of fissionable materials; the licensing and inspection of private and national plants engaged in nuclear research and the design of power-producing units; and the exchange of information on scientific and technical activities. The document did not treat the problem in legalistic terms, nor did it spell out the details of the administrative setup of the proposed international agency.

On June 14, at the first meeting of the members of the U.N. AEC, Bernard Baruch, the American representative, presented the official American government proposal for world-wide control of atomic energy. This plan called for the establishment of an international Atomic Development Authority with a monopoly over all raw materials and processes connected with atomic energy. It provided the U.N. Commission with the authority to inspect all establishments where atomic energy was being used, even for peacetime purposes, in order to prevent the misuse of facilities for the manufacture of bombs. There was to be no veto to the supervision and control of the organization.

At the second meeting, on June 19, Andrej Gromyko, the representative of Russia, set forth the official Soviet proposal. It was aimed at the destruction and outlawing of atomic bombs rather than control. Gromyko also urged the exchange of atomic information and the creation of a committee to study methods for supervising and enforcing the contract. The Soviet proposal, however, demanded the retention of veto in the case of enforcement action. The question of veto power thus became the first point of disagreement and initiated a controversy which was to deadlock almost every deliberation that followed.

Serious differences of opinion also arose on the question of inspection and control of atomic weapons. The Russians demanded that atomic weapons be destroyed first, as a prelude to the reduction in conventional arms. This was to be followed by a system of international inspection to prevent the future manufacture of both atomic and conventional weapons. The United States and the West agreed to the same steps, but insisted that they be carried out in the reverse order. Neither side would concede to the other. Criticism of the Baruch proposal from within the United States was most forcefully voiced by Henry Wallace. He advocated relaxation on the abolition of veto power, and suggested that the United States voluntarily interrupt the production of atomic bombs as a gesture of good will.

A report embodying the results of six months of continuous deliberation in the United Nations, a plan essentially in line with the Baruch proposal, was adopted on December 31, 1946, by unanimous vote, with Russia and Poland abstaining. This first report was turned over to the Security Council. The Russians were not so much opposed to the principles of the over-all plan, but they made it quite clear that they would not support a recommendation for the advance relinquishment of their veto power in the case of sanctions against violators of the controls.

We have already indicated elsewhere that while plans for inspection and control of atomic energy were being hotly debated in the United Nations AEC in 1946, the United States was busily engaged in testing nuclear weapons in the Pacific. It is obvious from the record that our administration somehow sought to use the American atomic monopoly both to secure an agreement from Russia on the abolition of nuclear weapons and to retain military supremacy at the same time. In effect, this gave the Russians the go ahead sign to attempt within their own power to achieve the same status on atomic energy which was already held by the West. The Russians, to be sure, were not going to accept the abolition of war on Western terms and sit by to wait for the West to distribute the peacetime benefits of atomic energy where and when they saw fit to do so. The logic of the situation rather demanded of Russia, as it did of Great

Britain at the same time, that constructive atomic endeavors as well as atomic weapons research be pursued in order to remain in the running as a first-rank power in world politics. In other words, after 1945 only atomic weapons constituted the badge of greatness in the sphere of power politics. Bargaining power henceforth would be equated with the stockpile of atomic weapons necessary to back up intentions, threats, and national policies.

During 1947 and 1948 there were broad discussions in the United Nations General Assembly and elsewhere on questions governing the general regulation and reduction of armaments. General Omar Bradley called for international control even at the expense of national sovereignty. General George C. Marshall felt that the United States should take the long view and turn over its secrets and all its atomic plants to the international atomic energy control in order to bring about the effective prohibition of atomic weapons. He did not believe that atomic bombs were the kind of weapons which a democracy should monopolize, for they would threaten the very basis of free government by sowing suspicion, fear, and distrust. The British Atomic Scientists' Association voiced the opinion that the Baruch plan and the Gromyko plan did not clash fundamentally. They suggested means of fusing the two plans into a workable scheme acceptable to all countries.

Gromyko in February 1947 submitted twelve amendments to the Baruch plan. In March he violently attacked certain aspects of the American plan and said that Russia considered international management of atomic plants through the Atomic Development Authority a threat to her economy. In other words, the Russians were willing to accept an international agency having the power of a police force with respect to atomic bombs (since she had none), but they were not willing to submit all of their atomic research and development activities to rigorous unlimited inspection. The Russians were obviously not going to accept a system of international control which would freeze their unfavorable position relative to the capitalistic world. P. M. S. Blackett, prominent wartime British atomic scientist, has said, "During the first two years after the war, I . . . gradually came to certain conclusions that were in marked conflict with official British and American opinion. . . . I guessed that . . . the Soviet Government would certainly stall on the West's proposal for international control of atomic weapons until they had built up their own stockpile. This is what they did, and I am convinced that Britain and America, if in the same situation, would have done exactly the same."[3]

SECURITY THROUGH WITCH HUNTING

On the domestic scene, Americans at this time were reviewing their own internal atomic setup. In hearings before the Senate Committee, Lilienthal and other AEC commissioners were interrogated on their alleged failure to maintain adequate security in the United States on atomic matters. Scientists rallied to the defense of AEC activities while some senators accused Lilienthal of being the spearhead of Communism in the United States. The old issue of civilian versus military control of atomic energy came up again: Why shouldn't the military liaison board sit in on all AEC hearings?

AEC commissioners were not the only suspects. The House Un-American Activities Committee released several reports making insinuations concerning the loyalty and trustworthiness of some of the most prominent scientists working in government circles. Loyalty clearance procedures in various research laboratories tightened up. Hysterical suspicions, loyalty tests, secret investigations, and guilt by association were the order of the day. The story of the miscarriage of American justice in the case of J. Robert Oppenheimer is too well known to require comment here.[4] On the whole, the American loyalty investigations were an outrageous disgrace to the individual scientists concerned, as well as to the nation. In testimony before the congressional investigating committee, Wernher von Braun, who is current director of the National Aeronautics and Space Administration, said: "In England, Oppenheimer would have been knighted."

While U.N. AEC debates continued without showing any sign of agreement on atomic control or inspection, there was much talk about world government and world constitution, and about the new role of atomic scientists in world politics. But there was also much talk about America's growing socialism, new types of defense, the dispersal of cities and vital industry, and the new balance of responsibility for atomic energy among the military services.

[3]P. M. S. Blackett, *The Listener,* September 11, 1958.
[4]Joseph and Stewart Alsop, *We Accuse!* (New York, 1954).

Before long, other nations were beginning to seriously question whether the United States could work for peace and war simultaneously through an atomic monopoly without drifting toward international coercion.   The big problem for the United States was apparently how to keep atomic weapons and still establish international atomic controls.   Would the United States, for example, go along with an indefinite international moratorium to delay the production of fissionable materials?   There was little sympathy with such proposals in the United States.

Toward the end of 1947, while various United States scientists on AEC projects were being suspended from their work because of security regulations, Soviet Foreign Minister Molotov told a Moscow audience, which was celebrating the thirtieth anniversary of the Russian revolution, that the secret of the atomic bomb had ceased to exist.   Even scientists in the United States took Molotov's statement to be a bluff.   According to most estimates, it was then considered that Russia would not possess an atomic weapon before 1952.

Beginning in 1948 the Soviet delegates moved consistently and progressively further away from the principles which the majority of the U.N. AEC members considered necessary as the basis for effective control.   They were still demanding that atomic weapons be outlawed and destroyed before an international control plan could be established.   They also felt that the majority of the proposals made by the United States would merely prolong the American atomic advantage and prevent atomic developments in Russia.

In May 1948 the U.N. AEC reported that it had reached an impasse in its work.   By majority vote the commission decided in favor of suspending its activities and recommended rather that the Security Council control atomic energy.   A Soviet resolution proposed that the commission should discard the three reports which had been issued thus far and start over from scratch.   That resolution found no support outside the Soviet bloc.

In February 1949, after nine months of suspension on deliberations, the U.N. AEC reconvened to reopen discussions on international control of atomic energy.   By April, at the end of five attempts by the commission to reach some kind of an agreement, Russia and the Western powers were as far apart on atomic energy controls as they had ever been.   This, in spite of the fact that the over-all plan worked out by the U.N. AEC had been approved by all members of the commission with the exception of the Soviet Union and its associated states. It had also been approved by the General Assembly of the United Nations by a vote of forty-six to six.

On July 29, 1949, the U.N. AEC again voted to end all deliberations on control. It was felt that in view of irreconcilable differences, further discussions "would tend to harden these differences and would serve no practicable or useful purpose until such time as the Sponsoring Powers have reported that there exists a basis for agreement." Henceforth all responsibilities were placed on the Big Five and Canada.

In America atomic scientists in 1949 were in an uproar about Senator Hickenlooper's charges that AEC Chairman Lilienthal be dismissed because of "incredible mismanagement" of the AEC. The charges centered in the fact that one ounce (!) of U-235 had been found missing from the Argonne National Laboratories in Chicago. The problem of how the United States was going to maintain atomic secrecy was discussed most by people who had not the slightest knowledge of the issues involved. But why, it was asked, should atomic scientists be consulted when most of them could not be trusted?

Walter Lippmann, writing on "Senators, Scientists and Secrecy," said:

The efforts of laymen, who know virtually nothing about nuclear physics, to determine what is a secret and how to guard it, is rather like what would happen if say Senator Hickenlooper woke up one morning and found he had been appointed the censor of the Chinese Nationalist press. I hope I do him no injustice in assuming that his ability to read Chinese is no greater than his knowledge of the science of nuclear physics. Now to Senator Hickenlooper—assuming him to be illiterate in Chinese—everything published in the Chinese papers would be an absolute secret, a complete and total mystery. How then would he proceed to make sure that nothing was published in the Nationalist press which would be of benefit to the Communists? One way, of course, would be to suspend publication of all the papers. If that did not seem feasible, he might get all the Chinese reporters, copyreaders and printers to sign their names to an oath not to reveal secrets. But that could not satisfy him because how could every Chinese reporter and copyreader know whether any particular piece of information was a secret or not?

So eventually, to continue but with apologies to Senator Hickenlooper, he would have to call in Chinese who can read Chinese and Chinese who happen to know all the military secrets of the Chinese. With their help he might make a reasonably efficient censor. Without their help, the best he could hope for when the record of his service was made up would be to get an A plus for effort and an A minus—because he had all the virtues except humility—for character.[5]

In the midst of the fiasco about the lost ounce of uranium and irresponsible talk about American atomic "secrets," the whole world was startled by reports of a successful atomic explosion within the Soviet Union.   The American atomic monopoly had been broken and only a technological edge remained in favor of the United States.

The United Nations thereafter faced an entirely new situation. It remained to be seen whether new plans for control could be discussed with the Soviet Union now that her status had been altered by such a major achievement in atomic energy.   United States scientists advocated less witch hunting among members of the AEC and among atomic scientists, and more work.   A new race for atomic weapons superiority was on.

The witch hunting continued unabated while an accelerated phase in the race for atomic superiority was in process.   After 1950 it was Senator Joseph McCarthy from Wisconsin who notably took it upon himself to inform Americans of the presence of "heretics" in the government and research laboratories. Singu larly adept at throwing around reckless accusations of the presence of hidden Communists in the United States, he succeeded in partially paralyzing the administration, the presidency, and the foreign service.   It was not until 1954 that his accusations were completely discredited after the televising of his dispute with the United States army.   McCarthy, nevertheless, had been able to inspire a peculiar loyalty and wield a tremendous influence over many Americans—to the delight of enemies of the United States and to the horror of foreign friends of the United States everywhere.

SOVIET A-BOMB ADDS NEW DIMENSION

At the Fourth United Nations Assembly in September 1949 the United States expressed its regrets that the United Nations had reached no agreement on international control of atomic weapons and on the prohibition of the use of atomic weapons. The United States, it was said, would go about its business as usual.   Vishinsky made no mention at all of Russian atomic

[5]Walter Lippman, *New York Times,* May 23, 1949.

bombs in his speech.   Instead, he attacked the Western position
and asked for immediate prohibition of the bomb.   At the same
time, the Soviet Union condemned the United States and the
United Kingdom for their war preparations and their armaments
race as reflected by "the inflation of military budgets inflicting
heavy burdens on the people, the establishment of numerous
military, naval and air bases on the territories of other countries,
the organization of military blocs of states pursuing aggressive
aims directed against peace-loving democratic countries, and the
implementation of other measures having aggressive purposes."
Ernest Bevin, Foreign Secretary of the United Kingdom, answered Vishinsky: "The Soviet representatives never cease to
harp on prohibition of the atomic weapon and to blame us and
others for failing to make prohibition a reality.   This is a stupid
charge.   We are as anxious as anyone for prohibition."   A five-
power statement in October blamed the Soviet Union for the
three-year stalemate.

In a November speech to the General Assembly, Vishinsky
reversed the earlier Soviet position on national quotas for the
production of fissionable materials.   In effect, this meant that
now the Russians would not go along with controls designed
to postpone the large-scale production of fissionable material.
Vishinsky claimed that the Soviet Union was already using
atomic energy to level mountains and divert rivers, and she
therefore needed much fissionable material.   The most hopeful
of earlier Soviet concessions was thus lost.   The six-power meetings which followed were largely repetitious statements of opposing opinions which we have already discussed.   Still, the assembly agreed to continue six-power consultations in secret.   No
agreement was in sight.   The Soviet delegation staged a walkout
in every United Nations organization in which Nationalist
Chinese sat.   Thus in 1950 the work of the U.N. AEC again
came to a standstill and there were no signs of any intentions to
resume talks.

In 1950 the United States AEC and the Department of
Defense announced a new series of atomic tests in the commission's proving ground at Eniwetok atoll in the Marshall
Islands.   In February, Truman announced the United States
decision concerning the development of the superbomb.   Toward
the end of the year and into 1951 the hottest topics of conversa-
tion were defense through urban and industrial dispersal, the

disloyalty of atomic scientists, and the dangers of the "dirty" hydrogen-cobalt bomb.

THE DISARMAMENT COMMISSION

After almost two years of deadlock on the problem of international atomic energy control, Truman in October 1950 proposed that the United Nations Fifth General Assembly set up a new U.N. disarmament commission.   Vishinsky suggested instead that the United Nations take another look at the earlier Soviet plan for international control—to outlaw the atomic bomb unconditionally.   The following month, at the end of November, during the Korean war, Truman startled the world by announcing in a press conference that the United States would take all necessary steps to meet the military situation, including "every weapon we have."   In December at the United Nations General Assembly, Truman again brought up the question of control and suggested that both conventional and atomic weapons be considered by a joint disarmament commission.   By vote, a new committee of twelve representatives was established to study controls and to report to the next regular session of the General Assembly.

A glimmer of hope thus came on January 11, 1952, when the United Nations Assembly set up its new Disarmament Commission to consider both nuclear and conventional armaments. The commission received the assignment to propose a treaty for the regulation, limitation, and balanced reduction of all armed forces and armaments; for the elimination of all major weapons adaptable to mass destruction; and for effective international control of atomic energy to ensure the use of atomic energy for peaceful purposes only. Before long it became increasingly clear that it would be only more difficult to reach agreement on such a broad basis. The establishment of the disarmament commission was virtually the only important point of agreement.

In April 1952 the United States submitted to the United Nations Disarmament Commission "Proposals for Progressive and Continuing Disclosure and Verification of Armed Forces and Armaments"—in effect, a proposal for an arms census. Nothing came of it, and nothing of fundamental importance happened on the question of atomic controls until Eisenhower's plan for an international pool of fissionable materials was announced in

1953, a plan which, we shall see, was not put into effect until 1955. Meantime, the Disarmament Commission meeting in London in 1954 ended its six weeks of closed session in failure. The problem of disarmament was then referred back to the parent body, the United Nations.

The story of atomic control negotiations which we have outlined above adds up to little more than a decade of disagreement. Indeed, the record reads like a series of ritualistic proposals in which each side prompted the other to exasperated frustrations. The outcome was that commissions never got down to business on any of the basic issues of how control was to be achieved. While the United States dogmatically stuck by its proposals, the Soviet Union continued to call for advance commitments and prohibitions which seemed unrealistic to the West. Questions which were addressed to the Soviet Union were either ignored or given a cold reception. Often the Soviet delegate would launch out into a long discussion in some other direction. In time, both sides aired their opinions with more candor, but also with more rigidity and less consideration for the other side. They understood each other, but understandings invariably led to a stalemate or deadlock.

We must mention here that a number of nations did not go along with United Nations proposals on atomic energy for reasons specific to their own private concerns which fell outside of United Nations big power politics. For example, India's attitude toward disarmament, international control of atomic energy, and collective enforcement measures was influenced by the desirability, she claimed, of improving the United Nations for the tasks of peace rather than for those of war. It was in this light that India examined all United Nations proposals concerning disarmament and international control of atomic energy. She did not, for example, support those provisions in the "Uniting for Peace" resolution which recommended that each member state maintain within its national armed forces elements so trained, organized, and equipped that they could be promptly made available to the United Nations.[6]

The United Nations also faced certain technical problems for which there was no precedent in the history of international

[6]See *India and the United Nations; report set up by the Indian Council of World Affairs.* Carnegie Endowment for International Peace (New York, 1957).

relations. For instance, the United Nations General Assembly was preoccupied for some time with attempts to reach an advance definition of "aggression." That was to be the starting point for the formulation of the policies of action for an international police force to handle aggressive moves on the part of a world power. It was rightly maintained that the hopes of securing peace by establishing a precise mechanical definition of "aggression" was only a snare and a delusion.[7] With nuclear warfare, it was pointed out, the initial act of defiance itself would be decisive of the whole conflict. The question was raised, for example, whether nation X would be bound by law not to look upon nation Y as its aggressor until after nation Y had attempted to destroy nation X with nuclear weapons—even if the spy of nation X delivered a twenty-four-hour notice of impending attack by nation Y. In other words, would a nation be an aggressor if it refused to wait until after having been struck?

INDUSTRY AND THE ATOMIC ENERGY ACT OF 1954

By 1954 many of the older big-power differences had hardened to the point where further discussions were of little value. Some of the earlier concerns simply lost their meaning and faded out of the picture after the Russians had detonated A-bombs and H-bombs. In general, after Stalin's death in 1953 the Russians engaged in their "peace" offensive with considerable vigor. The United States allegedly was already then in possession of a large number and a wide variety of nuclear weapons and had carried out a sufficient number of nuclear tests to feel its military strength. It was clear that somewhere, at the point of saturation of atomic bombs, the growing supply of fissionable materials in the United States could safely be diverted into industrial applications without jeopardizing the military advantage which had been acquired. But that, of course, meant releasing more information than could profitably be kept classified by secret governmental agencies.

After 1954 American private industry began to participate in the atomic energy program, not under government contract as had been the case since the war under the McMahon Act, but as agents operating in a system of free enterprise under the modified act of 1954. The Atomic Energy Act of 1954 was

[7]See Julius Stone, *Aggression and World Order, a critique of UN theories of aggression* (Berkeley, 1958).

the only major revision of the McMahon Bill in eight years. It administered a broader mandate to the AEC with the further understanding that future changes would be undertaken as specific needs arose. Prior to the revisions, industry spokesmen had felt that hardly any information of value had been made available for private enterprise. Without more frankness on atomic matters and more declassification of vital information, most industries felt that they could not safely venture into their own programs to build expensive atomic reactors. The status of domestic uranium mining was too uncertain. The potential liabilities with radiation hazards, licensing procedures, and regulations were too great; and the training of nuclear scientists and engineers was too costly. The problems which had held back industrial peacetime atomic energy development were taken up by Congressional hearings at the beginning of 1955. On the whole, the changes which were introduced had the healthy effect of publicly disseminating a great deal more atomic information. At the same time much of this information necessarily became available on an international basis to other nations of the world.

The Republican administration of President Eisenhower was quick to point out later that the initial declassification of much atomic energy information in the United States in 1954 came a full year before there were any changes on the part of the Soviet Union toward greater friendliness and increased co-operation in attitudes, policies, and plans. It should be mentioned in fairness to the Soviet side of this question that much of the material which was declassified by the United States had been arrived at independently by Soviet scientists by 1953. The Soviet accomplishment of A-bombs and H-bombs by 1953 was visible evidence of tremendous progress in nuclear weapons. It is perfectly clear that the intense Soviet-led campaign for outlawing nuclear weapons had passed its zenith when the Soviet stockpiling approached a level of substantial retaliation. The withholding and concealment of information from our own industrial establishments in 1954 would only have held back United States development.

The new freedom which resulted from declassifying much atomic energy information in 1954 indirectly opened up the most hopeful period of Soviet-American co-operation since the war, not on the question of international controls, but on a level of co-operative efforts among scientists probing the peacetime uses of atomic energy.

Geneva I: Conference on Peacetime Atom

By 1955, the tenth year of the arms race, neither the Communist nor the non-Communist world would relax its defense efforts. But something happened that year at the scientific Congress in Geneva which in retrospect seems more significant than most of the endless high-level diplomatic discussions which had taken place since 1945. Scientists in 1955 met to share information on atomic energy and discovered, as a by-product, that the areas of disagreement were much smaller than anyone had imagined—but only outside of the political sphere. All of the Big Three, for example, admitted that they had controlled fusion research projects under way.

Following a seven-year deadlock over the control of atomic energy since Baruch's plan in 1946, President Eisenhower on December 8, 1953, speaking before the United Nations General Assembly, proposed the formation of an international atomic energy commission under the United Nations to co-operate on the peacetime uses of atomic energy. It was his suggestion that the leading powers contribute uranium and other fissionable materials from their stockpiles to an international pool of atomic resources to "serve the needs rather than the fears of the world." Unlike the Baruch plan, Eisenhower's proposal did not call for international inspection and control of atomic facilities with surrender of national sovereignty. The proposal merely suggested an international agency to study and supervise the co-operation of atomic energy for peacetime purposes. The President, nevertheless, voiced the hope that the plan might eventually lead to a more satisfactory internationalization of the management, ownership, control, inspection, research, and development of the atom.

In September 1954 Secretary of State John Foster Dulles, speaking before the United Nations General Assembly, outlined President Eisenhower's plan for an international atomic pool of fissionable materials. He proposed, for 1955, the creation of an international atomic agency to represent nations from all regions of the world. Finally, he suggested that an international scientific and technical conference be scheduled for 1955 under the auspices of the United Nations. Simultaneously he announced the opening of a United States reactor training school where foreign students would be able to learn the working principles of atomic energy. Nuclear fuels for the building of experimental and industrial reactors were offered on a lend-lease basis. A substantial number of foreign medical and surgical experts were invited to participate in the work of our cancer hospitals.

Positive steps were taken in October 1954 by a United Nations committee headed by Ralph Bunche to discuss the United States program outlined by Dulles. Despite the negative attitude of the Soviet Union, the United States lost no time in pressing for conversations with other states which possessed advanced atomic energy programs. In the autumn of 1954 the United States began to take concrete steps to back up the Eisenhower atoms-for-peace proposal. The new chairman of the United States AEC, Admiral Strauss, enthusiastically supported the program. Foreign technicians were accepted for training in reactor technology at the Argonne National Laboratories. Uranium was distributed abroad, and technical publications were circulated. When the Soviet officials recognized that the United States and the United Nations would go ahead without Russia, Vishinsky reversed his stand and suggested changes which would make the resolution acceptable to the Soviet Union. On November 23 the resolution was unanimously accepted after the defeat of two amendments by the Soviet Union.

The text of the resolution recommended international co-operation in the peacetime uses of atomic energy, the creation of an international atomic energy agency, and an international conference on nuclear techniques scheduled for no later than August 1955. Dag Hammarskjöld, secretary of the United Nations, called together the seven-nation planning committee in January 1955 and set the conference in Geneva with August 8 as the opening date. H. J. Bhabha, the Indian United Nations representative and head of India's AEC, was chosen to head the conference. Russian physicist V. S. Vavilov was appointed Deputy Secretary-General. A panel chosen by Hammarskjöld then went to work to plan the details with a set of rules intended to keep out all political issues.

The International Conference on the Peaceful Uses of Atomic Energy was opened at Geneva on August 8, 1955, with a welcome by Conference President Bhabha of India. His address received world-wide attention when he predicted that "a method will be found for liberating fusion energy in a controlled manner within the next two decades. When that happens, the energy problems of the world will truly have been solved forever, for

the fuel will be as plentiful as the heavy hydrogen in the oceans."
This was a remarkable statement coming from an atomic scientist
who was representing a country in which 80 per cent of the
energy still comes from the primitive method of the burning of
dung.

Assembled at this meeting were 1,260 representatives and
advisers from 72 countries. Much interest was focused on the
meeting of the East and West scientists. The participating
nations in many cases had submitted their reports to the United
Nations for translation and dissemination in advance of the
Congress—without political implications and overtones. Data
from Brookhaven, New York, and Moscow were compared side
by side and printed in time for distribution at the conference.

For the occasion, the United States had shipped its $350,000
Oak Ridge "swimmingpool" research reactor to Geneva where
it was set up for display. The Soviet scientists had provided the
complete details of their 5000-kilowatt atomic power plant.
United Kingdom types of reactors and processes for separation
and disposal of fission products were demonstrated and discussed.
There were numerous displays, illustrating the applications of
tracer techniques in agriculture, medicine, and industry. Significantly, the conference also took on something of a businessman's
conclave where industrial executives bargained with one another
on new types of nuclear power plant equipment and analytical
devices for nuclear processes. United States industrial concerns
later felt that they had not been given sufficient freedom along
these lines. Scientists laid some of the blame on AEC Chairman
Lewis L. Strauss, under whose administration, they claimed, the
AEC had become more secretive and highly political.

The strongest single impression which American scientists
carried away from the Geneva conference was that of the perfectly tremendous progress which the Soviet scientists had made
in the atomic energy area in ten years. The technical competence
of the Soviet scientists, said a noted physicist, was only exceeded
by their friendliness and by their sincere scientific curiosity
concerning the accomplishments of American scientists working
in the same field. The meeting, referred to as Geneva I, was a
major landmark in scientific and cultural history. The proceedings of the conference were subsequently published by the United
Nations in sixteen volumes.

It was at Geneva I that the Soviet scientists released the first information on their research attempts with peacetime thermo-nuclear reactors. Subsequent developments, the following year, revealed that Soviet thermonuclear research was no mere bluff. In April 1956 the Soviet scientist, Igor Kurchatov, who had spoken at Geneva the previous year, was invited to give a lecture on thermonuclear fusion to the British atomic energy laboratory personnel at Harwell, England. It was a high-level technical lecture which was described as being honest, straightforward, and as devoid of propaganda as any lecture ought to be. There was more technical information on thermonuclear fusion in that talk in 1956 and in the Soviet scientific periodicals reporting the research of which Kurchatov spoke than in all the releases which the United States had made on that subject up to the end of 1957. In fact, it was suggested by the late Donald J. Hughes, who played such a unique role in the development of neutron physics at the Brookhaven National Laboratory, that, both at the Geneva conference of 1955 where the Russians reported in great detail on their experiments with neutrons and at Harwell in 1956, the Soviet scientists had released the greater bulk of all their basic work with nuclear energy.[8] With respect to fusion experiments specifically, Russia had released scientific information ahead of the United States in an area related to the peaceful applications of nuclear energy. The Soviet press and radio made the most of the fact that Russian scientists had been the first to break the classification barrier on controlled thermo-nuclear reactions. During the same year Kurchatov said that Soviet scientists would co-operate with Western scientists on thermonuclear research, provided their governments could come to an agreement to ban the use of nuclear weapons. In 1958 the offer was repeated.

In spite of the successes of the Geneva conference, the Disarma-ment Commission in 1955 failed to secure agreement among the major powers on a single proposal. By September 1955, after Geneva I, the Western proposals for disarmament were with-drawn and President Eisenhower said "the United States does now place a reservation upon all of its pre-Geneva substantive positions taken in this Sub-Committee as in the Disarmament Commission or in the United Nations on these questions in rela-tionship to levels of armament." This meant that all United

[8]Donald J. Hughes, *On Nuclear Energy* (Cambridge, Mass., 1957), pp. 238-244.

States proposals were suddenly retracted: manpower ceiling, elimination of nuclear stockpiles, and detailed plans for inspection and control. The reason for this withdrawal was allegedly that the Russian proposals were all either obscure or idealistic and impractical evasions of the real issue, or else outright bluff. Subsequently in 1956 and 1957 the Russians offered proposals which, at least on paper, were much more drastic on disarmament and inspection than the West was willing to consider. They were rebuffed by the West at every point, because it was then argued that any rigid control and inspection did not seem possible or practicable.

The argument for refusing to negotiate further with Russia can be summarized somewhat as follows: If there is no sure method of detecting bombs or of keeping tab of fissionable materials in the world, there is a real danger that a nation can possess a clandestine stock of nuclear weapons. The only practicable basis on which to proceed is to assume that a nation possessing nuclear weapons would use them in a war. In the case of the Russians, who cannot be trusted, there is no other alternative but to maintain one's own stockpile of nuclear weapons at least to repel aggression.

While there was no agreement on the question of disarmament in the United Nations Commission, Geneva I had provided the stimulus for the organization of other international efforts. In November 1955 the United Nations appointed a committee to study the effects of ionizing radiation and radioactive fallout. In the same year an all-European co-operative organization for research—European Organization for Nuclear Research, called CERN—was organized. Its first report was presented in Geneva in 1956. International nuclear conferences convened in 1956 and 1957 in Geneva, Paris, Amsterdam, Moscow, and Rochester, New York.

In the same year, the Soviet government established a Joint Institute of Nuclear Research as an organ to promote international nuclear co-operation, and the building of atomic power installations. It included Albania, Bulgaria, Communist China, Czechoslovakia, the Republic of Vietnam, East Germany, Hungary, the Republic of Korea, Mongolia, Poland, Romania, and the Soviet Union.

INTERNATIONAL ATOMIC ENERGY AGENCY

In 1956, one year after Geneva I, eighty-two nations met in

New York to draw up a charter for the creation of an International Atomic Energy Agency (IAEA) with headquarters in Vienna. It was proposed that the agency be established to act as a pool or clearinghouse to make fissionable materials available to the smaller countries engaged in peaceful atomic energy pursuits. President Eisenhower said that the United States would offer 11,000 pounds of nuclear fuel through the international agency and thereafter would match the contributions of all other nations to the agency's atomic pool until 1960. The Soviet Union was the first country to ratify the IAEA's charter. After three months of debate in the Senate, the United States became a member of IAEA. Thus, three and one-half years after President Eisenhower's initial dramatic gesture, the IAEA was finally established in July 1957 when the United States became the third atomic power to approve the charter.

Since the time of its generous original proposals, the United States government has hardly lived up to the obligations of its highly touted atoms-for-peace program. A detailed review of the history of the IAEA, which started with idealistic expectations about what atomic energy could do to aid underdeveloped nations, would reveal a relatively small record of positive accomplishments, mostly in the area of strictly technical assistance in working out co-operative administrative matters for countries willing to avail themselves of such services.[9]

Already in 1956, Dr. H. D. Smyth (AEC commissioner 1949 to 1954) charged the Eisenhower administration with failure to carry out its earlier promises for the program.[10] Smyth's criticism was partly directed toward reluctance on the part of the United States government to develop nuclear energy as a source of industrial power. How, asked Symth, was the United States to build reactors abroad without learning to build them at home? Failure of the AEC in this area, Smyth said, was endangering America's dominant position in the development of the new technology of power and was preventing the United States from fulfilling its obligation to help other countries obtain nuclear power. Smyth also criticized the AEC for withholding information not vital to national security. He called for a clear decision on declassification, adding: "Such a decision would release our

[9]See Stoessinger's paper in A. N. Holcombe, *Organizing Peace in the Nuclear Age* (New York, 1959).

[10] H. D. Smyth, *Foreign Affairs,* Oct. 1956, pp. 1-16.

work on the controlled thermonuclear reaction from the bonds of secrecy in which it is now entangled and would release other more prosaic data which our rivals can eventually get for themselves if they haven't already."

By 1959 both foreign and American authorities predicted that unless Congress would offer prompt and forceful support the IAEA would soon be doomed to failure. It was obvious that part of the program's failure was due to back-stage political moves by Lewis L. Strauss, former AEC chairman. This was admittedly only one side of the picture, since the Soviet Union had done everything in its power to frustrate the organization and its efforts.

In a stirring address before the American Association for the United Nations in March 1959, W. Sterling Cole, director-general of the IAEA, urged that his agency be allowed to perform the functions for which it had been established—the development of the atoms-for-peace program. Cole had reference to the fact that recent United States action had been taken to bypass the IAEA. He summarized his recommendations as follows:

The first decision which must be made is clear and straightforward. It is simply the decision that, having created an international body for defined purposes in connection with atomic energy, the Agency should be supported not only with generous financial contributions—as has been the case of the United States—but fully and without qualifications in its operational aspects. We can be only partially effective if some nations maintain parallel machinery to do the same thing as the Agency but subject to individual nation selection, manipulation and control.[11]

Notwithstanding these criticisms of the lack of United States co-operation with IAEA, there had been some definite signs of progress. IAEA nuclear conferences and symposia were scheduled in 1959 and 1960 at Vienna, Saclay (France), Warsaw, Monaco, Karlsruhe, Copenhagen, and Prague. These conclaves were organized to bring together scientists from major atomic energy installations the world over: radiologists, oceanographers, geologists, and other experts working on the peaceful aspects of atomic energy and the question of radiation in science and industry.

Plans through the IAEA were also being made to set up isotope training centers in various countries. Preliminary atomic

[11]W. Sterling Cole, *Science,* April 10, 1959, p. 951.

energy assistance missions through IAEA were approved for Argentina, Brazil, Venezuela, China (Taiwan), Japan, Korea, the Philippines, Vietnam, Burma, Greece, Africa, the Middle East, and the United Arab Republic. At the Boris Kidric Institute near Belgrade, experiments were undertaken in 1960 to study reactor accidents under IAEA and the Yugoslav Nuclear Energy Commission. During 1960 the IAEA also announced that it would undertake a project near Vienna to measure and analyze samples of air, water, food, and soil to help determine the degree of radioactivity in man's environment. Steps were also taken to obtain international control and safeguards over materials used to fuel atomic reactors. Director Cole urged the United States, Britain, and France to set an example by placing some of their reactors under the agency's supervision to demonstrate the feasibility and desirability of international controls. The AEC foresaw in these suggestions some apparently insurmountable problems; e.g., how was the agency going to inspect fissionable materials produced in reactors now being reprocessed in plants engaged in military work?

Geneva II

The Second United Nations International Conference on the Peaceful Uses of Atomic Energy convened in the Palais des Nations in Geneva, September 1 to 13, 1958, with some 5,600 participants from seventy nations. A comprehensive review of the conference appeared in the twenty-fifth Semiannual Report of the U.S. AEC. About 2,500 papers (double the number presented at the 1955 conference) were submitted (not all read) on all aspects of the experimental and practical phases of peacetime atomic energy. Hugh S. Taylor mentioned in his on-the-spot coverage of Geneva II that the great interest shown for atomic energy over that of other pressing problems of the world, and the lavish governmental support which was obvious at the conference, had something to do with "economics, the need for power, the search for prosperity, anxiety, prestige and propaganda."[12]

One of the most praiseworthy aspects of Geneva II was the positive advance toward a breakdown of the secrecy restrictions which had been expressed as a hope at Geneva I in 1955. Pro-

[12]Hugh S. Taylor, *American Scientist,* Dec., 1958, pp. 325-330.

fessor Perrin of France characterized the general conference attitude in his address to the opening session when he said, referring to secrecy: "Its most harmful effect is to prevent science from acting as the link that its universal character makes it so uniquely capable of being; and to engender distrust and to poison human relations in the sphere which should best allow an intermingling of civilization."

In 1955, at Geneva I, the barrier of secrecy had been greatly reduced; in 1958, at Geneva II, secrecy had almost been eliminated, except in essential military matters. The United States and Great Britain announced on August 30, as a prelude to Geneva II, that they were lifting all secrecy from their research on the control of thermonuclear fusion. Simultaneously the Soviet Union disclosed the existence of its largest research tool, the OGRA, a device for studying the control of thermonuclear reactions. During the meeting the Russian delegation handed out four notebooks containing the results of its investigations on fusion research. Twelve volumes of up-to-date information on peacetime nuclear developments in the United States were also presented to each of the hundreds of official delegates of the countries represented at the conference.

In general, on the question of technical exchange of information, thermonuclear fusion stole the show at Geneva in 1958. Fifteen different governments reported on their research into thermonucleonics. The devices, equipment, working displays, and models for thermonuclear research occupied a specially constructed exhibition hall two blocks long.

Notable advances in full-scale uranium power station reactors were also given full treatment. There was general agreement that by 1975 most new high-output power stations in the world would be nuclear. Atomic power for underdeveloped countries was stressed in particular for India where the country's power requirements are now doubling every six to seven years. World reserves of high-grade uranium ore were re-estimated at ten million tons of uranium. Other topics of the Congress included the genetic effects of radiation, health, safety, inspection organizations, the new industrial uses of radioisotopes, and important advances in fundamental research and chemical technology. Many of these uses have already been mentioned elsewhere in our text. The proceedings of the conference entitled *Peaceful Uses of Atomic Energy* were published in English in a thirty-

three-volume work by the United Nations. Abridged editions
and translations were also prepared.

In November 1958 the United States signed an agreement
with the six-nation European Community for Atomic Energy
(*Euratom*). This included Belgium, France, Luxembourg, West
Germany, Italy, and the Netherlands. This organization had
been initiated in 1957 in response to Europe's growing demands
for electric power. The aim of *Euratom,* as declared in its
original *Treaty,* was "to continue, by establishing the conditions
necessary to the formation and rapid growth of nuclear industries, to an increase in the standard of living in the member
states and to the development of trade with other countries."
This was to be accomplished by facilitating investment and
assuring the setting up of installations fundamental to the development of nuclear energy within the community. By the end of
1959, Canada and *Euratom* had entered into agreements for a
ten-million-dollar peaceful atomic energy program. The proposed
target for *Euratom* was set at six nuclear-power installations to
produce one million kilowatts by 1963. Nuclear fuels were
offered by the United States at current prices, with 135 million
dollars of long-range credit for capital costs. In 1960 the AEC
announced that the joint United States-*Euratom* atomic power
program had been a failure. Increased supplies of low-cost
coal and oil for conventional power plants had made atomic
power less attractive to European countries than a number of
years earlier.

We should mention a number of other international organizations in the field of atomic energy. The Organization for European Economic Co-operation (OEEC) consists of seventeen
western European nations and includes the development of
nuclear industries among its several spheres of international
activity. Since 1954 the OEEC has been greatly concerned
with the probable supply of energy which will be available to
meet Europe's requirements in the next few decades. To this
end OEEC set up a committee of experts to survey the whole
European energy field and especially nuclear power developments.

Within the OEEC there is also a newly created European
Nuclear Energy Agency (ENEA) which plans co-operative pro-

grams in all major aspects of nonmilitary nuclear development. In addition, the ENEA has organized twelve of the seventeen-member nations of OEEC into *Eurochemic* which in turn has set up an international twelve-million-dollar company for reprocessing nuclear elements and recovering plutonium. The first plant, with United States AEC design assistance, was scheduled to begin operation in Mol, Belgium, in 1961. The purpose of this international jointly-owned company was to prevent each country from having to develop its own facilities. The company at Mol was also supposed to serve as an experimental pilot plant for the building of larger installations, such as a boiling water reactor at Halden in Norway. In March of 1959 the ENEA agreed to support the construction in England of its third joint undertaking, viz., an experimental high-temperature, gas-cooled reactor to be known as the "dragon."

In April 1959 the Organization of American States, Pan American Union established an Inter-American Nuclear Energy Commission (IANEC) to plan for the peaceful application of nuclear energy in the Western Hemisphere. Representatives met for the first time in October 1959 and planned co-operative programs for training, education, and research in the nuclear sciences and for dissemination of atomic information in Latin America.

THE BOMB TEST BAN

Before we leave the subject of the international control of atomic energy, we shall summarize the attempts on the part of the major powers to reach agreement on the debate over whether or not to end nuclear testing. We know that the fundamental points of view of the East and West on disarmament measures are quite different. Nevertheless, concrete proposals for a cessation of nuclear weapons tests, by both sides, have led to many honest negotiations and a considerable measure of agreement on a number of important matters.

On June 14, 1946, the United States submitted Baruch's plan for an international agency to control atomic power and to destroy existing atomic weapons. Five days later, Russia made a counter-proposal to ban the production of atomic weapons but without international control. Russia's first atomic explosion in 1949 ended the United States bomb monopoly. In 1955 the United States proposed an "open skies" policy for mutual aerial inspection through exchange of air survey facilities. Russia rejected the policy.

Shortly after the Russians had tested a new thermonuclear bomb in November 1955, Radio Moscow issued a statement requesting "that countries which possess nuclear weapons pledge to discontinue their testing." In December, Soviet Premier Bulganin, Secretary Khrushchev, and Prime Minister Nehru of India called for the "unconditional prohibition of the production, use, and experimenting of nuclear and thermonuclear weapons." British Prime Minister Eden replied that his government would not consider discontinuance of the tests before it could test its own thermonuclear weapons. Secretary Dulles replied that a test ban was out of the question without a safe disarmament plan. Weapons testing continued unabated. A letter by Malik, made public at the Soviet embassy in London, said that Russia was prepared to abandon bomb testing as soon as the Western powers would give a similar pledge. In England the Soviet plan was looked upon as a propaganda move to strengthen the Labor Party's opposition to the tests.

On May 10, 1957, the Soviet Union again asked British Parliament and United States Congress to agree to an immediate halt of nuclear weapons tests. Simultaneously Russia called for the organization of an interparliamentary committee of the three countries to discuss the banning of the production and testing of nuclear weapons.

On March 31, 1958, Foreign Minister Gromyko announced that the Soviet Union would unilaterally suspend all testing of nuclear bombs. No time limit was given, but Gromyko stated that the Soviet Union would resume its tests if other countries continued theirs. He mentioned that it would be more difficult to reach an agreement to ban nuclear tests as soon as powers outside of the Big Three would possess atomic weapons. The United States State Department responded by saying that Russia previously had refused to co-operate with the United Nations disarmament commission. It was suggested that mere statements without intention and without a system of verification were of no value. During the month of April the AEC began a new series of tests in the Pacific.

In July 1958 an International Conference on Nuclear Test Control convened in Geneva to discuss the feasibility of a system for policing a world-wide test ban. The meeting had been called by President Eisenhower and was based on an earlier study by a professional panel in the United States under the direction of the acknowledged expert in the detection field, Hans Bethe of Cornell University. After two months of sessions at Geneva the conclusion was reached that testing control posts would be feasible under an international co-ordinating control organ. The three major powers thereupon agreed to continue negotiations on the question of detailed technical means of detecting nuclear explosives anywhere in the world.

President Eisenhower then announced on August 22, 1958, that the United States was suspending all nuclear tests for one year effective October 31, 1958, in order to enter into East-West three-power talks on long-range plans to halt nuclear weapons testing. A few hours after Eisenhower announced his proposal, the British government issued a similar statement. Russia through Khrushchev expressed its willingness on August 30 to join the United States and Great Britain on talks. On October 30 the United States completed its series of tests in Nevada.

In Congress both Republicans and Democrats voiced praise for the United States ban offer. Secretary of State Dulles and Under Secretary of State Herter both favored the suspension of the tests—unqualifiedly and without any of the delays which might nullify the hoped-for effect of the announcement on world opinion. New AEC chairman McCone argued against the suspension of nuclear tests, saying that this would interrupt plans designed to study the peaceful uses of atomic explosions. Deputy Defense Secretary Quarles and Chairman of the Joint Chief of Staff Twining were outspokenly against suspension of tests. The Pentagon made it clear that the program of equipping military forces with nuclear weapons would be continued.

On October 3 the Russians announced that they would resume their tests because the United States had continued her tests after the Russian-announced suspension of March 31. Two nuclear explosions were staged by Russia on November 1 and 2 while the Geneva conference was beginning its talks. Eisenhower declared: "This action by the Soviet Union relieves the United States from any obligation under its offer to suspend nuclear-weapons tests. However, we shall continue suspension of such tests for the time being, and we understand that the United Kingdom will do likewise. We hope that the Soviet Union will also do so. If there is not shortly a corresponding renunciation by the Soviet Union, the United States will be obliged to reconsider its position." London made a similar announcement. The next move would have to come from Russia. The Russians completed their tests on November 3 in Siberia.

By the end of the year, when the Berlin situation had reached the most precarious state since the blockade of 1948, the three major powers had stopped all nuclear tests. Khrushchev's acceptance of the Western offer to begin diplomatic talks, nevertheless, was accompanied with so many criticisms of the United States position that the final political agreement seemed very remote. Both sides had made some concessions. Eisenhower had given up the long-standing United States position that test explosions should be halted only on condition that there would be a simultaneous agreement to stop the production of nuclear weapons. Khrushchev had agreed to halt the tests and leave control and inspection to be worked out later.

Some members of the AEC voiced the opinion that such a test ban would be of greater military advantage for the Soviet Union than for the United States, because it would interrupt our program for developing nuclear missile warheads. It was felt that the Soviet Union, fully appreciate of the possible advantage of a test cessation, would therefore welcome the suspension. On the other hand, it was also suggested that test suspensions would hinder the Russians in the development of small-size atomic weapons for tactical battlefield use, provided they were unable to continue work along these lines by concealing their small tests.

As the talks got under way toward the end of 1958, it was immediately apparent that both sides were in hopeless disagreement even on the order in which problems should be tackled. The United States and United Kingdom pressed for discussions about technical methods of test controls. Russia insisted that all three powers should first commit themselves to a *permanent* ban to end atomic and hydrogen weapons testing. After four weeks of procedural wrangles, the Russians moved toward the Western position by agreeing to discuss a plan for inseparably linking the ban on nuclear tests with the organization to police such a ban. It began to appear as if the Big Three were on the threshold of an agreement to draft a treaty in which both sides could offer proposals as to the contents of such an agreement.

When they got down to brass tacks, new difficulties arose. They finally came to agree on one article: that the treaty, when and if completed, should be left open for signature by any country. It was stipulated, however, that this article, which would lay down the agreement of all signatory nations to prohibit nuclear weapons tests, should have no legal validity until the whole treaty was drawn up and ratified by the three major governments. The second article which was accepted by the conferees was simply to agree on the need for a control system to police the ban.

The much more difficult problem which came up early in 1959 was to reach some unity on a specific international system to prevent violations of the ban. It was soon seen that some of the actual details of bomb test detection would cut across areas of highly restricted technical information. From the start, the Soviet Union objected to the tight inspection system suggested by the United States. Eventually the talks boiled down to the question of the technical feasibility of detecting small underground blasts. When the Soviet delegates realized that the Americans themselves were not completely in agreement on all the technical aspects of the problem, they expressed their doubts about the sincerity of the United States's desire to end the testing of nuclear weapons. The United States and Great Britain subsequently rejected the Soviet proposal for veto rights on policing the test ban.

In March 1959 the United States government called on a panel of earthquake specialists to map a program aimed at foolproof detection of nuclear blasts. The main difficulty, it was learned, would be to distinguish between the shock waves of earthquakes and those produced by underground atomic blasts. Surface and aerial blasts would be detectable in a number of ways which would make on-the-spot inspection unessential. But seismic experts agreed that small underground five kiloton explosions, similar to the type fired in Nevada in October 1958 could not be detected with absolute assurance. After four months of meetings, the three-power talks were stalemated on every key issue. Nevertheless, both sides were willing to keep talking in the hope that the other might sooner or later give in on some point.

There were a number of roadblocks which prevented East-West agreement. The Soviet delegates kept insisting, as prerequisite to all other details, that the three powers should first agree to declare a permanent ban on testing. Furthermore, Russia wanted the weapons ban to be based on trust, while the United States and the United Kingdom insisted that the ban should be monitored by elaborate technical controls which would eliminate any need for trust. According to the Western argument, nations which cannot trust each other are forced to devise instrumental means of checking up on one another to see whether each will live up to an agreement to stop exploding nuclear bombs. According to this argument: concealment is easy; detection is difficult; trust under such circumstances is naive and unrealistic, because it has no technological basis of operation.

The criteria for distinguishing earthquakes from explosions were discussed in great detail during the Geneva negotiations. It was decided that control stations should be located about every 600 miles apart in regions where earthquakes normally occur, and about 1,000 miles apart in other regions. This would come to about twenty stations in Russia. It was further estimated that about fifty to a hundred earthquakes annually in the Soviet Union would not be distinguishable from underground explosions. It was, therefore, argued by the West that the only sure way of identifying the seismic records would be to send inspection teams to the location of a disturbance. Unfortunately, a combination of seismographs placed at several stations can locate the center of a disturbance to an accuracy of only about five miles. This would mean that the inspection team would have to explore an area of about 100 square miles.

In January 1959, Dr. Albert Latter had announced that the tremors from underground bombs could be muffled by a factor of 300 by setting them off in enormous underground cavities. Dr. Latter's so-called "decoupling" or "big hole" theory was experimentally verified with small conventional explosions early in 1959 in a salt mine in Louisiana. From this it was calculated that the explosion from a twenty-kiloton weapon could be decoupled in a spherical hole 500 feet in diameter, if placed at a depth of 3,000 feet below the earth's surface. Thus, the Carlsbad Caverns would be sufficiently large to muffle ten-kiloton explosions. The cost of excavating a hole big enough for a twenty-kiloton explosion was estimated by oil industry experts at about ten million dollars.

The big question which was raised, of course, was whether any country really would put itself to such expense in order to construct big holes merely to be able to cheat on the test ban. Since repeated seismic disturbances coming from any one such big hole would look suspicious and warrant sending an outside inspection team to the site, many big holes would have to be constructed in order to make positive progress with respect to the development of weapons. To violate the test ban treaty without being detected, a nation would practically have to use a different big hole for each test in its program. Cheating on such a scale and under these conditions would be difficult, if not impossible.

By the end of May 1959, a major difficulty developed over the question of manning the inspection posts. According to the Western plan, British and United States technicians were to be stationed at the control posts on Soviet territory, in order to provide fool-proof policing of the ban. The Soviet delegates felt that foreign technical inspection teams would be in a position to set up espionage rings in the Soviet Union under the guise of an international control of the test ban.

In effect, Russia was willing to accept world-wide inspection, with control posts, on condition that Russian personnel be assigned to the posts in Soviet territory. The West felt that such an arrangement, as well as any kind of inspection which would be subject to veto, would not permit an international agency to operate on Soviet territory with the freedom necessary for effective control. If, for example, an underground explosion were suspected in the Soviet Union, it might be necessary, according to the Western argument, to send an inspection team to the spot from the outside to determine what had actually happened. The Russians wanted rather to reserve the right to exercise a veto over any decision to send foreign inspectors into the Soviet zone, while the West demanded veto-free day-to-day freedom to operate according to the wishes of the international inspection agency.

British Prime Minister Macmillan proposed that the impasse on the on-site inspections might be avoided by limiting the number of veto-free inspections permitted each year. The American delegation was interested in this proposal, but Khrushchev refused to agree to a scientific study that would indicate how many inspectors would be necessary to detect nuclear explosions.

There were many other complications. For example, China with its tremendous territory would necessarily have to be included among the countries in which control posts were to be located in order to maintain effective world-wide monitoring of tests. But even if the Soviet and Western officials were to agree on a control system, how would this be worked out when Communist China was not recognized by the United States and had not been admitted to the United Nations?

After eight months in session (72 meetings), the Geneva conference for a ban on nuclear weapons tests went into a recess on March 19, 1959, with plans to reconvene on April 13. By then the conferees had adopted only three additional articles for their draft treaty: that the proposed ban treaty should be of an indefinite duration; that it be registered with the United Nations; and that the control situation be reviewed after two years.

In a letter dated April 13, 1959, President Eisenhower proposed a new limited agreement which would prohibit tests on the surface of the earth and up to an altitude of thirty-one miles. This proposal was offered as a preliminary step designed to permit detection by a system of observation posts without any on-the-spot inspection—since the Soviet Union had rejected the latter. In effect, this proposal would have bypassed the deadlock created by the Soviet demand for veto. Khrushchev replied on April 23 that this plan was "an unfair deal" and added that his government would insist on the simultaneous ban on tests "in the atmosphere, underground, under water, and at great altitudes."

In July of the same year a panel of seismic experts, a subgroup of the President's Science Advisory Committee, made plans for a multimillion-dollar two-year research program to study uncertainties over detection and concealment of underground nuclear blasts—the main uncertainty obstructing East-West agreement. Scientists also suggested that satellites might prove to be useful for patrolling sneak explosions at high altitudes.

On August 26 the United States announced that it would continue its test suspension until December 31, 1959, and thereafter only on a week-to-week basis. Russia said it would not stage any tests as long as the West refrained from doing so.

On November 20 the United Nations General Assembly voted

51 to 16, with 15 abstentions, to ask France to refrain from a planned atomic test in the Sahara. France proceeded with its plans despite the protests.

By the end of 1959 the committee of scientists from the United States, Britain, and Russia, studying the technical aspects of a control system to police the ban, submitted a report which indicated that no agreement had been reached on the major issue of criteria to be used to determine whether earth tremors recorded by control posts were caused by natural earthquakes or underground nuclear explosions.

In its annual report to Congress in January 1960, the AEC disclosed that the United States had ruled out H-bomb tests and big underground nuclear blasts for 1960. A-weapon tests in Nevada and nuclear shots in space were not so excluded.

On February 11, 1960, after fifteen months of negotiations on tests at Geneva, and two days prior to France's explosion of a fission bomb in the Sahara desert (the first nuclear detonation since Russia's explosion of November 3, 1958, in Siberia) President Eisenhower announced a new United States plan for international restriction on nuclear tests which was aimed, first, at breaking the deadlock with the Russians and, second, with consolidating negotiations made up to that time.

Up to that point there had been some measure of progress on peripheral issues, but virtually none on the crucial problem —how to set up mutually acceptable guarantees of compliance with the ban. Briefly, the Western argument up to this point had been that small underground explosions were so difficult to detect that they could easily be confused with tremors from earthquakes. Refusing to place their faith in anything but scientific devices and strict inspection, the United States had stood fast by the principle that a *total* ban on tests would not be acceptable until more accurate detection devices were developed.

Among Americans, Edward Teller notably opposed the continued cessation of tests. He took the view that the Russians were bent on violation; that the United States would be throwing away its lead in nuclear weapons development by continuing the test ban. In debates with Bertrand Russell before a television audience, Teller argued that it was reasonable to assume that the Russians were or would be carrying out such tests. He concluded that the situation would lead to Soviet military superiority and eventually to blackmailing the Western world into complete capitulation under Russian Communism. During hearings before the Joint Atomic Energy Committee of Congress, Teller recommended that the United States launch a research program for new methods of decoupling underground explosions. According to his argument, the United States should know all possible means of concealment in order to develop a detection system to deal with violations.

Eisenhower's February proposal for the ban covered all reliably detectable tests in the atmosphere, the ocean, and all those regions of space and beneath the surface of the earth where monitoring was known to be possible and where effective controls could be agreed on. Low-powered underground (subterranean) test explosions were to be exempted from the ban as not being subject to effective monitoring. What the new proposal in effect boldly suggested was: Let's allow the cheating we can't be caught at.

This new United States position was partly the result of the experiments which had been conducted by the AEC in a salt mine in Louisiana. There were other motives behind Eisenhower's new proposal. Both the Defense Department and the AEC had generally opposed cessation of nuclear tests on grounds that it would freeze American tactical weapons development. Eager to conduct small underground tests, the Pentagon and the AEC had maintained that such tests were essential to the perfection of nuclear warheads for the Polaris and Minuteman missiles, the anti-missile missile, and a better tactical weapon for the army.

The Soviet Union rejected Eisenhower's plan as unworkable. On February 16 at Geneva they offered a new version of their own plan to cover *all* tests, and to check on atom blasts by limiting on-site inspections to a small predetermined quota. In this plan the Russians set aside their own criteria for defining suspicious events and accepted criteria based on standards which had been proposed by the United States, i.e., the investigation to see whether seismic disturbances were earthquakes or secret tests. Alongside these Soviet concessions came the warning that if the United States gave nuclear weapons to its allies, Russia would do the same for its allies.

On March 19 at Geneva, the Soviet delegate Semyon Tsarapkin called for a special meeting of the three nations to offer the Russian counterpart of Eisenhower's proposal. This was the

188th meeting on atomic tests since the Geneva talks began in the summer of 1958. Tsarapkin announced Soviet willingness to accept Eisenhower's proposal on one condition: that the three nations agree not only to a controlled ban of high-powered blasts, but also to an *unpoliced* moratorium on small underground explosions. It was explained that during the moratorium it might be possible to undertake joint scientific experiments designed to improve detection devices. The duration of the moratorium was not fixed, but observers implied that the Russians had a four to five-year period in mind; the West, two to three years.

Opposition in the United States to the Soviet proposal arose over fears of the consequences to the security of the United States. It was suggested, for example, that the ban would result in an armory of American ICBM nuclear warheads one tenth the size of the Soviet armory. It was also feared that over a period of four to five years the atomic laboratories of the United States would disintegrate. The Russians, it was said, would be able to count on strict adherence by this country to any pact on a test ban, but that without an adequate inspection system the United States would not be equally confident that the Russians would really adhere to the ban.

The British, represented by Prime Minister Macmillan and his staff who conferred with Eisenhower at Camp David in Maryland, were more favorably inclined to look upon the Soviet long-term proposal for a moratorium on all tests as being well worth serious exploration. The British, in fact, were willing to accept a treaty for a moratorium based on mutual trust, in hopes that the East and West would be able eventually to secure sufficiently sensitive testing devices to record small-scale underground tests.

It was recognized in this country that the Soviet proposal would confront President Eisenhower with one of the most difficult decisions he had faced in foreign affairs. The problem was all the more complex in that some United States detection specialists expressed doubts that underground detections could be perfected even after a period of intensive research.

The Soviet suggestion became the subject of lively debate in the United States. Influential groups in Washington largely gave their support to the continuation of nuclear testing. Nevertheless, Hans Bethe, the principal administration scientific adviser on test ban technical provisions, stated:

No international agreement can be entirely foolproof. It must always be partly based on faith in the other party's good intentions. The only thing that technical methods of inspection can do is to reduce the area in which one needs to rely on good faith. This is accomplished by the present Russian compromise proposal; the area of faith is reduced in scope to small, underground explosions and in time to a few years. This seems to me an entirely acceptable risk.[13]

By the end of March a United States counter-offer seemed to be developing which would favor a one-year moratorium within the Soviet plan. It was based on the belief that a joint research plan with the Russians would eventually lead to a system of earthquake analysis which would prevent anyone from cheating. During the interim, the Soviet Union, it was thought, would not attempt to cheat if there were even a remote chance of being caught.

A joint statement released by President Eisenhower and Prime Minister Macmillan on March 29, 1960, favored the acceptance of the Soviet proposal for a moratorium on underground nuclear tests (provisionally, and not for more than two years), provided Russia would accept a satisfactory system of international inspection, including an adequate quota of on-site inspections and satisfactory agreement on the composition of the control commission, control post staffing, and voting matters. The treaty, Eisenhower said, would be subject to approval by a two-thirds vote in the United States Senate.

Following the announcement of the Eisenhower-Macmillan statement, a wave of optimism spread through the State Department when it appeared that the Big Three were at last on the verge of reaching agreement on a limited test ban. This optimism bore along with it the Democrats and Republicans who were seeking to become President Eisenhower's successor. There seemed to be closer agreement on testing than at any time in the past.

The feeling did not last. The Eisenhower-Macmillan decisions went counter to many high-ranking American officials who were convinced that Soviet Russia would gain great advantages over the United States by a moratorium on tests. It was suggested that the whole field of defense against surprise attack might be

[13]*New York Times,* March 27, 1960.

sacrificed by the United States if such a plan were to go into effect. The West, it was said, would be putting its trust solely in Russia's word during the moratorium. On the other hand, some State Department officials felt that cheating with clandestine small-yield tests would entail a risk of detection or disclosure which the Soviet Union could ill afford to risk. Finally, it was also felt that an outright rejection of the Soviet test-ban proposal would be a dangerous propaganda setback for the West in the eyes of the rest of the world.

Four days of scientific testimony before the Joint Congressional Committee on Atomic Energy, however, threw additional serious doubts upon many details of the technical mechanism which could be used to police the ban. The foremost arguments which emerged had to do with the fact that the act of concealing a nuclear test had advanced much more rapidly than the act of detection. It was stated, for example, that in large concealed underground caverns the detection threshold was closer to the equivalent of 100,000 tons than to 19,000 tons of TNT— especially in view of the feasibility of constructing large underground chambers which could muffle explosions by a factor of 300. Thus, a fully muffled explosion of the strength of the Hiroshima bomb would pass completely unnoticed if the proposed network were in use. Leading atomic scientists said that the Geneva system of 180 seismographic stations spaced around the globe would be hopelessly inadequate as a reliable system for enforcing a ban on all tests. In the Soviet Union alone, it was estimated that, instead of the twenty contemplated control posts, there would have to be six hundred.

There was no doubt in the minds of many scientists by the end of April 1960 that enormous technical problems were involved in establishing a reliable system for detecting underground atomic explosions. But it was even clearer that political and diplomatic relations with respect to the tests had not yet caught up with the technical developments.

General Disarmament Conference—1960

Simultaneous with the Big Three Conference on the nuclear test ban in its sixteenth month at Geneva, five Communist nations and five Western nations met for a general disarmament conference in the United Nations Geneva headquarters on March 15, 1960. The talks of the two groups, although not officially connected on paper, dovetailed and were intimately linked to the problem of nuclear weapons. Specifically, the issue of controls was the key to the success of either set of negotiations. A Big Three agreement on a test ban inevitably would have given the ten-nation disarmament talk its major boost.

The general disarmament talks were the first since the fall of 1957 when the long-stalemated negotiations in London were broken off. In this instance, for the 1960 meetings, British Foreign Secretary Selwyn Lloyd had prepared a three-stage disarmament plan for negotiation with Russia which included handing atomic weapons over to an international agency and cutbacks by stages in both conventional and nuclear weapons. The United States had not by March 15 laid out any effective plans for entering into the disarmament talks. In fact, the State Department found its own top secret Coolidge report "negative" on the whole disarmament problem. It was much more concerned with security.

Conducted with some quibbling and the usual maneuvering with words, the Geneva disarmament conference sessions were, nevertheless, businesslike in manner and moderately free from harangues and mutual accusations. The atmosphere of the talks was noticeably better than the rigid and harsh confrontations which had characterized most of the earlier East-West talks. In previous disarmament negotiations, the Russians, it was usually said, had not believed that the Americans wanted disarmament; the Americans, it was said, had not believed that the Russians wanted controls. Reproaches of this kind were less common in 1960 as the delegates settled down to the more serious business of discussing the political machinery necessary for conciliation, and the power necessary to impose sanctions. Both sides had made provisions for involving other countries in the disarming process. Communist China, for example, was mentioned explicitly in the Russian plan, implicitly in the Western plan.

Western delegates therefore believed that the Russians were genuinely seeking negotiation opportunities. More specifically, the test ban talks had seemed to reach a wide measure of agreement on the detection and control of atomic blasts—even without concurring on the feasibility of detecting and controlling small underground blasts.

The issue of atomic inspection and controls ran throughout

the whole disarmament debate like the problem of the chicken and the egg. Which comes first? The Russians said that if the major powers would only agree on an over-all plan for disarmament first, then they could talk later about the details of inspection. The West, on the other hand, said that it would be futile to agree on a disarmament system before reaching agreement on how each separate measure would be inspected and verified.

THE U-2 PLANE INCIDENT

On May Day 1960 the Russians captured the pilot of a Lockheed U-2 jet which had been shot down near Sverdlovsk, 1,200 miles from the Afghan-Soviet border. The plane, which had left Pakistan and was en route across Russia to a Norwegian air base, was on a spying mission for the United States Central Intelligence Agency. The pilot was allegedly caught during high-altitude aerial espionage and admitted taking photographs of Russian airfields and guided missile and nuclear installations.

An atmosphere of embarrassed silence prevailed in Washington on May 7 as Premier Khrushchev jubilantly reported the incident. The report was followed by Khrushchev's assertion that Americans had sent the plane into the Soviet Union as a provocation aimed at sabotaging the East-West talks in Geneva and the Big-Four summit meeting which was scheduled to open in Paris on May 16. Shortly thereafter, Washington admitted that the American plane shot down in Russia "probably" was on an intelligence mission "to obtain information now concealed behind the Iron Curtain."

On the same day on which Khrushchev released his report, the White House announced a greatly expanded United States plan to improve the detection of underground nuclear explosions. Known as Project Vela, the program called for increased basic research in seismology; procurement of instruments for a world-wide seismic research program; construction and operation of prototype seismic detection stations; and an experimental program of underground blasts encompassing both conventional explosives and, where necessary, nuclear detonations.

According to the official announcement:

Such nuclear explosions as are essential to a full understanding of both the capabilities of the presently proposed detection system and the potential for improvements in this system would be carried out under fully contained conditions and would produce no radioactive fallout. In order to develop sufficient reliable data from the program, it is anticipated that it will be necessary to conduct a series of explosions of various sizes, in differing types of geological formations.

Recently, the Soviet negotiators at Geneva concurred with the proposal that underground nuclear explosions should be conducted to improve the capability of the proposed control network to detect and identify underground explosions.

They have also indicated a willingness to discuss research and development in the seismic detection area with the United States and the United Kingdom. Agreement has been reached to convene a group of U.S.S.R., United Kingdom and United States scientists in Geneva on May 11 to exchange information on the seismic activities of the three nations as a basis for future determination of the areas in which co-ordination or joint research would be most fruitful.

Government agencies, including the Department of Defense, the Atomic Energy Commission, and the Department of Commerce and the Department of Interior, as well as universities and private organizations, will participate in carrying out the United States program of research and development related to the detection and identification of nuclear detonations.[14]

It was stressed in Washington that the decision to conduct such tests was neither a pre-summit maneuver nor timed with the spy-plane incident. Eisenhower later stated a second time that the underground trials would be supervised by a body representing Britain, Russia, and the United States; and that no *weapons* whatever would be used. Many of the tests, it was stated, would not even involve nuclear materials.

The day on which Khrushchev flew to Paris for the summit, mass meetings in every major Soviet city featured leading Communist personalities denouncing United States aggression in connection with the spy-plane incident. In Paris, at the summit on May 16, Khrushchev deliberately brought the meeting to an abrupt halt when he announced that the Soviet Union would take no further action on a peace treaty for another six to eight months—i.e., until after the inauguration of a new president in the United States. Having wrecked the summit and insulted President Eisenhower, Khrushchev returned to Moscow.

Moscow accused Washington of ruining the Paris meetings by staging the May 1 flight of an American reconnaissance plane over Russia. Khrushchev, in a letter to Eisenhower, asserted that the Soviet Union had been forced to break off the ten-

[14]*New York Times,* May 8, 1960.

nation talks because the Western allies were using them as a pretext to stall while stepping up the arms race at home. A note from the State Department invited the Russians to return to Geneva to undertake again the task of serious negotiation. The request was ignored. In Washington it was said that Moscow had planned to torpedo the Big-Four conference long before the U-2 incident occurred. The U-2 incident had provided the excuse to do so. Adlai Stevenson said: "It was President Eisenhower and the administration who gave Mr. Khrushchev the sledge-hammer and the crowbar to wreck the summit."

Thomas Barman, diplomatic correspondent, expressed the feeling of many in his post-mortem analysis of the summit when he said in a B.B.C. broadcast: "I think the lesson of this catastrophe at the 'summit' conference is the bankruptcy really of this 'summit' diplomacy. What I am hoping for is that we shall have a little peace and quiet now, and absence of 'summit' conferences and less talk about them; that the normal machinery of diplomacy will get to work, the experts talking quietly behind the scenes without publicity, without press conferences."[15]

Despite the collapse of the summit talks, the technical side of the test ban negotiations continued while the United Nations began a debate over the U-2 incident. Observers were inclined to believe that the Russians would not initiate major alterations in the thus-far agreed-on policies for a test ban. Nevertheless, recent events indicated that further progress and real action would be slowed down appreciably and perhaps postponed until the next summit conference (six to eight months hence) or at least until the tensions were relaxed. Certainly no one expected to complete the much-hoped-for test ban treaty for many months.

Joseph Turner, assistant editor of *Science*, pointed out in June that "down in the valley . . . at the level of physics, medical science, and the arts, the world was treated to the sight of another aspect of the East-West dialogue continuing undisturbed."[16] While Premier Khrushchev had withdrawn his invitation to President Eisenhower to visit the Kremlin, a number of American physicists were visiting various high-energy research centers in the Soviet Union; Soviet atomic scientists in thermonuclear research were visiting American atomic laboratories. This was

[15]*The Listener*, May 26, 1960, pp. 911-913.
[16]*Science*, June 10, 1960, p. 1703.

the outcome of earlier agreements by the two nations to exchange
visits of scientists working in such fields as thermonuclear research, high energy physics, neutron physics, power reactor development, and all types of unclassified information on the peaceful
uses of atomic energy. At the same time, American medical
scientists attended a poliomyelitis conference in Moscow; Soviet
medical scientists were in conference at Johns Hopkins University
and elsewhere on heart disease and related problems. While
negotiations at the summit were characterized by angry shouts
and abuses, scientists continued to co-operate "down in the
valley."

One effect of the summit collapse in Paris was that by the
end of June the test ban negotiations in Geneva had reached
another deadlock when the Soviet Union refused to go along
with the United States proposal for more research to control
underground tests. The United States had offered to share all
test results with Russia and to admit Soviet observers to the test
site. When United States delegates explained that they likewise
expected to be invited to witness tests conducted within the
Soviet Union, Tsarapkin, the chief Soviet delegate in the East-
West negotiations over the test ban, retorted that there would
be no such test explosions in the Soviet Union. The United
States also offered to place boxes containing all of the test bombs
under international supervision. The Russians, however, demanded that they be permitted to take a look not only at the
boxes but at the bomb devices themselves.

Reversal of the Soviet stand on its own research program,
without any explanation, was looked upon in the West as an
opportunity for the Russians to stall the negotiations. It was
conjectured that Moscow was no longer eager to sign a treaty
with the Eisenhower administration, but would rather wait until
after the presidential election before pushing the talks any further.
In short, there were signs that the United States was in for a
renewed period of threat, counter-threat, and heightened tension
in the cold war. It was a reminder that peace hangs on the
accident of political events, personal vanity, and human mis-
calculations.

On top of the debacle in Paris, where the U-2 affair gave
Russia the excuse for torpedoing the summit conference, Presi-
dent Eisenhower was forced in humiliation to cancel a visit to
Japan which he had gone halfway around the world to make.

Most newspapers linked the anti-United States demonstrations in Tokyo with leftist-inspired violence through the National Federation of Students. In the background was a much more substantial disapproval of Premier Kishi's "undemocratic" government which had set up a serious conflict between the occupational government's mandate and the proposed Japanese-American Mutual Security Pact which would place military installations on the Japanese homeland and thus make her vulnerable to attack in case of war. The only country in the world which had experienced an atomic bomb firsthand, had over a period of fifteen years also developed a strong pacifism which was peculiarly alive to all the issues of war and especially to a Japan keyed to missiles with nuclear warheads.

The general reaction which was expressed in numerous places was that the United States in mid-1960, during the last busy weeks of the eighty-sixth Congress, had suffered very serious setbacks in the eyes of the whole world. The Communists had scored a number of major propaganda triumphs.

On June 27, 1960, the entire Soviet bloc walked out of the ten-nation East-West disarmament talks, curtly ignoring a new American plan for a world disarmament treaty which was to be presented by Frederick M. Eaton, chief United States disarmament negotiator at Geneva. Soviet Deputy Foreign Minister Valerian Zorin and delegates from Czechoslovakia, Poland, Romania, and Bulgaria charged that the West had refused to discuss any genuine disarmament measures and dramatically announced that the Soviet Union would place its new plan for general and complete disarmament before the United Nations General Assembly. French delegate Jules Moch shouted: "This is a scandal! It is hooliganism."[17] But the Communist representatives filed out of the chamber. This action by the Soviet bloc brought to an end the ten-nation conference which had opened March 16, 1960. Zorin had succeeded in torpedoing the Geneva disarmament meetings in much the same way that Khrushchev had torpedoed the Paris summit conference.

THE TEST BAN TALKS IN RETROSPECT

At the current mid-1960 stage of developments in the test ban talks, it might be worthwhile to try and recall the specific factors

[17]*New York Times*, July 3, 1960.

which originally brought about the three-power decision to consider the possibility of a nuclear weapons test ban treaty. A number of factors can at least be suggested:

The rising storm of persistent protest to testing—coming from scientists and from the general public all over the world; Russia's repeated suggestion, since May 1955, that bomb testing be halted; signs of better liaison between United States scientists and the United States government, following the work of presidential science advisers; the success of Geneva I and the anticipations for co-operation at Geneva II; and, improvement in the technical methods of sneak bomb detection by gas analysis in the mass spectrograph and by means of acoustic and seismographic techniques. Even prior to the official atom test ban, Hans Bethe had reported that detection was technically feasible. Without the earlier East-West technical discussions on the detection of sneak bombs, it is highly questionable whether the United States or Russia would have come to the agreement of a test halt in the first place. The Geneva conference not only had suggested that detection was feasible, but had also provided the blueprint of a preliminary workable world-wide system of monitoring and detection.

Apart from all of these contributory factors, we cannot overlook the fact that on this side of the iron curtain the stockpile of nuclear weapons probably had reached its point of saturation by the end of 1958. No other nation had carried out nearly as many tests as the United States. The AEC, the Defense Department, and Congress all had agreed that the United States could equip intermediate range and intercontinental ballistic missiles with nuclear warheads. The Pacific tests had made that certain. A high-altitude test in August 1958 had carried an atomic warhead aloft by a ground-to-sky rocket. It was aimed at perfecting the defenses against bombers and intercontinental ballistic missiles. In any case, the United States had completed its most important series of tests. It would take about two years to prepare for another series of big tests like the Eniwetok tests. The United States could keep "preparing" for new tests during the moratorium. Meantime, the United States would also speed up its "space program," and try hard to catch up with the Soviet lead. AEC efforts could be shifted to the development of nuclear-power propulsion for rockets and ram-jet aircraft. On the face of things it appeared that the United States suggestion to ban tests for one year came in response to a multitude of pressures from all sides—scientific and technical, moral and ethical, social and political. The military had relatively little to lose.

Beyond these considerations, the most cogent argument for the East-West talks was the opportunity to take a long look at the possibility of averting a surprise nuclear "Pearl Harbor." United States military policy was supposedly committed to the doctrines of nuclear bombs for deterrence, i.e., the United States was committed to the use of nuclear bombs only to reprise enemy attack. It would not use them first; she would not be the aggressor. It is, of course, not an easy matter, in a specific case, to define what is and what is not aggression, especially in view of Soviet diplomacy which is geared to a slowly creeping insidious wait-and-see kind of policy rather than to sudden outright, obvious attack.

When we look at these questions from the viewpoint of individuals on the other side of the iron curtain, what reasons might we suggest to explain the fact that the Russians have demonstrated a serious attempt to arrive at some agreement which would put a halt to nuclear testing? American and British negotiators and representatives of the United Nations General Assembly have all been convinced that the Russians mean business in this area; and that they fully understand and foresee the future implications of whatever agreement they have accepted thus far.

In the first place, we recognize that any nuclear test cessation agreement would have tremendous propaganda value for the Soviet Union. They first proposed it in 1955 and they have backed that proposal consistently ever since. As Hanson Baldwin has said, "The test cessation could . . . strengthen the image of peace-loving paternalistic Russian Communism among the neutral and uncommitted nations—all the more so since the United States has been put into a position of seeming to drag its feet on the issue."[18]

We would also suggest that the economic motive behind the desire to limit nuclear weapons developments is an important factor for the future growth of the Soviet Union in terms of shifting its economic strain away from the production of nuclear

[18]*New York Times,* Feb. 14, 1960.

weapons and arms in general to the expansion of capital goods and consumer industries.

In support of this project we quote from Modelski's analysis of atomic energy in the states of the Communist bloc. He says: "The specific features that lend strength to the [Soviet] atomic programme . . . are also the causes of basic weakness in the Soviet-type economies, and ultimately in their entire system. Governments can make the nuclear or any other programme very strong indeed, but in doing so they undermine the balance of their economic structure because they deprive other vital parts of the economy of necessary resources."

Thus Modelski points out that the fundamental imbalance of Communist economies, stemming from their political environment, is the main obstacle to long-term successful economic progress. He says:

> The frenzied industrialization programmes of the past three decades have left the Soviet Union, and are now leaving other Communist countries, with a lop-sided economic system: powerful heavy industries but an enfeebled agriculture, and great weaknesses in industries that cater for the consumer. Another few years of campaigning for increased production of maize, wheat, or milk and meat will not suffice to iron out this fundamental defect.

By contrast:

> Industrial growth proceeds from a smaller economic basis in the Soviet [Union] than in the United States, yet has to shoulder an armament burden of equal magnitude. If to these burdens are added the difficulties that stem directly from politics—conflicts within the political leadership, divergencies between the Communist party apparatus and the industrial bureaucracy, rising demands of the non-Russian nationalities within the Soviet Union, uneasy relations with the East European satellite countries or with mainland China—the picture that emerges is a system whose prospects of expansion at a high rate are imperilled by instabilities. These instabilities do not, however, justify any minimizing of the immediate Soviet strength in nuclear technology, no matter how profound their ultimate effect may be.[19]

In the third place, we note that much has been said in certain quarters in this country concerning the manner in which test cessation would freeze United States tactical weapons development and thereby prevent United States technical gains over the Soviet Union. This is debatable on both sides, and we have already taken up these matters.

[19]G. A. Modelski, *Atomic Energy in the Soviet Bloc* (Melbourne, 1959), pp. 215, 216.

According to all indications, a more realistic concern of the Russians is the potential danger of adding other nations to the "nuclear club" before testing is stopped by international control. A number of observers have indicated that the Soviet worry about the dissemination of nuclear weapons to other powers is focused on West Germany and Communist China, both of which she has good reasons to mistrust in the long run. A growing and unmanageable "nuclear club" is, of course, a major concern for each of the Big Three, especially in view of recent experiences which revealed that France was able to raise herself to membership in the club without the sanction of any of the Big Three.

We recognize that the West and the Communists are equally anxious to reach an agreement to ban atomic weapons tests. The West insists on making the inspection and control system as foolproof as is technically feasible and as little dependent on mutual trust as is possible when dealing with a ruthless, shrewd, and expedient bargainer. The Communists by contrast are intent on making the treaty as loose as possible, without an all-out ban based on mutual trust until such time as technically feasible methods of detection can be discovered and agreed on for practical enforcement.

The implication of our foregoing discussion is that by the very nature of the problem the inspection and control of nuclear weapons testing, even with an intricate, complex, and expensive system which would demand the time of a very large staff of scientists and technicians, is one of staggering proportions. It might, in fact, be questionable whether several thousand men with seismographs and calculating machines could provide more than a further deterrent to violation of any treaty. Foolproof absolute detection is not something which can be counted on in the near future, if ever. And yet we know that scientists have patiently persisted in the discussions at their formal council tables in Geneva, exhausting the alternatives which are available in an attempt to find a formula for a system to which both East and West can agree. "Never before," says Hanson Baldwin, "has any conference moved as far as this one apparently has toward an international control and inspection system. And probably never again, at least in the foreseeable future, will any arms control or arms limitation conference achieve very much if this one ultimately fails."[20]

[20]New York Times, Feb. 14, 1960.

At the time of this writing the debate over whether or not to end nuclear testing has reached international proportions. It is the opinion of this author that no one has yet offered such cogent reasons for stopping the tests as Professor Hans Bethe of Cornell University. Professor Bethe received the President's Medal of Merit in 1946 for his work in aiding the development of the A-bomb and more recently has been intimately connected with the detection problem as one of the world's recognized experts on this subject.

Professor Bethe has stressed the fact that the Russians have accepted the major principle on which the United States has insisted, viz., that there should be a control system for the test cessation agreement. He says, "This in itself is an important result of the negotiations, and we must not jeopardize this achievement by either breaking off the negotiations or by making unreasonable demands which we know Russia cannot fulfill."[21] He adds, "I do not think the Russians intend to violate a treaty banning weapons tests; I do not think that the Russians could risk cheating, even if there is only a small likelihood of being detected. . . . I believe that the Soviet Union, which is posing as a peace-loving nation, whether rightly or wrongly, simply cannot afford to be caught in a violation, and, therefore, I think that it will not try to cheat."

With great insight and clarity Professor Bethe then goes on to give his reasons for these beliefs. In first place, he questions whether it would be worthwhile for the Russians to muffle tests according to the big hole theory even if they were able to get by without getting caught. This is because it takes many nuclear tests below the ground to develop something worthwhile in terms of weapons. We have already pointed out some of the difficulties and expense involved in constructing a new big hole for every test in the series. Thus, cheating on a massive scale is simply not feasible. Bethe mentions that if we were to follow Teller's suggestion to keep abreast of possible novel means of underground decoupling, we would, in effect, be "drawing up a blueprint for a violator of the treaty, and also do the engineering development for him."

In second place, Bethe maintains "that it is technically feasible to devise a system of detection stations and inspections which

[21]Hans A. Bethe, *The Atlantic Monthly*, August 1960, pp. 43-51.

will give reasonable assurance against clandestine testing, with the possible exception of very small, decoupled tests."

In third place, Bethe believes that the Russians now would stand to gain most from large tests of the kind that cannot possibly be concealed. Thus, it would be greatly to their advantage not to continue the test ban. His argument is that if the Russians really had wanted nuclear weapons of small yield they would have accepted the pattern first suggested by President Eisenhower's proposal of February 11.

Bethe says:

If we had stopped nuclear testing when the Russians first suggested doing so, at the beginning of 1956, we would presumably have had a very great superiority in hydrogen bombs. . . .

There can be no doubt that, since 1956, the Russians have gained in nuclear weapons, relative to us. It is my belief that this is quite natural: the country that is behind will catch up; the country that is ahead will not make so much progress in the future. . . .

This being so, further testing by both sides would bring the Russian capability closer and closer to ours. If we stop testing now, we may reserve at least the little bit of military advantage in nuclear weapons that we still possess.

It is certainly late enough. So I come to the conclusion that, even from the purely military point of view, for our military strength compared with Russia's, we would gain by a test cessation agreement.

Bethe concludes:

At this time we can still get something if we agree to stop nuclear testing. But we have a wasting asset here. Before long, I believe, public opinion in the world will force us to stop nuclear testing without our getting anything in exchange. At present we get in exchange recognition by Russia of stations on Russian soil and of the principle of controlled disarmament. We may further get in exchange the restriction of the nuclear club to three members.

Opponents of the test cessation agreement want to have a perfect agreement; they want to have an agreement in which we can be sure to detect each and every violation, no matter how small. I think that by insisting on perfection we shall end up with nothing.

In this analysis our attention has been directed again to the fact that the objective study of the means of disarmament, by experts in science and technology, is closely tied in with the ultimate political and ideological agreements which can be reached between nations. If modern wars have been made possible largely through the efforts of scientists, the making of peace also depends to a large extent on their efforts.

chapter 8

THE ORGANIZED CONCERNS AND
APPEALS OF SCIENTISTS

Since World War II the scientist has been called on frequently to clarify his views with respect to questions which touch on the political, social, and moral implications of atomic energy. To what extent does the scientist who is engaged in research and development feel that he should be held answerable for the outcome of his work? Where and when does the scientist take it upon himself to pass judgment on the results of his own objectives and accomplishments? Should it be within his power to determine the uses to which his discoveries will be put? Where should he define the boundary conditions of research beyond which he could not proceed without being guilty of betraying mankind? To what extent should he feel obligated to make explicit to the public the character and significance of his work? These questions, and others, have plagued atomic scientists to an extraordinary degree and have created a new dimension of give and take between scientists and the public which is somewhat unique.

The Copernican-Galilean revolution in astronomy, the Newtonian model of a mechanistic universe, the controversy over Darwinian evolution, and the far-reaching implications of Einstein's relativity theory—these were some of the major historical developments which brought forth strong public reactions in the past. They left society altered in the process. Atomic energy struck into modern society like a thunderbolt during wartime, and since then, for good or evil, has affected almost every segment of the globe.

Scientists discovered in 1945, almost overnight, that they had acquired a position of great influence in our society—an influence which reached deeply into the question of man's survival. How the scientists have responded to the challenge of atomic energy since 1945 is of great interest to us. It forms the subject matter of this chapter.

EXTREMES IN SCIENTIFIC RESPONSIBILITY

There are two extreme views of the scientist's responsibility for the social consequences of his research. According to one view, the scientist's responsibility ends simply with his willingness to work, directly or indirectly, for the government or any other "responsible" agency. According to this view, the scientist has no hand in the formation or execution of any policy matters beyond providing accurate and expert factual information. Someone has said that being a good scientist, according to this view, "no more gives one special privileges in determining national policy than being a good information clerk at an airport entitles one to select destinations for travelers."[1]

According to the other extreme, the scientist is honor bound to weigh, to the best of his abilities, all of the consequences of any research before it is undertaken. If it should be judged that such research will be more of a threat to the world than a benefit, he should refuse his services.

Scientists who argue in favor of social responsibility know that it is impossible to foresee the future applications of pure scientific research, since all forms of knowledge can be used for beneficial or nonbeneficial purposes according to the user's wish. But such scientists feel that there is no need to deliberately prostitute one's talents in the service of scientific projects which are obviously designed for man's destruction. Whether or not a scientist will agree to work on a given research project will depend on whether or not he approves morally of the goal of the project. No one suggests that it will be an easy task to make a clear-cut choice between a constructive and a destructive activity. To some extent this may even be a matter of opinion. For example, it has been mentioned that Louis Pasteur's work on fermentation might seem beneficial to some because it led to pasteurization. To others it might seem nonbeneficial because it solved the problem of wine diseases in France and led to the increased production of alcohol and possibly to increased alcoholism.[2]

[1] Joseph Turner, *Science,* April 8, 1960, p. 1013.
[2] Donald L. McRae, *Science,* June 17, 1960, p. 1818.

Irrespective of the scientist's decision as to the direction which his work may take, there is no question about the fact that many atomic scientists have come to the conviction, or at least the consensus of opinion, that they must now pay some attention to the practical outcome of their labor. Many a scientist, in fact, has faced the serious problem of making a decision as to whether or not he will allow himself to be engaged in scientific research which he cannot approve without reserve on moral grounds. He can no longer push that question aside in the hope that governments and societies will automatically turn his ideas and discoveries to the betterment of mankind.

In an address of August 25, 1955, at the annual conference of the International Liaison Committee of Organizations for Peace in Oosterbeek, The Netherlands, Dr. J. Bronowski, director of the Central Research Establishment of the National Coal Board in England had the following to say:

> My claim is . . . that the individual scientist should exercise his own personal conscience. This is his duty. What is the duty of government in this respect? It is to make it possible for him to exercise his conscience. The responsibility of government in this is to create the conditions in which the scientist can say "No!" to projects in which he does not want to take part. He must even be able to give advice which is distasteful to those in authority, and still must not be hounded out of public life, or prevented from making a living. . . . This is the duty which citizens owe to scientists, to insist that governments shall make it possible for scientists to be conscientious objectors if they wish.[3]

What this adds up to is a two-way moral contract with society which allows scientists the freedom of conscience to work at what they would want to do and to refuse to work at what they would not want to do. It also means freedom to speak about what they do. But the scientist must likewise hold up his end of the moral contract. He must not abuse this freedom against society or use it as an excuse for hiding mediocrity or a violation in trust. In this respect he is no different from any other individual. All men must needs be debtors to their societies in some way or another. Above all, the scientist must recognize that to integrate the scientific with the political, economic, and cultural factors requires competent individuals who understand the relationship of science to these other factors. It is not within the area of most scientists' competence and training to

[3]J. Bronowski, The Dilemma of the Scientist (London, 1955), pp. 5, 6.

handle problems over so broad a spectrum of knowledge.

Scientists have had much more to say on atomic energy than we can possibly summarize here. They have done it with the zeal of evangelists bent on saving man from eternal damnation. This has been new terrain for them. They have lobbied on political questions and talked international affairs—sometimes ill-informed and sometimes naively—but mostly with sincerity and with enthusiasm. They have discovered, even when there has been general agreement among their own ranks on the facts and figures, that the opinions and interpretations of experts and colleagues in the same field are often poles apart. The give and take has created a vigorously critical scientific community in debate with itself, its accomplishments, its ultimate objectives. On the whole it has been a gentlemanly fight—a battle of wits and of calculations and counter-calculations—but not without people "telling each other off."

THE DUTY TO INTERFERE

Our story of the organized reactions of scientists to atomic energy originates in the atomic laboratories of the Manhattan project in Chicago and Los Alamos, 1944-1945. It begins with attempts on the part of a number of directors of research to influence the United States government in the manner of its use of the atomic bomb.[4]

In the critical months preceding Hiroshima and Nagasaki, many atomic scientists had begun to question the wisdom of using the bomb to bring the Japanese war to an end. In July 1944, Zay Jeffries, a consultant to the project, addressed a letter to Compton, who was then director of the metallurgical project at Chicago. He urged the preparation of a prospectus which would outline some of the problems on atomic energy which our nation would confront. Before the end of the month, Compton had asked Jeffries to form a committee on "postwar work on nucleonics." Comments and memoranda were collected and put into a combined "Jeffries Report" which in the spring of 1945 was made available by Compton to Stimson's Interim Committee which we have already had occasion to mention in chapter 2. The details of how and exactly when

[4]See especially Alice K. Smith, *Bulletin of Atomic Scientists,* October 1958, pp. 288-312; also, A. H. Compton, *Atomic Quest, A Personal Narrative* (New York, 1956).

this communication and others were transmitted are not available, but we know that in June 1945, following a meeting with four scientists in an advisory capacity (Compton, Fermi, Lawrence, and Oppenheimer), the committee unanimously adopted the recommendation to use the atomic bomb without warning against Japan as soon as possible.

In the spring of 1945, probably partly as a result of the circulation of ideas from the Jeffries Report, many scientists in Chicago began to consider the international implications of the military use of the bomb on Japan. A Committee on the Social and Political Implications of Atomic Energy was formed with Nobel Prize winner and Nazi exile James Franck as chairman. Alternatives to the use of the bomb were discussed by a small group and drawn up in a report for the Secretary of War in June 1945. This "Franck Report" outlined some of the probable consequences which would result from use of the bomb as a means of sudden destruction in war. The committee wrote:

> We believe that these considerations make the use of nuclear bombs for an early unannounced attack against Japan inadvisable. If the United States were to be the first to release this new means of indiscriminate destruction upon mankind, she would sacrifice public support throughout the world, precipitate the race for armaments, and prejudice the possibility of reaching an international agreement on the future control of such weapons. Much more favorable conditions for the eventual achievement of such an agreement could be created if nuclear bombs were first revealed to the world by a demonstration in an appropriately selected uninhabited area.

The Franck Report had not yet been drafted when the interim committee meeting took place (May 31 and June 1) although similar considerations were probably discussed there. There is no evidence to indicate when Secretary of War Stimson saw the report, although it was taken to Washington by Franck after its completion on June 11. It is known that by July 1 plans by the War Department had already been made for dropping an atomic bomb; targets had been discussed.

Another petition, initiated by Dr. Leo Szilard and signed by sixty-three scientists, was addressed to President Truman and forwarded to Washington on July 17. It stressed the moral argument against the military use of the bomb. There were counterpetitions from some scientists who felt the bomb should be used with convincing warnings.

On July 1, Compton asked the director of the University of

Chicago Metallurgical Laboratory, Farrington Daniels, to take a poll among the scientists in the laboratory. On July 12, four days prior to the first experimental A-bomb test in New Mexico, Daniels asked the scientists to vote by voluntary and informal secret ballot on one of five procedures by which the bomb might be put to use in the Japanese war: 1) By the most effective way to bring prompt Japanese surrender at minimum human cost to the armed forces; 2) By military demonstration in Japan followed by renewed opportunity for surrender before making full use of the weapon; 3) By an experimental demonstration in our country with representatives of Japan present, followed by new opportunity to surrender before making full use of the weapon; 4) By withholding military use, but making public demonstration of the weapon's effectiveness; 5) By maintaining all developments as secret as possible and refraining from using them in the war. About half of the men voted. The outcome of the poll in each of the five categories was respectively: 23, 69, 39, 16, and 3 votes—showing that only about 15 per cent favored full military use.

How Compton interpreted these figures in his communication to the White House has not been made public, but it is likely that he felt that most scientists favored the official policy of using the bomb in some way or other to end the war but by means no more drastic than were needed to bring surrender. In any case, it is questionable that the opinions reached Washington in time to influence those making the decisions.

In Berkeley and Los Alamos, opinions were sounded in a less formal way. At Los Alamos the group of scientists working under the leadership of J. R. Oppenheimer voiced no great objections to the use of the bomb against Japan, but laid much emphasis on informing the Russians of our intentions before we dropped the bomb. This view we know was shared by Secretary of War Stimson, who urged Truman to inform Stalin at Potsdam of plans to use the bomb.

Daniels has indicated[5] that after July 1 a considerable number of scientists were given a chance individually to discuss in private session, with him and a committee, the social and political implications of the atomic bomb. This procedure was used because the military did not approve of holding general meetings

[5]Smith, *loc. cit.* pp. 307, 308.

to discuss such questions. Immediate and long-range plans were given a thorough going over. Eugene Rabinowitch (now editor of the *Bulletin of Atomic Scientists* and research professor of biophysics at the University of Illinois) was notably active in many of the preliminary discussions which eventually gave rise to the organizing of scientists for responsibility toward atomic energy.

On July 6 President Truman's party left for Potsdam. On August 2 and 3 Truman, while at sea en route back to Washington, authorized the dropping of the bomb. Hiroshima was bombed on the sixth of August.

Before the end of 1945, scientists of the newly-disclosed laboratories of the Manhattan District (Chicago, Oak Ridge, Los Alamos) spontaneously organized independent local groups to discuss and bring into the open what they knew about atomic energy. When the May-Johnson Bill for control of atomic energy had been drafted in the War Department, it was scheduled for a quick House passage without a genuine hearing and debate. Atomic scientists sent a group of enthusiastic, albeit inexperienced, lobbyists to Washington to contest the military control of domestic atomic energy. Nurtured by the controversy over domestic atomic energy legislation, representatives from four groups of atomic scientists met in Washington, D. C., in December 1945 to form the Federation of Atomic Scientists.

In Chicago the Committee on Social and Political Implications late in 1945 had elected Eugene Rabinowitch as their chairman. Thereafter the group met weekly to organize a campaign to inform other scientists and the American public on atomic energy and its potential meaning in international affairs, atomic power, and proposals for world government. This group, known as the Atomic Scientists of Chicago, published its first issue of the *Bulletin of the Atomic Scientists of Chicago* on December 15, 1945, under the editorship of H. H. Goldsmith and E. Rabinowitch. The atomic scientists who were active in this organization and its publication were convinced that the discovery of the atomic bomb had introduced a radical change in the role which science had to play in public affairs. "They believed," in the words of Rabinowitch, "that mankind was entering unawares, into a new age, fraught with unprecedented dangers of destruction." They felt that henceforth they would have to do their duty of interfering, as scientists, with the political and military decisions of the nation.

FEDERATION OF AMERICAN SCIENTISTS

Seven groups of scientists from the wartime laboratories and universities, including the Federation of Atomic Scientists and the Association of Los Alamos Scientists, organized on January 6, 1946, to form the Federation of American Scientists (FAS). Local chapters of the FAS were subsequently established in a dozen or so places.

The over-all objective of this society was to set up an organization which would be able to participate actively in political issues where the opinions of scientists were relevant. It was hoped that the society would help to meet the increasingly apparent responsibility of scientists in promoting the welfare of mankind and the achievement of a stable world—by placing science in the national life where its maximum contribution would be felt by all the people. To this end they urged that the United States help initiate and perpetuate an effective system of world control of atomic energy based on full cooperation among all nations.

Since the time of formation of the FAS in 1946, when the press dubbed its members "The League of Frightened Men," this organization, through the *Bulletin of Atomic Scientists* and its *FAS Newsletter,* has represented the voice of scientists who, conscious of their social responsibilities in the atomic age, have advocated organized democratic participation. The influence of these men has been felt in the press, in the halls of Congress, and in the United Nations. In many organized campaigns the FAS has severely criticized the position of the United States with respect to its atomic energy program. From the start, the FAS has diligently sought to minimize the military applications of atomic energy through feasible methods of domestic and international control and through the dissemination of information on the peacetime uses of atomic energy in research, industry, and power production.

For many years the FAS was the largest and most effective United States organization devoted exclusively to the problem raised by the interaction of science and society—maintaining its own Washington listening and action center as a scientists' lobby. For example, in 1946 the FAS played a major role in defeating the May-Johnson Bill (atomic energy under military control) and in furthering domestic legislation for civilian control of atomic energy through the Atomic Energy Act (McMahon Bill) of 1946. At the same time, the FAS strongly urged the United States to propose international control of atomic energy through the United Nations.

We shall see later in this chapter how the FAS on a number of occasions implemented its policies both in the area of domestic legislation and in international affairs. On the domestic scene the FAS has been instrumental in influencing the government against overzealous militarization and accelerated armaments production. The organization has also had a strong hand in directing national policy to provide a more favorable climate for scientific research. The FAS has combated overstringent security measures, opposed loyalty oaths, and attempted to remove restrictions on the international exchange of persons and information. It has opposed unwarranted attacks on science and scientists. The FAS has also had an active part in problems connected with civil defense and the creation of the National Science Foundation. The FAS has repeatedly emphasized the importance of cultivating scientific resources in this country as related to scientific manpower and the proper balance between basic and applied research.

Most recently the FAS has testified before Congress, urging that international agreement be sought for the banning of any further nuclear weapons tests, under supervision of a United Nations monitoring agency; and that the government explore as a second step an international ban on the testing of intercontinental ballistic missiles. The FAS has urged that an objective scientific evaluation of the radiation hazards from fallout be made independent of any military or policy considerations. The FAS has also labored for the civilian control of outer space developments, a United Nations police force as a first step to peace, and active United States support for the atoms-for-peace program.

BULLETIN OF THE ATOMIC SCIENTISTS

A few comments should be made here about the *Bulletin of the Atomic Scientists,* which since 1945 has achieved world-wide circulation and fame as a most important medium of disseminating atomic information and opinion. While living for a decade from hand to mouth and operating at a substantial deficit, the *Bulletin* continued even in its early days to carry to its readers atomic energy news, along with articles by leading people on the technical, political, and moral implications of atomic energy. A critical nontechnical journal, the *Bulletin* was designed to spur public-spirited action by the wide dissemination of authoritative atomic energy information. Although certain views were given considerable editorial support, all sides were aired by permitting people of widely differing opinions to express their views. This was done in a spirit of dedication to the welfare of the world community, and in the belief that the truths of modern science, properly interpreted, would contribute to a better understanding of the new problems which confronted the human race. More than any other specific accomplishment, perhaps, has been the *Bulletin's* contribution to lessening the tensions between East and West by suggesting means of using science as a servant of mankind rather than as a threat against current enemies, and by opening the doors to an exchange of views between American and foreign scientists.

In 1951, five years after its first publication, editor Rabinowitch wrote that the *Bulletin* had been founded as

part of the conspiracy to preserve our civilization by scaring men into rationality. . . . Men wise in history, or practical politics, or proud of their common sense, told us that wars have always been—and will always be; that national and ideological enmities cannot be made to lapse simply because physicists have found that certain nuclei fission in a chain reaction. The scientists were supposed to be so naive politically as to ignore this! . . . While scientists went around explaining to members of Congress, Elks, Rotary, and Women's Clubs the destructive potentialities of atomic energy; while they watched, first with hope, then with anxiety and, finally with despair, the proceedings of the United Nations Atomic Energy Commission; while they joined with prominent laymen, educators, and social scientists—and a few politicians who have recognized the emergency—in groups agitating for the reorganization of the world under enforceable international law, the Soviet leaders pursued their power-political aims, as if they still lived in the seventeenth century, and the non-Soviet nations countered by moves of the same kind, if of lesser ruthlessness.[6]

No one who has followed the records since that time will question the importance of the FAS as an organization and the

[6]Eugene Rabinowitch, *Bulletin of Atomic Scientists,* Jan. 1951, pp. 3, 4.

Bulletin as a publication in shaping public and international opinions and actions on atomic energy.

SCIENTISTS ORGANIZE FOR SOCIAL RESPONSIBILITY

Let us now direct our attention to a year by year study of the organized concerns and appeals of scientists in the United States and elsewhere. As we move along, we shall have something to say about the circumstances which led to the organization of a number of other groups of scientists who felt constrained to make their concerted efforts felt on the local and on the international level.

The British Atomic Scientists Association, a much smaller group than the FAS, was organized in 1946 by scientists who had worked on atomic energy projects in Britain, the United States, and Canada. Their journal, the *Atomic Scientists' News,* has been devoted largely to the issues of British domestic atomic energy legislation, international control, and activities in public education devoted to the dissemination of information and discussion of political problems arising from atomic energy. A diverse political group, the members have seldom made statements in public unless complete agreement could be achieved in their council.

In London the organization of a world-wide federation of national associations of scientific workers held its first meeting on July 20 and 21, 1946. This organziation has been concerned with the responsibility of science in advancing human welfare and has worked for the fullest utilization of science in promoting peace, international co-operation in science and technology particularly through the United Nations, and the preservation and encouragement of the freedom and co-ordination of scientists everywhere.

The Association of Scientists for Atomic Education was organized in January 1947, in Washington, D. C., by scientists representing eight different regions of the United States. This organization and the Emergency Committee of Atomic Scientists (formed July 1946) drew up plans for joint action in 1947. Unlike the FAS, which is also concerned with legislative matters, these two organizations have restricted themselves to educational objectives such as the promotion of public discussion and evaluation of various proposals for the effective international control of atomic energy.

In September 1949 a group of American scientists and engineers who were increasingly alarmed by the use of science for destruction met at Haverford, Pennsylvania, and organized the *Society for Social Responsibility in Science* (SSRS), believing "that science and technology should contribute fully to the benefit of mankind, and never to its harm or destruction." According to its constitution, the purpose of this organization was "to foster throughout the world a functioning co-operative tradition of personal moral responsibility for the consequences for humanity of professional activity, with emphasis on constructive alternatives to militarism . . . to embody in this tradition the principle that the individual must abstain from destructive work and devote himself to constructive work, drawing the line between the two according to his own moral judgment . . . to ascertain through open and free discussion the boundary between constructive and destructive work to serve as a guide for individual and group discussion and action. . . ."[7] These purposes of the society have been implemented through the years by: a) A strong educational program to provide for open and democratic discussion of constructive action, especially as it concerns scientific workers in solving problems of peace and war; b) An employment service to locate positions for those individuals whose convictions necessitate leaving or refusing destructive work; and c) Giving counsel and assistance to constructive projects.

While the Society for Social Responsibility in Science brings together those who have drawn or wish to draw some line as to what may be acceptable work for a scientist, even at considerable risk or sacrifice, it has published no official list of types of constructive and destructive work. Projects sponsored by military establishments or projects of a definitely military nature sponsored by industrial or civilian organizations are suggested as possible types of destructive work. Not all of its members, however, draw such sharp boundary lines between constructive and destructive work. The SSRS differs from other organizations in placing its emphasis on the individual moral judgments of its members as to abstention from destructive work. The society, among other activities, has taken part in a number of nationally-attended panel discussions on the basic moral issues

[7]*SSRS Newsletter,* Sept. 1949. See also *Ibid.,* "The Aims of the SSRS," July-Aug. 1960.

of scientists, and has given technical advice to the United Nations Technical Assistance Administration and other foundations.

The SSRS by 1959 had members in seventeen countries, including five Nobel Prize winners; it circulated its *SSRS Newsletter* in forty-one countries. Recently the *SSRS Newsletter* devoted much attention to the dissemination of information in regard to the question of the hazards of radiation and fallout. It strongly urged its members to inform the general public on these matters. The organization also consistently called for more thorough world-wide scientific studies of the effects of radiation. The *SSRS Newsletter* emphasizes a policy of calling scientists to social responsibility and not merely of pacifism toward nuclear science. To quote scientist Max Born, who is a member of this group: "It is only a manner of speech to say that the atom has become dangerous . . . the source of the danger is in all of us, because it is the weakness and passion of ordinary human beings."

Nuclear Weapons Testing Is the Worst Crime

In 1950, when Truman announced the decision of the United States to engage in H-bomb development, the FAS Council released the following statement:

We can be sure that if we make hydrogen bombs the Russians will build them too; we must have no illusions of security based on monopoly of a super-weapon. . . . Superficially the super-bomb appears to threaten our rival, but the President and the people must see that the threat lies nowhere sharper than here. American scientists are of many minds on many issues, but on one we unite: our country must turn from the false security of bombs to the slow difficult task of gaining security by a positive approach to peace by mutual agreement, to peace by gradual disarmament, to peace by worldwide economic reconstruction and development.

The policy of our country has faced in two directions. We have sought to achieve international control of atomic energy on the one hand, while basing our military planning on atomic armaments. The question which faces us today is whether the United States will persist in its avowed policy of seeking peace through agreement or whether it will pay lip service to this policy while relying on force.

The decision on the hydrogen bomb can be interpreted by the world as a symbol that we have now set our course. We have placed a terrible weight in the balance for destruction. A greater weight must now be placed on the side of real security and peace.[8]

[8]*FAS Newsletter*, Feb. 14, 1950.

Similar statements were issued in 1950 by the Council of the SSRS, by prominent scientists meeting at the New York Physical Society and by scientists meeting under sponsorship of the National Council of the Arts, Sciences, and Professions.

In July 1953 at The Congress for Freedom in Hamburg, Germany, representatives from nineteen Western countries met to discuss theoretical and practical problems of scientific research and to protest the treatment of science and scientists in totalitarian countries. The congress sent the following message to colleagues behind the iron curtain:

We should like to convey our fraternal greetings to our fellow scientists separated from us by political power. We are convinced that you, our unhappy co-workers, have never ceased to feel a profound loyalty to those ideas of free inquiry without which science itself would never have arisen. We look forward to the day when you can sit down with us as free men at such a conference as this to discuss our common problems in a spirit of sincerity and objectivity that you must surely cherish under the most difficult circumstances.[9]

The SSRS in October 1953 issued a resolution rallying fellow scientists to act in response to the deplorable "serious growth of fear" which was inhibiting free expression among scientists. We quote from this report:

It is time that we scientists learn to lose our fear of being "labeled" for saying things we profoundly believe in. This fear must be overcome if we are to preserve the trust and fellowship, the loyalty to truth, and the freedom of inquiry which we recognize as fundamental to science and to a high level of civilization.[10]

In May 1954 the Japanese Society for the Study of Organic Evolution sent an open letter to many of their colleagues in genetics around the world, appealing for support against the testing of hydrogen bombs:

It is our duty . . . to transmit the chromosomes received from our ancestors, without a bit of injury. Since the last war . . . biologists are making a progress in their thought that biological science can not be separable from the ethics concerning the evolution of human society and wisdom. . . .

It is time to appeal for the abeyance of attempts of such tremendous destruction. We hope that you, the Western evolutionists, would take the leadership of this appeal, because you are the men most conscious of the destructive influence due to the radiation upon the life on the earth.[11]

[9]*Bulletin of Atomic Scientists,* Sept. 1953, p. 288.
[10]*Science,* Dec. 11, 1953, p. 3.
[11]*Science,* Oct. 8, 1954, p. 9A.

The FAS, in a public release (March 1955), proposed the establishment of a United Nations committee to study and assess the potential dangers of atomic and thermonuclear bomb tests. This was the first time that anyone had ever specifically suggested such a United Nations commission. In the United States, the National Academy of Sciences in April announced that it would undertake a broad appraisal of knowledge concerning the effects of atomic radiation on living organisms. The academy received financial support from the Rockefeller Foundation and the promised co-operation of the AEC. A United Nations Scientific Committee on the Effects of Atomic Radiation was established in December of 1955. Its first report was released in August 1958.

Nine eminent scientists, six of them Nobel Prize winners, sent a statement in July 1955 to each of the major powers which either had or were in process of acquiring nuclear weapons. Albert Einstein had nominated Bertrand Russell to draft a statement which advocated the abolition of thermonuclear weapons as a first step to the abolition of war in general. Einstein signed the following statement two days before his death:

Most of us are not neutral in feeling, but, as human beings, we have to remember that, if the issues between East and West are to be decided in any manner that can give any possible satisfaction to anybody, whether Communist or anti-Communist, whether Asian or European or American, whether white or black, then these issues must not be decided by war. We should wish this to be understood, both in the East and in the West.

There lies before us, if we choose, continual progress in happiness, knowledge and wisdom. Shall we, instead, choose death because we cannot forget our quarrels? We appeal, as human beings, to human beings: Remember your humanity, and forget the rest. If you can do so, the way lies open to a new paradise; if you cannot, there lies before you the risk of universal death.

We invite this congress, and through it the scientists of the world and the general public, to subscribe to the following resolutions.

In view of the fact that in any future world war nuclear weapons will certainly be employed, and that such weapons threaten the continued existence of mankind, we urge the governments of the world to realize and to acknowledge publicly that their purpose cannot be furthered by a world war, and we urge them, consequently, to find peaceful means for the settlement of all matters of dispute between them.[12]

One week later, July 15, 1955, at the end of the fifth annual Lindau (Germany) conference, eighteen Nobel Prize winners

[12]*Science,* July 29, 1955, pp. 189, 190.

of different countries, races, religious faiths, and political convictions signed another statement which reads in part:

We believe that a government betrays itself by thinking that fear of these weapons will prevent wars for a long time. Fear and tension have often led to wars. We also believe it is wrong to speculate that smaller conflicts would continue to be solved by the use of conventional weapons.

In extreme danger, no nation will refrain from using a weapon which science can help to produce.

All nations must come to the conclusion to refrain from the use of power as an ultimate means of statesmanship. If they won't do this they will cease to exist.[13]

The FAS in October 1955 suggested three positive steps by which the United States could further the international exchange of ideas which had been begun at Geneva I: To press ahead with the atoms-for-peace program; to reduce restrictions on travel across United States borders; and to re-evaluate existing government restrictions on the flow of information.

In January 1956 the Scientists' Committee on Security formally organized an independent volunteer group to expand its former activities in the area of science and security. The committee's function was to act as a clearinghouse for information and responsible scientific opinion on matters of information and personnel security.

The FAS in August 1956 recommended to the Democratic Platform Committee that "as a preliminary step toward complete and universal enforceable disarmament . . . international agreement be sought for the banning of any further nuclear test explosions."[14]

In February 1957, 350 Japanese physicists addressed an appeal to their British colleagues to try to persuade the British government to stop their H-bomb tests at Christmas Island in the Pacific. A national wave of protest to atomic weapons testing had arisen in Japan from concerns over radioactive fallout and from losses to Japan's vital fishing industry through restricted waters. The Japanese physicists stated: "We consider it our most important duty to warn all Governments that a continuation of the nuclear weapons testing is the worst sort of crime against all human beings."[15] Macmillan rejected the appeal.

[13]*Ibid.,* p. 190.
[14]*Bulletin of Atomic Scientists,* Sept. 1956, p. 268.
[15]*Peace News,* London, March 22, 1957.

The British exploded their first H-bomb at Christmas Island on May 15.

Japan's National Meteorological Observatory announced in April 1957 that radioactivity over Japan was reaching unusual proportions as a result of Soviet and British tests. Japan, Indonesia, and Hawaii broadcasted further appeals to cancel tests. The tests continued. Meanwhile the United States had been conducting its series of low-yield nuclear explosions in Nevada.

THE PETITION OF NINE THOUSAND

In February 1957 the Council of the FAS urged the United States to seek world-wide cessation of nuclear weapons tests without making this contingent upon achieving more far-reaching goals in arms limitation. We quote:

> The Russians, and others, propose the reasonable step of stopping nuclear tests which, if carried out, would be no more to their advantage than to ours. We, however, refuse to consider this proposal alone, but tie it to other more far-reaching proposals which require detailed inspection and for this reason may continue to postpone progress indefinitely.[16]

In April 1957, eighteen prominent German scientists led by Otto Hahn signed a declaration saying that they deplored the decision to equip the West German Armed Forces with nuclear weapons and would refuse to take part in any nuclear weapons development. The declaration had been sparked by Göttingen's C. F. von Weizsäcker who first wrote a letter in November of 1956 to Germany's Minister of Atomic Affairs. In a public statement the German scientists declared: "Today one tactical atomic bomb can destroy a small city; one hydrogen bomb can make uninhabitable a region the size of the industrial Ruhr. . . . None of the undersigned would be ready in any way to take part in producing, testing or using atomic weapons."[17] This action led to conversations with German government officials in January 1957.

A new declaration by the German scientists later in 1957 contained three main points: 1) The West cannot in the long run protect its own freedom and the peace of the world by atomic armaments. To avoid these armaments is in its own interest as well as in that of the East. 2) Diplomacy and

[16]*Bulletin of Atomic Scientists,* April 1957, p. 138.
[17]*Süddeutsche Zeitung,* April 13, 1957.

political calculations are not enough to bring this truth to general recognition.   Therefore scientists must speak up and the people must make their will known.   3) To be convincing in recommending atomic disarmament to all, a country must convince the world that it does not want atomic arms for itself.   The final point:

> We do not feel competent to make concrete proposals for the policies of the great powers.   We think that today a small country such as the Federal Republic can protect itself best and promote world peace by renouncing explicitly and voluntarily the possession of atomic weapons of any kind.   Be that as it may, none of the undersigned would be ready in any way to take part in the production, the tests, or the application of atomic weapons.   At the same time, we emphasize the utmost importance of the peaceful applications of atomic energy, which should be supported with all means, and we will participate in this task as we did before.[18]

In May 1957 Linus Pauling initiated an appeal by American scientists to the governments and peoples of the world, urging that immediate action be taken to effect an international agreement to stop the testing of all nuclear weapons.   By June 1957 the appeal had been signed by about 2,000 American scientists and was submitted to President Eisenhower.   The appeal stated:

> Each nuclear bomb test spreads an added burden of radioactive elements over every part of the world.   Each added amount of radiation causes damage to the health of human beings all over the world and causes damage to the pool of human germ plasm such as to lead to an increase in the number of seriously defective children that will be born in future generations.

The appeal further urged "that an international agreement to stop the testing of nuclear bombs be made now."[19]   By January 1958 the list of signers of the document was over 9,000 and included thirty-six Nobel laureates and scientists from forty-four countries.   The petition was then presented to the United Nations by Linus Pauling.   In June 1960 the Senate Internal Security Subcommittee issued a formal demand that Pauling hand over, by August 9, the names of the people who had helped to obtain the signatures for the petition to the United Nations. Pauling replied: "My conscience will not allow me to protect myself by sacrificing idealistic young people.   I am convinced that these names would be used for reprisal."   Pauling was told

[18]*Bulletin of Atomic Scientists*, June 1957, p. 228.
[19]*New York Times,* June 4, 1957.

that he would be considered for contempt of Congress unless
he changed his mind and released the names.

The Council of the British Atomic Scientists' Association
Committee, which had been appointed to study the problem of
radiation hazards, released its report in June 1957, stating:

> If H-bomb tests continue at the present rate, the dose of radiation
> to the reproductive organs . . . which may cause damage to future gen-
> erations, has been estimated . . . to be of the order of one percent of
> that resulting from the natural level of radiation. Of greater impact,
> however, is the damage which may result to the present generation,
> mainly from one radioactive substance—strontium-90. . . . By the year
> 1970 the radiation dose to bone from all the tests carried out up to the
> autumn of 1956 will range from nine percent to 45 percent of the dose
> received from all natural sources, including the radium which is normally
> present in bone.

The report went on to say that all the evidence was still
inconclusive to assess fallout more carefully.[20]

THE FIRST PUGWASH CONFERENCE

In July 1957, twenty-two renowned scientists drawn from ten
nations and coming from both sides of the iron curtain met at
Pugwash, Nova Scotia, "to assess the perils to humanity which
have arisen as a result of the development of weapons of mass
destruction." These scientists reviewed the question of the hazards of nuclear warfare and radioactive fallout and the responsibilities of scientists. The statement which was issued by this
first Pugwash conference (Pugwash I) advocated working toward the total abolition of war and the threat of war hanging
over mankind. We quote:

> War must be finally eliminated, not merely regulated by limiting the
> weapons which may be used. For this purpose, it is necessary to reduce
> tension among the nations; to promote mutual understanding among the
> peoples; to strive for the ending of the arms race; and to provide an
> adequate control system so as to give substantial protection, and permit
> the development of mutual confidence.[21]

The Pugwash statement, furthermore, recommended that scientists help prevent war through public enlightenment on the
destructive and constructive uses of atomic energy and by the
formation of national policies. One of the committees concluded that the radiation hazards of nuclear tests carried out

[20]*Bulletin of Atomic Scientists,* June 1957, pp. 202, 203.
[21]*SSRS Newsletter,* Aug. 1957.

to that time were small when compared with other hazards to which mankind is subject from natural causes. The principal radiation effect was seen to be due to strontium-90. Assuming that the occurrence of leukemia and bone cancer by radiation was proportional to the dose, even down to very small doses, the committee estimated that the tests conducted over six years would be responsible for an increase of about one per cent over the natural incidence of leukemia and bone cancer. Over thirty years that would amount to about one-hundred thousand additional cases. These would hardly be identifiable with certainty among the ten million or so normal cases of the diseases. The committee stated: "Nevertheless, because of the world-wide distribution of fission products, and the fact that some areas may be subject to effects much above the average, close attention to the dangers should be maintained, especially if tests of bombs which give large radioactive fallout continue to be made." The committee also issued a word of caution on the hazards associated with the peacetime uses of industrial atomic power.

Radiation evaluating committees in 1957 were emphasizing the importance of putting the effects of various sources of radiation into their proper perspective. In line with this suggestion, the Pugwash conference in 1957 concluded:

The radiation received by the average individual from medical x-rays is, in countries of highly-developed techniques, considerably greater than the fallout radiation from tests at the recent rate. This does not mean, however, either that we should stop using x-rays, or that we should not be concerned about fallout from tests. Great benefits to man are obtained from the use of x-rays as well as from the industrial use of nuclear energy. The new awareness concerning the deleterious effects of radiation is leading to greater improved techniques in use of x-rays and to more rigorous precautions in the application of nuclear energy. By these means it will be possible to reduce the doses received from medical and industrial radiation to levels that are justifiable in the light of the benefits obtained. It is useful to remember that modern industrialized society involves many developments with harmful side effects, as in the case, for example, of the fumes from automobiles and from industrial establishments. Accurate evaluation of the damage caused in this way has not been made; but, even if it should turn out to be considerable, no one would expect to stop using all automobile engines or noxious industrial processes.[22]

[22]*Bulletin of Atomic Scientists*, Nov. 1957, pp. 314-317.

Atom Test Ban Proposed

As a reaction to the Pugwash conference, the Presidium of the Soviet Academy of Sciences adopted a statement (August 8, 1957) concerning the prohibition of atomic weapons and their tests. The statement was signed by 196 Soviet scientists and supported the idea of a broad conference concerning the prohibition of atomic weapons. The Soviet scientists declared:

> We believe . . . that scientists of all countries should show their common concern with the dangers which threaten mankind, and combine their efforts in the fight for immediate prohibition of atomic weapons and of its tests and the prevention of wars. We Soviet scientists express our full readiness for common effort with scientists of any other country, to discuss any proposals directed toward the prevention of atomic war, the creation of secure peace, and tranquility for all mankind.

In August 1957, forty-three British scientists issued a manifesto urging scientists to join them in using science for peaceful purposes only. All of these scientists were members of the Society of Friends. Like the eighteen West German atomic scientists, they announced their refusal to co-operate in the production of nuclear weapons. The British scientists declared:

> We believe that scientists must always be prepared to re-examine their premises in the light of new situations. . . . History has proved that the most trusted of politicians may be wrong and their errors in the era of nuclear weapons may well prove fatal to civilization. . . . We welcome the statement of the West German scientists although we go further in refusing to co-operate in the production of any weapons of war.[23]

In November 1957, 155 eminent Soviet scientists issued a communication calling for "a broad international conference of scientists" to discuss the dangers to mankind of a thermonuclear war. The statement read:

> Let not only atomic scientists of all countries but also representatives of other disciplines, biologists, medical scientists, philosophers of all schools, economists, historians, sociologists, educators, etc., express their weighty opinions in a broad international meeting of the most important representatives of science. In such a tense time, full of danger of a general destructive war, scientists cannot remain aside.[24]

In February 1958 the FAS released a statement supporting an immediate nuclear test ban, the United Nations control of space research, and a United Nations police force as the first

[23]*SSRS Newsletter,* Sept. 1957.
[24]*New York Herald Tribune,* Nov. 8, 1957.

steps toward peace. As to the test ban, the statement pointed out:

Both the United States and the Soviet Union have accepted in principle the desirability of such a test ban. First, it would prevent the entry into the nuclear arms race of still more nations . . . Second, it would allay the fears aroused by the potential hazards of radioactive fallout. . . . Finally there is good reason to hope that the success of negotiations in this matter . . . might go far toward establishing a more favorable atmosphere for subsequent negotiation of the many political and military problems requiring resolution.[25]

In April 1958 a group of scientists and other well-known figures filed suit against the Federal District Court in Washington, D. C., requesting that members of the AEC be prohibited from conducting any more weapons tests. The list of people who filed this suit includes some of the best-known world figures who have been associated in recent public announcements with the peace movement: British mathematician and philosopher, Bertrand Russell; Socialist party leader, Norman Thomas; 1954 chemistry Nobel Prize winner, Linus Pauling; Wisconsin biochemist, Karl Link; University College of London crystallographer and Quaker, Kathleen Lonsdale; Germany's President of the Evangelical Church, Martin Niemöller; Japanese religious leader, Toyohiko Kagawa; American Friends Service Committee spokesman, Clarence Pickett; IFOR leader, André Trocmé; and South African human rights leader, Michael Scott. Pauling announced at a news conference that efforts were being made to bring similar suits against Great Britain and the Soviet Union. The petition said: "No power has been delegated to Congress by the Constitution to enact legislation as a result of which the atmosphere will be contaminated and the lives and progeny of the population damaged."[26] The lawsuit was designed to arouse public opinion against the danger of radioactive fallout. A federal judge rejected the suit on July 31, 1958, overruling the argument that the tests were unconstitutional or lacked congressional authorization.

The second international Pugwash conference of twenty-two noted scientists met at Lac Beauport, Quebec, from March 31 to April 11, 1958. The dangers resulting from the arms race were presented, along with suggestions of means for curbing it.

[25]*Bulletin of Atomic Scientists,* March 1958, p. 125.
[26]*Bulletin of Atomic Scientists,* June 1958, p. 239.

In May 1958 a group of 618 British scientists presented an appeal to British Prime Minister Harold Macmillan, urging immediate action to halt the testing of nuclear weapons. The signers included sixty-nine fellows of the Royal Society and ninety-three professors of science and medicine at British universities. Nobel Prize winner Sir John Boyd Orr, Sir Charles Darwin, former director of the British National Physical Laboratory, and Julian Huxley, former director of UNESCO, were among the signers. The appeal read in part as follows: "Each added amount of radiation causes damage to the health of human beings all over the world and causes damage to the pool of human germ plasm such as to lead to an increase in the number of seriously defective children that will be born in future generations."[27]

The appeal was accompanied by the following letter from Bertrand Russell:

I hope that this appeal from those most qualified to judge will be carefully considered by you together with the fact that a large majority of the British people are in favor of the suspension of the British tests. May I add that I personally feel that it is intolerable that Britain should continue its present series of tests, despite the suspension by the Soviet Government. A unique opportunity now exists to reduce the nuclear peril which confronts us all. I hope that you and your Government will accept the opinion not only of the many eminent scientists but of millions of ordinary people and call an immediate halt to the present series at Christmas Island.

Macmillan rejected the appeal, saying that it was essential to rely on the nuclear deterrent in order to prevent aggression, adding: "It must never be forgotten that the whole purpose of our policy is to save countless millions from death and suffering. This must be balanced against the possible future hazards associated with nuclear tests."[28] Shortly after this announcement by the prime minister, the British H-bomb tests at Christmas Island in the Pacific were unexpectedly canceled after only one of three scheduled tests had been completed. No reasons were given for discontinuing the tests.

In July 1958 Kanji Suda, chief of the Hydrographic Section of the Maritime Safety Agency, announced that Japanese scientists would not send out any more ships for the oceanographic

[27]*Science,* July 4, 1958, pp. 18, 19.
[28]*Ibid.*

surveys of the International Geophysical Year, unless the United States suspended its nuclear testing in the Pacific. This action was taken when two ships, the Satsuma and the Tokuyo, ran into radioactive rains and sea water following a United States nuclear explosion. The ships were well outside the danger zone established by the U.S. AEC. Suda reported that their IGY surveys of sea currents near the equator were completely spoiled by the fallout. Ill crew members were examined by American and Japanese medical teams and were stated to have been unharmed.

The third Pugwash conference of nuclear scientists met from September 14 to 20, 1958, in Kitzbühel and Vienna, Austria. These scientists unanimously voiced the opinion that faith in defensive measures against nuclear warfare was unfounded and might even contribute to the outbreak of a war. Believing that even localized limited wars could lead to wars of catastrophic consequence, the scientists drew up some of the requirements for ending the arms race. This was based, as a first step, on an international agreement for the cessation of all nuclear tests and an effective detection and control system. They spelled out what it would mean to reduce mutual apprehension by political adjustment and the establishment of an active global co-operative effort in atomic energy. There was considerable discussion of the effect of fallout in terms of both short and long-range damage to humans, and suggestions for co-operative technical studies of the problems by scientists of all nations. The responsibility of educating people to the dangers and potentialities of modern science was stressed at the meeting, especially through the efforts of scientists who possess competence in special areas where the public is ill-informed.

The Pugwash statement which was signed by scientists from eighteen countries, East and West, concluded as follows:

Scientists are either admired for their contribution to national security, or damned for having brought mankind into jeopardy by their invention of weapons of mass destruction. The increasing material support which science now enjoys in many countries is mainly due to its importance, direct or indirect, to the military strength of the nation and to its degree of success in the arms race. This diverts science from its true purpose, which is to increase human knowledge, and to promote man's mastery over the forces of nature for the benefit of all.

We deplore the conditions which lead to this situation, and appeal to all peoples and their governments to establish conditions of lasting and stable peace.[29]

On October 5, 1958, the three-thousand-member Union of German Societies for Physics met at Essen and issued a statement condemning the nuclear arms race. The statement reads as follows:

German physicists are deeply concerned at the increase of nuclear armaments everywhere. The Union of German Societies of Physics therefore once more warns the public that the use of these weapons in war will inevitably lead to the annihilation of millions of people and to complete devastation through radioactivity.

The physicists, who desire their work to benefit mankind, repeat their previous warning as to the consequences which a criminal misuse of the results of their research might have. They wish to state with all possible emphasis that nuclear weapons are capable of the wholesale destruction of all races and will expose to the horrors of death by radiation even those nations which are not involved in the conflict.

On behalf of its 3000 members, the Union of German Societies of Physics again urgently appeals to the public, and in particular to responsible politicians in all governments and parliaments, to give unceasing and constant support to any attempts at a peaceful settlement between the States and at last bring to an end the atomic arms race, including nuclear tests.[30]

The FAS Executive Committee addressed an open letter to President Eisenhower in October 1958, urging him to halt the new series of ten nuclear tests scheduled to take place in Nevada just prior to the test-ban negotiations which had been scheduled with Russia for October 31. The letter read in part:

The Federation of American Scientists urges you, Mr. President, to stop the proposed Nevada test series. Such action on your part would emphasize our earnest desire that an agreement be reached to halt nuclear weapons testing as a first step towards disarmament and world peace. Even if extensive preparations have been made and important information will be gained from these tests, the adverse propaganda effect must be seriously considered. A declaration on your part that these tests will not be held would re-establish our high purposes in the eyes of the world and insure all concerned of our true desire to take steps aimed at achieving a stable peace.[31]

The tests were not canceled.

In November 1958 after the suspension of tests the FAS said

[29]*Science*, Oct. 31, 1958, p. 1073.
[30]*SSRS Newsletter*, Oct. 1958.
[31]*Science,* Oct. 3, 1958, p. 761.

that the United States, United Kingdom, and Russia had enough nuclear bombs to kill every person in the world. They urged the United States to press for a permanent ban on nuclear weapons tests under international control.

The Council of the American Association for the Advancement of Science, in a Resolution Control of Nuclear Tests (January 1959), voiced its concern for the need of continuing studies of the effects on human population of increasing levels of radioactivity. They also emphasized the importance of channeling nuclear energy efforts into constructive rather than destructive purposes. Finally they expressed the profound hope that the Geneva Conference test-ban negotiations would prove successful. "We believe," said the resolution, "that these negotiations represent a bright hope for the translation of scientific knowledge into effective public policy on a question which—literally—involves the survival of civilization."[32]

On February 13, 1959, a group of well-known scientists signed their names to a full-page advertisement in the *New York Times* addressed to Eisenhower, Khrushchev, and Macmillan, urging special effort to make the Geneva atomic bomb test-ban negotiations a success. The advertisement was sponsored by the National Committee for a Sane Nuclear Policy, an organization formed in 1958 by Clarence Pickett of the American Friends Service Committee and Norman Cousins of the *Saturday Review*. SSRS members, religious leaders, and peace workers joined in signing the appeal which began as follows:

The people of the world have hopefully watched your representatives meet in Geneva. They have been heartened by the progress which has been made in writing a treaty to end nuclear weapons tests. The negotiations have brought us the first rays of light in the twelve years of darkness since the cold war began. The men meeting in Geneva have given us hope—hope that the dangers of radioactive fallout will not be increased in the years to come, hope that the world need not continue to drift toward extinction in a suicidal arms race.[33]

In March 1959 the Executive Committee of the FAS released a statement on the nuclear test-ban negotiations which were in process at Geneva. They deplored the fact that the negotiations seemed to have reached a stalemate and suggested points at which roadblocks might be removed by improving the reliability

[32]*Science,* Jan. 16, 1959, p. 137.
[33]*New York Times*, Feb. 13, 1959.

of monitoring tests, by providing safeguards against espionage and by removing the Soviet Union's insistence on veto rights over the composition and operation of the inspection teams. We quote the final comment:

> There is . . . an American program, called Project Plowshare, which is meant to develop peaceful applications of nuclear explosions. The carrying through of the peaceful tests program is certainly less important now than is the chance of agreement on a workable test ban and its policing. If exemption of peaceful explosions from the test ban threatens the success of an agreement, Plowshare should not be insisted on. It is really extraneous to the basic issue of arriving at a better chance of peace.
>
> In particular, the scheduled nuclear explosions this summer under Project Plowshare could very well lead to unrestricted resumption of Russian weapons tests. No gain from Plowshare would compensate for this unfortunate result.[34]

The fourth Pugwash conference met at Baden, near Vienna, June 25 to July 4, 1959, to discuss arms control and world security. No public statement was issued, the intention of the conference being to engage in extensive and frank examination of concrete problems connected with armament and world security. The fifth Pugwash conference met at Pugwash, Nova Scotia, August 24 to 29, 1959, to discuss biological and chemical warfare. The sixth conference is scheduled to meet in Moscow.

On August 6, 1959, thirty distinguished scientists representing many countries met at Hiroshima to participate in the Fifth World Conference against A-bombs and H-bombs. Linus Pauling was a key speaker. The delegates issued an appeal to all scientists from which we quote: "We pledge ourselves that we will not cooperate in scientific research for the purposes of war and destruction, and we appeal to the world that science be not used in any way incompatible with the principles of humanity."[35]

The conference was picketed by anti-Communist organizations and denounced by the Japanese government for its partisan direction. Citizens of Hiroshima were reported to be increasingly resentful of the exploitation of their sufferings for political purposes.[36]

On Easter Sunday, 1960, a crowd of 75,000 (a line six miles long) marched through Trafalgar Square to protest nuclear weapons and to attend a meeting sponsored by the Campaign

[34]*Science,* March 20, 1959, p. 767.
[35]*SSRS Newsletter,* Oct. 1959.
[36]*New York Times,* Aug. 8, 1959.

for Nuclear Disarmament. It was the largest popular rally in London in the past one-hundred years. Simultaneously there were similar demonstrations in West Germany and in Glasgow, Scotland.

"Clock of Doom" Moves Back

January 1, 1960, marked the dawn of a new decade. A new spirit had been fanned by those aware of the stake mankind had in its own preservation. Editor Rabinowitch of the *Bulletin of Atomic Scientists* wrote:

> These are the signs that a turning away from the path of traditional power policy is becoming psychologically possible. We do not doubt that, as of now, the mainstream of political events is still dominated by traditional thinking and by the inertia of established institutions. The outlines of a new world community are but vaguely discernible behind the traditional structure of divided humanity. Nevertheless, in recognition of these new hopeful elements in the world picture, we are moving the "clock of doom" on the *Bulletin's* cover a few minutes back from midnight. In doing so, we are not succumbing to a facile optimism, engendered by a change in the climate of our diplomatic relations with the Soviet Union, or to the exhilaration engendered by the personal contacts of the leaders of the great powers and their visits to different countries of the world. We want to express in this move our belief that a new cohesive force has entered the interplay of forces shaping the fate of mankind, and is making the future of man a little less foreboding.
>
> When, in the past, the *Bulletin* clock was moved forward closer to midnight, it was on the occasion of events—the first Soviet atom bomb, the first hydrogen bomb—symbolic of mankind's drift toward the abyss of a nuclear war. The recent advent of intercontinental missiles is another stage of the same drift; the forthcoming test of a French nuclear bomb in Sahara, symbolic as it is of the beginning of the world-wide spread of nuclear weapons, will be another. No similar landmark can be pointed out indicating progress on the road to world community, but there has been, in recent years, an accumulation of facts and words which suggest that this hopeful trend is gathering force. The feeling seems justified that a turn of the road may have been reached, that mankind may have begun moving, however hesitantly, away from the dead end of its history; and so, with a hesitant hand, we are setting back the *Bulletin's* clock.[37]

Self-Control, Sobriety, and Unselfishness

In the preceding pages we have followed some of the group reactions toward atomic energy on the part of scientists from

[37]Eugene Rabinowitch, "The Dawn of a New Decade," *Bulletin of Atomic Scientists,* Jan. 1960, pp. 2-6.

all over the world. We have seen that scientists have gone
out of their way to voice their opinions and to suggest definite
forms of political action on the local as well as the international
scene. It was once commonly thought that scientists did not
and should not have much part to play in deciding how scientific discoveries were to be used. But today the scientist is no
longer that type of isolationist. He is the most disturbed man
on earth. If he does not feel that it is his duty to tell the world
which particular path to take, he, nevertheless, as the record
shows, has felt very keenly the responsibility to present the facts
so that the proper decisions can be made. This corresponds
with what Bronowski calls "the responsibility of knowledge"
in contrast to the responsibility of power. According to this
view, scientific responsibility must act not to impose the will
of the specialist on the community, but to help the community
to form and to know its own.

Bronowski's attitude is by no means generally shared by all
scientists, some of whom believe that no one now is in a better
position to provide the facts and to appreciate them and trans-
late them into policies of action and control in the area of
atomic energy than the scientist himself. According to this
view, the scientist would press hard in some areas to exert his
influence instead of giving over this duty to the statesman. He
would do it individually or more effectively by organized action.
Many scientists, for example, would now be happy to face
radical decisions in regard to bomb testing. While they would
agree that much more research needs to be done in studying
the effects of radioactive fallout, they would hold that existing
knowledge is already adequate to press for the prohibition of
test explosions by international agreement for the sake of a
humane policy for mankind as a whole.

In the last analysis, we would do well to recognize, however,
that, while it is relatively simple to sit on the sideline and idealis-
tically express opinions and press for action, it is not so simple
to officially confront the international atomic energy situation,
where the hard cold facts limit the realistic alternatives which
are open. Regardless of party politics, the people who have
been specifically charged with carrying out United States policy
in these matters have frequently found it impossible to accept
many proposals made by sincere and responsible scientists. In
fact, some of the most capable scientists in our country, when

placed into official positions of great responsibility, have experienced that their personal views were either markedly altered when they got down to the difficult business of dealing with the Soviet Union or else they have discovered that some of the most desired and worthy long-range objectives could not be carried through realistically without the most radical steps of compromise.

Let us conclude this chapter with a quotation from a 1956 convocation address by Farrington Daniels of the University of Wisconsin:

It will take all the wisdom of our statesmen, all the international good will that we can encourage, all the United Nations can do and all that our young potential leaders can do to avoid international destruction and to continue on the road to abundant industrial energy. Let us not think either that all of the responsibility lies on the other side of the iron curtain. Men in our country have power over life and death such as we never before imagined. It is up to us to make sure that public opinion is vigorously expressed and that no irresponsible person ever gets into a position of power over our atoms. Our present energy-rich civilization is like a new super high-powered automobile—it calls for self-control, sobriety, and consideration.

We now have the sources of energy and the technologies with which to give vital help to the non-industrialized countries. We have a broader base for unselfishness—the whole world—than any other nation has ever had. Let us give this help freely and wisely. The best road to happiness for a nation, as well as for an individual, is unselfishness.[38]

[38]Farrington Daniels, "Pathway to Progress," *Wisconsin Alumnus,* Feb. 15, 1957, p. 11.

chapter 9

THE RESPONSES OF RELIGIOUS GROUPS

In this last chapter we want to discuss the organized concerns and responses to atomic energy on the part of a number of religious groups. It is appropriate that we do this in view of the fact that this book was an outgrowth of talks between a small group of Mennonites who met in Chicago in September of 1958 to consider the question of the Christian's responsibility to developments in the field of atomic energy. We emphasize that what follows represents no more than a survey of a number of positions taken by a select group of religious organizations. Furthermore, our analysis is restricted to statements which have been released in an official or semi-official way in an attempt to influence governmental policy or to alert the public to action in one way or another. In a number of instances the information presented is based on private communications directed by the author to persons representing church organizations in some official capacity.

To the extent that individuals of a religious faith explicitly profess any decided opinions in connection with problems related to warfare (atomic or otherwise), it is convenient to recognize three distinctly different historic positions. Each of these positions is well represented among the religious groups of the Hebraic-Christian tradition which will be considered in this chapter.

In first place, we mention the viewpoint according to which it is maintained that, since the state derives its ultimate sanction from God, the individual must support war and go to war if the state asks the individual to do so. This view is common wherever the Christian community or the church is so intimately bound up with the state that in wartime the church co-operates with the state in its decision to act in a certain way, whatever that decision may be. This position has been the dominant one in large segments of the Protestant world in the past.

In second place, we have those groups which emphasize various conceptions of the "just war." The latter is usually defined according to the dictates of individual conscience, or else as given by some higher church council. This view may or may not conflict with the decisions of the state in a particular situation. The concept of the "just war" presupposes that there is some way of differentiating between just (or righteous) wars and unjust (or unrighteous) wars, and between just and unjust methods of waging them. Here we find many shades of opinion. It has been argued, for example, that whereas some wars were once legitimately designated as "just wars," modern nuclear technology has rendered war a moral absurdity.

Accordingly, it has been said that nuclear warfare cannot be justified because of the fact that there are now almost no limits to the amount of chaos which can result from it. On the other hand, it has also been argued that since Communism as an ideology and as a political system constitutes the gravest danger confronting the moral and civilizational values of the Western world, the West should be prepared to use any available "just" means to undertake a "holy war" against a completely unprincipled order of life which threatens all of the traditions of civilized mankind. The most direct statements in defense of the "just war" have come from the Roman Catholic Church, but Protestants have also supported this view.

To a third group, namely the pacifists, who cannot justify warfare on any terms, the expression "just war" is semantic nonsense. Here we include liberal religious pacifism which emphasizes the goodness of man and seeks to gradually eliminate war through social and political schemes based on principles of nonviolence as exemplified in the life of Jesus. We also include biblical nonresistant pacifism which locates its emphasis in the redemptive and renewing work of Christ rather than in any kind of political expediency or humanistic ideology.

Among Christian pacifists one can also distinguish between so-called absolute pacifists and relative pacifists. The former unqualifiedly embrace the principle of nonviolence and assert that all war is a transgression against the Christian law of love made known to man through Christ, especially in the Sermon on the Mount. Accordingly, war and the use of force and violence are intrinsically evil. To the relative Christian pacifist not all wars but only modern nuclear warfare may be considered to be intrinsically evil. The rationale behind this viewpoint is that nuclear warfare is potentially so destructive that the consequences of every other conceivable alternative would be more desirable. There are some points of contiguity between this kind of pacifism and the view of the "just war." In general, all individuals who call themselves pacifists would, nevertheless, express their concerns in a somewhat more unified practical way than nonpacifists who object to nuclear warfare because it can no longer be justified. There are various interpretations within each of these groups, and there are, of course, secular pacifists for whom the New Testament interpretation of war is just one of many religious and humanistic expressions of the futility of all organized killings.

We shall have occasion in what follows to discuss reactions to atomic warfare on the part of religious groups which represent each of these religious positions. Rather than organize our discussion around one position or another, however, we prefer to consider some representative reactions to atomic energy on the part of Roman Catholics, Protestants, Jews, and the historic peace churches, respectively.

The "Just War" in Catholic Doctrine

In general, the Catholics in this country and elsewhere are far too divided on atomic energy questions for any official declaration of protest, let us say, against atom bomb tests. This does not mean, however, that there is a lack of strong conviction one way or the other among individual members of the Catholic community.

The idea of a "just war" has occupied the minds of men since classical times. Socrates, so Plato tells us, urged that the warfare between Greeks, should it unfortunately occur, ought to be conducted with restraint. The Romans established a place for "the just and pious war" in their public and religious law. Medieval theologians and canonists formed a variety of opinions about the just war. Thus, certain of the early fathers of the church debated whether or not participation in any war was sinful; whether the calling of a Christian and that of a soldier were compatible. Justin Martyr and Tatian in the second century, Tertullian, Origen, Cyprian, and Hippolytus in the third century, Arnobius, Eusebius, and Lactantius in the fourth century regarded war as organized iniquity.[1] In St. Thomas' writings the just war was seen as the chosen instrument of God for the punishment of the wicked and the legally guilty. In the sixteenth and seventeenth centuries, jurists like Vitorio, Suarez, and Grotius incorporated the notion of the just war into modern international law.

In the eighteenth and nineteenth centuries the justness of war virtually became legally irrelevant. Wars became the just prerogative of national sovereignty. It was only in the twentieth century, after two centuries of emphasis on all-out war, total victory, total enemy ruin, and unconditional surrender, that wars were again looked upon as a questionable means of solving international disputes. At the Pact of Paris in 1928 and later in the United Nations the just war again took on its earlier meaning.[2] According to the United Nations, for example, the resort to war is justified only as an inherent right of self-defense, or as a collective enforcement action ordered by a group of nations against the illegal aggressor.

In a very real sense the most prevalent contemporary Catholic emphasis is, therefore, one of return to the classical concept of the just war. It goes without saying that this view of the just war is by no means limited to conservative Catholics. It is perhaps also the most commonly accepted view among Protestants, who, nevertheless, have written much less explicitly on this issue.

As an expression of the conservative position of Catholic Christians in this country, we shall cite the views of Thomas E. Murray (member of the U.S. AEC, 1950-1957), a prominent Catholic layman and businessman who has been honored thrice by the pope for his charities. In his talk to the Catholic Association for International Peace in Washington, D. C., in 1957, Murray outlined the meaning of the just war in terms of nuclear weapons.[3]

According to Murray's position, war is not always immoral. It is only when armed force is not subject to *any* moral re-

[1]C. J. Cadoux, *The Early Christian Attitude to War* (London, 1940).
[2]Gerald Draper, "The Idea of the Just War," *The Listener*, Aug. 14, 1958.
[3]Thomas E. Murray, *Catholic Mind,* March-April, 1957.

straints, as in barbarism, that it becomes immoral. Accordingly, it is the Christian's task to civilize warfare in such a manner that wars can be fought to achieve justice. The modern dilemma, since the development of atomic bombs, is that man is now confronted with the possibility of using force to destroy all human security. The implication is that whereas war was once a legitimate means of moral action, while it could still limit its purposes and methods according to the norms of justice, modern warfare has ruptured the tradition of civilized warfare. In fact, the modern concept of "total victory," meaning total enemy ruin or unconditional surrender, has become the chief cause of war's immorality—and this, according to Murray, is regression to a type of barbarism.

No one will deny that according to this view everything depends on defining "justice" in a given circumstance—especially in the case of potential nuclear warfare. According to Murray, justice must be defined with reference to the areas of diplomacy, politics, and economics. Where the conflict is spiritual—as it is with Communism—the war is primarily a cold war, since the sword of the spirit is the word of God. Still, Murray emphasizes that the military has its place in maintaining the capacity to deter unjust aggression, the argument being that at times one can only restrain an enemy by convincing him that it would be too costly to be the aggressor. This is accomplished by being better prepared than the enemy.

Accordingly, warfare is not evil or unjust if one determines in advance of the contingency of war what policies will be consistent within the tradition of civilized warfare. A realistic appraisal of the modern situation will show, says Murray, that nuclear weapons cannot be outlawed; for to abandon the production of nuclear weapons would be to abandon the cause of justice to the point where it could not be defended effectively.

The road of justice, according to this traditional view, must rest on a firmly defined ideology and a flexible military policy. This is to sanction a policy of "rational nuclear armament," by means of which the dangers of defeat must be averted while giving moral principles and military policies their proper primacy. In practice it means limiting the size of thermonuclear weapons so as to avoid more destruction and radiation damage than is necessary. It means equipping a nation with a wide range of small conventional-size atomic weapons so that it never need be forced into using a larger weapon where a smaller one will do. The object must always be: not the greatest amount of destruction for the smallest amount of effort, but the least amount of destruction consistent with a limited, moral, civilized war which is just. This demands the technical ability to fight limited wars in which the destruction does not go beyond what is necessary in order to mete out justice. This is a total commitment to the moral use of force, on penalty of moral self-destruction. If this is the only way to protect a nation's moral spirit and its constitutional commonwealth, it must, nevertheless, be accomplished without setting up a conflict between the military duty to achieve success in the face of an enemy's threat and the moral duty of man to be just in the sight of God.

In a more recent treatment,[4] Mr. Murray brings his philosophy to bear on the analysis of events since the time of the test ban. He greatly deplores the fact that our administration has suspended its nuclear bomb tests, since this will allow the Russians to accomplish their own strategic objective of forestalling the further development of American weapons. He believes that the United States is drifting into a Soviet trap at Geneva, by which through signing a treaty, we will be legally freezing our nuclear weapons development program before we meet our weapons needs and before an adequate inspection system can be constructed and put into operation. This is seen as a dangerous threat to our national security, for it will give the Russians an excellent opportunity not merely to catch up with us in nuclear weapons technology, but to outdistance us as well, especially in the refinement of small tactical atomic weapons. Murray proposes that it would be much more realistic to continue testing small nuclear weapons which, short of being totally destructive, can be used with discrimination.

In another place Murray proposes the "orderly destruction, on a matching basis, of existing hydrogen bombs—megaton weapons—in the United States and Soviet stockpiles under international supervision." He adds:

Given the nature of man, international politics cannot dispense with the use, or at least the threat, of force any more than human society can dispense with law, which requires force to back it up. On the

[4]Thomas E. Murray, *Nuclear Policy for War and Peace* (Cleveland, 1960).

other hand, international politics perishes as an art if power is allowed
to suffer moral degradation and become mere violence, which is destructive of the very idea of force and of law too.

Murray recognizes that the destruction of megaton weapons
in matching lots by the United States and the Communists leaves
open to the latter a chance for cheating in order to launch a
total attack on the United States. He says:

I readily grant that no moral scruples hinder Communism in the pursuit of its aims. But it does not follow that Communism recognizes no
restraint at all on its use of force in pursuit of its aims. The supreme
restraint is imposed by the very Communist dogma of world revolution
which is supposed to usher in a new era of world organization. The
dogma supposes that there will be a productive world and masses of
people to organize. Hence the dogma forbids use of unlimited nuclear
violence that could imperil the sheer existence of peoples and world alike.

"In other words," says Murray, "Communism is not committed to the political ineptitude of unlimited violence. The
Communist purpose is always to use apt force, whenever useful
or necessary. Here lies the real risk for the United States."[5]

The implications of the just war are spelled out with great
clarity in Murray's several analyses, but many Catholics do not
support his definition of the just war. They have said that if
the society we aim at cannot be brought about by big-scale
violence, then discriminate small-scale violence will not help
either. Both produce an atmosphere of conflict and disruption
in which any attempt to forcibly impose ideas on large groups
of people in the world is bound ultimately to fail.

It has often been argued, against the view of the just war,
that the traditional criteria of a just war are no longer relevant
now that world-wide atomic destruction has become possible.
The most common arguments are that the use of nuclear weapons is likely to produce more evil than the good which can be
achieved by victory; that, in any case, there is no reasonable
prospect of victory for either combatant; that the employment
of immoral methods to achieve morally just ends is unjustifiable.

According to the noted British Catholic philosopher, E. I.
Watkin, even if nuclear warfare cannot be justified according
to any of the above arguments, this does not invalidate the
Catholic canons of the just war which are entrenched in reason
and ecclesiastical tradition. These canons nakedly deny, he

[5]Thomas E. Murray, *Wisconsin State Journal,* Feb. 14, 1960.

says, that an end sufficiently good justifies any means whatsoever. Thus Watkin believes that even the evil of world-wide subjection to Communist governments is not so great that the employment of any means for preventing it is justifiable. Each issue, he says, must be judged solely on its merits in the light of the principles traditional in Catholicism— principles which are determined by the dispassionate use of reason unclouded and undeflected by the emotions aroused by nationalism or by particular sympathies, antipathies, and interests.[6]

Again, according to John Courtney Murray, S. J., one of United States Catholicism's most creative and penetrative thinkers, it is a mistake to adopt any argument based singly upon: a) absolute or relative Christian pacifism; b) the concept of the just "holy war"; or, c) the reliance on an international organization committed by its charter to the preservation of peace by pacific settlement of international disputes. Father Murray says:

> If . . . one adopts a single standpoint of argument, and adheres to it narrowly and exclusively, one will not find one's way to an integral and morally defensible position on the problem of war. On the other hand, all of the three standpoints mentioned [above] do derive from real aspects of the problem itself. In consequence, each of them must be exploited, if the problem is to be understood in its full scope.[7]

Father Murray suggests that three basic questions are in need of careful exploration. The first concerns a definition of the exact nature of the conflict. It will put all other questions into perspective. The nature of the present conflict, he says, is characterized by the pope's statement that there is a "line of rupture which divides the entire international community into opposed blocs." The result is that "coexistence in truth" is not possible, since there is no common acceptance of a "norm recognized by all as morally obligatory and therefore inviolable."

This is not a geographic line of rupture, but a spiritual and moral one, running through the West as well as between East and West. "It cannot," says Murray, "be a question of maintaining that both East and West are so full of moral ambiguities that the line of rupture between them either does not exist or is impossible to discern. . . . One must avoid both a moral simpli-

---

[6] See Mr. Watkin's essay in *Morals and Missiles,* ed. by C. S. Thompson (London, 1959).

[7] John C. Murray, "God, Man and Nuclear War," *Catholic Mind,* May-June 1959, pp. 274-288.

cism and a moral scepticism in the analysis of international conflict." In other words, Father Murray maintains that the analysis of the exact nature of the real conflict between East and West in terms of ideologies is prerequisite to setting up any standard "against which to match the evils of war."

Father Murray's second point has to do with the study of the means which are available "for insuring the defense of the values that are at stake in the international conflict." Otherwise, he says, one can give no concrete meaning to the concept of war as *ultima ratio*.

Finally, Father Murray considers the question of arms as a last resort. He suggests two propositions as a guide for Catholics: 1) "All wars of aggression, whether just or unjust, fall under the ban of moral proscription." 2) "A defensive war to repress injustice is morally admissible both in principle and in fact." These propositions provide "a way between the false extremes of pacifism and bellicism." The second of these propositions, says Father Murray, is "far from being a contradiction of the basic Christian will to peace; [it] is the strongest possible affirmation of this will. There is no peace without justice, law and order . . . the precept of peace itself requires that peace be defended against violation."

Father Murray, therefore, sees no reason why the traditional principle of defensive warfare should not be explicitly extended to include atomic warfare—when nations are driven to this end "by the brutal facts of international life."

The Obligation of Submitting to Injustice

The Catholic church has never in modern times condoned the position of all-out war. In 1917 Pope Benedict XV proposed a negotiated peace. The historic Catholic position of a just war has more recently been defined on numerous occasions by Pope Pius XII.[8] In a radio message to the world, December 24, 1941, entitled "Limitation of Armaments," Pope Pius XII rejected the notion of "total war." He criticized the unchecked arms race and suggested a limitation on the manufacture and possession of offensive weapons. In 1944 in his Christmas

[8]*The Pope Speaks, The Teachings of Pope Pius XII,* compiled and edited with the assistance of the Vatican Archives, by Michael Chinigo (New York, 1957).

address, the pope stated: "If ever a generation has had to appreciate in the depths of its conscience the call: 'War on war,' it is certainly the present generation. . . . The theory of war as an apt and proportionate means of solving international conflicts is now out of date."

In 1945 the Vatican vigorously opposed the unlimited obliteration bombing of Hiroshima and Nagasaki on the grounds that although this was easy, quick, and cheap destruction, it did not provide any immunity to civilian populations. On another occasion, in a message entitled "The Atomic Age" (inauguration of the twelfth year of the Pontifical Academy of Sciences, February 8, 1958), the pope asked how an atomic bomb could be used in a just war if St. Augustine in the *Civitate Dei* found it painful, even in his day, to think of the horrors of a just war. In the *Encyclical* of December 6, 1950, "Atomic Weapons," the pope expressed the need for renewal of conscience, repression of passions, calming of hatreds, putting into practice the norms of justice, the more equitable distribution of wealth, and reciprocal charity.

On October 19, 1953, in an address to military doctors, the pope said:

The only constraint to wage war is defense against an injustice of the utmost gravity which strikes the entire community and which cannot be coped with by any other means. . . . Defending oneself against any kind of injustice, however, is not sufficient reason to resort to war. When the losses that it brings are not comparable to those of the "injustice tolerated," one may have the obligation of "submitting to the injustice."

In his Christmas message of 1955 the pope said: "Our peace program cannot approve of an indiscriminate coexistence at all costs with everybody; certainly not at the cost of truth and justice. These irremovable boundary marks, in effect, demand complete observance. . . ." In his broadcast to the world at Easter 1956, the pope gave his blessing to the peaceful uses of nuclear energy but referred to the homicidal and suicidal madness of the atomic weapons race. On November 2, 1956, an *Encyclical* by Pope Pius XII drew with absolute firmness the line separating "the road of justice" and "the steep slope of violence." To take the road of justice, he said, was to shake off the mad logic of sheer barbarism and massacre and to rely on limited warfare which finds its justification and final authority in a moral order sanctioned by God.

In his Christmas broadcast to the world in 1956, during the time of the Hungarian revolution, the pope stated:

It is clear that in the present circumstances a situation may arise in a nation wherein, after every effort to avoid war has been expended in vain, war (for effective self-defense and with the hope of a favorable outcome against unjust attack) could not be considered unlawful. If, therefore, a body representative of the people and a government—both having been chosen by free elections—in a moment of extreme danger decide, by legitimate instruments of internal and external policy, on defensive precautions, and carry out the plans which they consider necessary, they do not act immorally; so that a Catholic citizen cannot invoke his own conscience in order to refuse to serve and fulfill those duties the law imposes. On this matter We feel that We are in perfect harmony with Our predecessors.

CATHOLIC PACIFISM ON SEVERAL LEVELS

According to a Catholic view as represented, for example, in the group which publishes *The Commonweal,* there is no such thing as a just war. The Christian is called upon, rather, in the name of Christ, to search for an alternative to modern war. War is irreconcilable with Christian morality. To accept pacifism as the practical and theoretical answer is, therefore, inescapable, even, if need be, by sidestepping the unrealistic circumlocution of Catholic theologians.

According to Zahn,[9] who represents this pacifist view, the traditional Catholic position conceivably could lead to a situation similar to the one in which German Catholics under Hitler were led to reason that, since not every part of Hitler's wars were "unjust," open support to some aspects of Hitler's war effort was justifiable. What should the liberal Catholic pacifist do under such a situation? He should, according to Zahn, neither retreat to the catacombs nor become a martyr; he should accept the risks of the situation into which his active pacifism would lead him.

To put it very bluntly, the Catholic pacifist in the West today would, according to Zahn, put his trust in the belief that the "Christian Truth does not depend upon the continued existence of Western Civilization." It might well be that "a Communist victory could arise from the Christian West's inability to meet hydrogen atrocity with hydrogen atrocity [which] would put

[9]Zahn, *The Commonweal,* Jan. 10, 1958.

Christians to a test so severe that it defies imagination." Still, this is "the gamble we take by accepting Christ in the first place." In the last analysis "Is it not true that the forces of evil have the 'advantage' of an unrestricted choice of weapons, while the children of light are always bound by moral considerations and restrictions?" If so, says Zahn, the Christian must be prepared to meet even this terrible challenge—so as not to bring death and destruction on others in the name of the mystical body of Christ.

According to a Catholic position of somewhat different emphasis,[10] the Christian must counter absolute violence with absolute nonviolence as the early Christians did and as Gandhi did. Here nonviolence is the supreme principle. Whereas the moral Catholic theologian might be led to ask how far the Christian can go in any particular direction without committing sin, the Catholic pacifist committed to nonviolence would say that the gospel of Christ is less concerned with the avoidance of sin (under the law) than to exemplify the ideal of life which Christ set before His disciples in the Sermon on the Mount. This is a summons to a new way of life where all human values are of no count in comparison with the kingdom of God. As to Communism, if it is to be overcome, this must be done by a spiritual force greater than its own. By compromising, the whole strength of resistance is lost.

On the extreme left there is *The Catholic Worker* which seldom makes official pronouncements, but rather directs all of its efforts against the system of capitalism, the state, and war. This is largely a radical movement of the extreme (non-Communist) left organized by a small number of lay Catholics who believe that capitalism is as complete an evil as Communism itself. "*The Catholic Worker's* distinctive positions can be labeled, as far as labels are ever accurate, as distributism, anarchism, pacifism, personalism, voluntarism, decentralism, agrarianism, and, in a special sense, Christian communism."[11] Members of the Catholic Worker movement have recently voiced their disapproval against war in general and against atomic armaments in particular through picketing AEC establishments and through fasting as a penance "for our atomic sins."

The Catholic pacifist's position relative to statements by the

[10]Griffiths, *The Commonweal,* Dec. 27, 1957.
[11]McCloskey, "The Catholic Worker Movement," *The Catholic Worker,* May 1957.

pope has been defended by James W. Douglass in *The Catholic
Worker*.[12]   Mr. Douglass begins by saying that Catholic ethics
considers the killing of one man by another as an act indifferent
in itself.   The intention of the killer and the circumstances
surrounding his act must be known in order to determine whether
or not the killing is morally justified.   In the case of a state
which defends itself by bombing proper military targets—which
in human terms means massed combatants—the unintentional
killing of innocent civilians is normally justified by Catholic
theologians as the accidental by-products of a legitimate and
just war.   However, the individual who does not follow the
Catholic church's "traditional but nondogmatic conditions for a
just war has imposed upon himself the obligation of finding
some other measure of morality in war which is consistent with
his conscience."

According to Douglass, the irreconcilability of total nuclear
war and morality has become a dilemma for Catholic militarists.
The dilemma has been dealt with in various ways:

> By a silent front which ignored the new moral problem of the Bomb;
> by a deistic nationalism which made "God and country" one supreme
> entity subverted by the pacifist; by a seizure of isolated parts of moral
> principles to justify the new weapon; and most recently, by painting the
> Catholic pacifist as an outlaw from the Church by alluding to some of
> the public statements of Pope XII.

Douglass adds: "The latter method is now the most frequently
used to demonstrate that the pacifist is subjectively in good faith
but objectively wrong."

What does the Catholic pacifist have to say in reply to this?
Douglass claims that "the attempt to establish a case against
pacifism by carefully selected quotations from Pope Pius XII's
messages is futile for more than one reason.   First, Pope Pius
XII has never issued an ex cathedra pronouncement on the
pacifist position.   Every statement he has made on the question
has been that of a learned man speaking in a fallible, nondogmatic manner.   His view of the pacifist seemed to shift, too,
from one address to another.   Douglass, furthermore, points out
that no pope has ever passed public judgment on the justness
of a particular war.   Rather, he says: "Catholic tradition has
given us nondogmatic principles of judging wars, but the church
does not serve as the individual's own conscience. . . .   St. Paul's

[12]James W. Douglass, "Nuclear Challenge to Conscience," *The Catholic
Worker,* Oct. 1959.

admonition that we must 'obey God, rather than men' has not been superseded by the dictates of modern nationalism."

Somewhere between the views of the above discussed Catholic conservatives and Catholic liberals there are those who advocate that Christians must diligently search for the practical moral principles upon which foreign policy really *can* be based. According to Cagley,[13] the action of Christians should be dominated neither by an out-and-out perfectionist pacifism nor by the Machiavellian type of planned absolute firmness with emphasis on predetermined civilized warfare. The main argument which is advanced here is that political morality must recognize power since it is rooted in the fact that "men are not of good will"; i.e., a morality which sidesteps coming to terms with power in foreign policy is inadequate. For if there are very great evils in the world, the Catholic who wants to do something about them may (if he is not cautious) end up doing something which could call down even greater evils. The Christian is therefore left with the agony of using power responsibly through controlled practical prudence, worldly wisdom, and the principles of political morality. This, says Cagley, cannot be dictated in advance by Catholic theologians anywhere.

THE WORLD COUNCIL OF CHURCHES

There is no world council to speak for Protestant Christendom in the authoritative manner in which the Vatican in Rome speaks for Catholics the world over. Consequently, we might anticipate much more over-all latitude and much greater heterogeneity in the so-called "official" Protestant statements on questions related to atomic energy in war and peace. The best we can do here is to compare and contrast the positions and actions which have been taken by major national and international church councils.

The most important of these is the World Council of Churches (WCC) with headquarters in Geneva. The WCC is composed of about 170 member churches (denominations) in fifty countries throughout the world, involving some 170 million people. Practically all major Protestant, Eastern Orthodox, and Anglican churches in the United States are included. The WCC and the Commission of the Churches on International Affairs (CCIA),

[13]Cagley, *The Commonweal,* Jan. 10, 1958.

a joint agency of the WCC and the International Missionary Council, have issued a number of important statements on nuclear weapons as related to disarmament and testing.[14]

The Executive Committee of the WCC in session at Bossey, Switzerland, in February 1950, appealed to the governments of the world for a "gigantic new peace effort." Simultaneously they denounced the H-bomb as "a perversion . . . against the moral order by which man is bound," and a "sin against God." In July of the same year the Central Committee of the WCC, meeting in Toronto, urged international discussions to end "such methods of modern warfare as the use of atomic and bacteriological weapons and obliteration bombing [which] involve force and destruction of life on so terrible a scale as to imperil the very basis on which law and civilization can exist."

The statement on nuclear weapons issued by the Second Assembly of the WCC in Evanston (August 1954) included the following remarks:

It is not enough for the churches to proclaim that war is evil. They must study afresh the Christian approaches to peace, taking into account both Christian pacifism as a mode of witness and the conviction of Christians that in certain circumstances military action is justifiable. Whatever views Christians hold in respect of these approaches, they must seek out, analyze, and help to remove the psychological and social, the political and economic causes of war. Without forsaking their conviction that all weapons of war are evil, the churches should press for restraints on their use. Christians in all lands must plead with their governments to be patient and persistent in their search for means to limit weapons and advance disarmament. But even this is not enough.

The report went on to say that an international order of truth and peace would require effective international inspection and control without endangering the security of individual states, the elimination and prohibition of nuclear weapons of mass destruction, the reduction of armaments to a minimum, and the development of methods for peaceful rectification of existing injustices. To resolve the stalemate between East and West the assembly recommended that nations pledge to refrain from the use of all nuclear weapons, and that violations of such a pledge be

[14]For all the WCC "Statements on Nuclear Weapons," 1950 to 1958, see *Information* F/3-58, Geneva, June 23, 1958. See also the *Annual Reports* of 1956-1957 and 1958-1959 of the Officers of the Commission of the Churches on International Affairs, established by the WCC and the International Missionary Council.

handled by the United Nations which recognizes the right of national self-defense. Positive action by the Assembly was recommended in the form of commissions to reduce tension through social, political, and economic measures, and through strong moral support in the use of atomic power for the benefit of mankind.

In August 1955 the Central Committee of the WCC at Davos, Switzerland, in a statement on "Disarmament and Peaceful Change," supported the expressed desire of the United Nations General Assembly "to promote energetically the use of atomic energy to the end that it will serve only the peaceful pursuits of mankind." The Central Committee also supported "the proposal to establish an International Atomic Energy Agency . . . constituted within the framework of the United Nations." It was suggested that the United Nations "establish an international commission of scientists and technicians to identify the essential scientific requirements for an adequate system" of control and inspection.

In July 1956 the CCIA Executive Committee, meeting in Herrenalb, Germany, urged that although

experimental tests are a part of the armament effort . . . tests of nuclear weapons should be discontinued under international agreement as soon as possible. . . . Meanwhile, as the basis of impartial international investigations . . . the people should be promptly told what the effect of radiation actually is so that they may know how to choose, if they must, between the possible danger of health now and the threat of war if the present balance of power is disturbed.

Finally:

The churches, both internationally and in their several countries, must challenge governments to shape their policies in accordance with the demands of moral authority rather than those of mere pragmatic expediency . . . Public opinion must be free, informed and morally responsible, so that it can exercise effective influence to ensure that commitments will be honored.

The Central Committee of the WCC, meeting at Galyatetö, Hungary, in August 1956, issued the following statement:

Mankind is fearful of actual or potential danger from experimental tests of nuclear weapons. We call upon the churches to appeal to their governments and the U. N. to negotiate such an agreement for the discontinuance, or limitation and control of these tests, as to end any such danger. Provision must be made to safeguard both the health of the people and the security of the nations. In order that human resources may be directed toward constructive ends, the churches should continue insistently to press for an adequate system of disarmament and a peaceful settlement of the unresolved issues which confront the world.

On July 24, 1957, the CCIA Executive Committee meeting at New Haven, Connecticut, issued a statement entitled Atomic Tests and Disarmament. In part this statement reads:

The main concern must always be the prevention of war itself, for the evil of war is an offense to the spiritual nature of man. But since any war carries increasing danger of becoming an atomic war, this task makes the prevention of war, which shocks the conscience of mankind with a peculiar repugnance, all the more imperative. . . . The total problem involved is so baffling and complex that no man can speak with certainty. All must humbly confront the issues, for all are involved. The mounting stockpiles of atomic weapons and increasing dependence upon atomic deterrents heighten the danger that atomic weapons will at some point actually be used. Yet, in the judgment of many, our present insecure peace rests mainly upon the possession of atomic deterrents on both sides of a divided world and upon the suicidal character of atomic war. This paradox does not relieve us of the need to examine our goals and the means thereto.

The committee went on to make five specific suggestions:

To stop, by international agreement, the testing of nuclear weapons . . . such agreement should be related to general disarmament.

To bring to a halt the production of nuclear weapons, under such controls as will most fully ensure compliance . . . stopping the production of nuclear weapons is more fundamental than stopping nuclear tests.

To develop measures which will reduce national armaments, nuclear and conventional, with provision for necessary safeguards as such measures are progressively taken.

To accelerate international co-operation in the development of atomic power for peaceful purposes, under proper safeguards.

To establish more effective mechanisms for peaceful settlement of international disputes and for peaceful change. . . . If all . . . efforts fail, they [the nations] must strive to deal with conflicts without recourse to atomic weapons.

The statement concluded:

Easy solutions cannot be expected for the problems which plague man in an atomic age, both because the problems themselves are complex and man himself is sinful. God stands in judgment over all the nations of the world, and it is not for man to presume to identify his cause with the fullness of God's purposes. For it is man's disobedience which is the basic cause of his despair and frustration. Christians, who share with all men in the guilt of the world, have, nevertheless, a hope which transcends the failures and successes of history, and a faith which overcomes fear.

If persistent efforts bring no sufficient agreement on any of the inter-related objectives, Christians can oppose counsels of despair and still strive to establish true conditions of peace. Moreover, there is a risk for the sake of peace which Christians, especially in countries projecting tests of nuclear weapons, are justified in advocating, in the hope of break-ing through the barriers of distrust.

On August 5, 1957, the Central Committee of the WCC commended the above statement of the Executive Committee of the CCIA and gave it a wide distribution in all of its member churches—adding the following:

There are . . . certain moral principles affecting the whole issue of atomic warfare which we desire to emphasize. The Central Committee reaffirms the conviction expressed at its Toronto meeting in 1950. . . . The condemnation of such methods [of atomic warfare] finds broad support in the fact that total war, in the sense of warfare without any limitation in the methods employed, is universally in conflict with the conscience of mankind. We also believe that the use of such methods of warfare inevitably involves spiritual degradation for any nation that uses them.

We are bound to ask whether any nation is justified in continuing the testing of nuclear weapons while the magnitude of the dangers is so little known and while effective means of protection against these dan-gers are lacking. We must ask further whether any nation is justified in deciding on its own responsibility to conduct such tests, when the people of other nations in all parts of the world who have not agreed may have to bear the consequences. Therefore, we call upon each nation conducting tests to give full recognition to this moral responsibility as well as to considerations of national defense and international security.

Nothing less than the abolition of war itself should be the goal of the nations and their leaders and of all citizens. The attainment of this goal constitutes a solemn challenge to our particular generation. We welcome and support every honest effort now being made to limit and control armaments of all kinds and to establish conditions for a secure peace. We repeat the Evanston appeal for prohibition of all weapons of mass destruction, including atomic and hydrogen bombs, with pro-vision for international inspection and control.

We know that a comprehensive program for disarmament must pro-ceed by stages, and we realize how much depends upon the deepening of confidence between the nations. But we urge that as a first step governments conducting tests should forego them, at least for a trial period, either together, or individually in the hope that the others will do the same, a new confidence be born, and foundations be laid for reliable agreements.

We therefore appeal to all our brethren to act with Christian courage,

[15]*Atomic Tests and Disarmament,* a pamphlet published by the CCIA (New York, 1957).

246

and to pray to Almighty God to guide the peoples and their governments aright.[15]

By Central Committee action in 1958 the WCC, Division of Studies, published a provisional study document on the prevention of war in the atomic age. The study was released at the WCC's Nyborg, Denmark, session in August and was offered as a first step to the churches for their reflection and discussion.[16] This document was the outcome of three years of work by a fourteen-member committee, pacifists and nonpacifists, of scientists, philosophers, historians, theologians, and military men. The committee appointed by the CCIA in 1955, under the chairmanship of Sir Thomas Taylor of Aberdeen, had been set up to examine the scientific data and political realities "on atomic energy in the light of basic Christian convictions."

The report was not offered as an official view or statement of policy of the WCC, but was intended as "a contribution to Christian research and inquiry on a vital issue of our time," and as "a stimulus to widespread reflection and discussion on the urgent issues which it raises for the faith and witness of the Churches." It dealt with the realistic appraisal of the atomic situation in terms of war prevention, arguments for and against pacifism, and the clarification of concepts such as the meaning of "just war." Opinions were divided among those who advocated the "possession of nuclear weapons and the means of their delivery, but of never using them in all-out warfare"; those who declared themselves in favor of a "refusal of either the possession or use of the hydrogen bomb"; and those who rejected "not only the H-bomb but participation in war itself." A critique by the CCIA Executive Committee was appended to the report. It was stated that the study was "but a first step in a continuing study process."

In February 1959 the Executive Committee of the CCIA adopted a Statement wherein it sought to relate the previous positions of its churches to the difficulties which were obstructing agreement at the Geneva conference on the cessation of tests—particularly the procedures of the control commission, the staffing of control posts, and the duration of the agreement for the cessation of testing. The statement was then transmitted to the

[16]World Council of Churches—Division of Studies, *A Provisional Study Document on "Christians and the Prevention of War in an Atomic Age—A Theological Discussion"* (Geneva, 43 pp., Aug. 27, 1958).

heads of the delegations at the Geneva Conference: David Ormsby-Gore of the United Kingdom, Semyon K. Tsarapkin of Russia, and J. J. Wadsworth of the United States.

In August 1959 the Executive Committee of the CCIA, meeting in Spittal, Austria, and the Central Committee of the WCC, meeting in Rhodes, Greece, addressed themselves to the atomic situation in an effort to achieve agreement on the cessation of tests.   They formally adopted statements the relevant parts of which are here quoted:

> The World Council of Churches has at various times urged the cessation of nuclear weapons testing with the provision for international inspection and control, notably in Statements on Atomic Tests and Disarmament adopted in New Haven in 1957. . . . On reaffirming these former statements in all their present relevance, we now as members of the Central Committee call attention to certain matters which we consider immediately urgent.
>
> We urge the powers not to resume tests unilaterally, in order that statesmen may have time to achieve agreements and the international situation may not deteriorate. A treaty to cease all tests—atmosphere, space and underground—should be urgently sought not least since it will represent the beginning of specific controls, may lead to measures of disarmament verified by international inspection and control, and will help to eliminate dreaded risks to health.
>
> Tests for peaceful purposes or for more certainly identifying possible underground explosions should henceforth be under international control.   In particular, so long as international control is under discussion, powers which have not made tests as yet should not launch them anywhere for military purposes.
>
> We affirm that no nation is justified in deciding on its own responsibility to conduct weapons tests when the people of other nations who have not given their consent may have to bear the consequences.   Therefore, we call upon each nation contemplating tests to give full recognition to this moral responsibility as well as to considerations of national defense and international security.[17]

In September 1959 a memorandum of the CCIA's August 1959 statement was submitted to more than 700 United Nations delegates and alternates.

Meeting in Buenos Aires in February 1960, the twelve-member Executive Committee of the WCC called on the nuclear powers of the world to keep working for an agreement for total cessation of atomic tests.   The appeal followed up the previous statements of the council's ninety-member Central Committee in 1957 and

---

[17]*Christianity and Crisis,* Nov. 16, 1959, p. 168.   See also WCC Release New York, NB/44-59, Sept. 29, 1959.

1959 which have already been discussed above. Reaffirming
its concern for world disarmament the committee said: "The
conclusion of a treaty to cease nuclear weapons testing . . .
would contribute to greater confidence and provide for the
forthcoming meeting of the Committee of Ten on Disarmament
both a healthy climate and an agreed start on procedure for
international inspection." The CCIA Committee also reiterated
a call to the French government not to carry out bomb tests
in the Sahara.[18]

In May 1960, Dr. O. F. Nolde, director of the CCIA, sent
an open letter to the heads of governments convening at the
Summit Conference in Paris. The letter stated:

Many people ask themselves what the Summit Conference can accomplish. Knowledge of stubborn international realities and of past
failures dulls the edge of expectation. Yet yearning for progress towards
peace continues to survive every recurring disappointment.

In connection with the Summit Conference, the heads of the governments immediately concerned should be able to resolve in substance
the few major differences which continue to obstruct final agreement
on the cessation of nuclear weapons testing. The stage ought to be set
for the Geneva Conference thereafter promptly to complete the draft
of a treaty banning all tests where inspection and control are now possible, as well as arrangements for a moratorium on smaller underground
tests with an international research program to devise more effective
methods of detection. . . .

The current impasse imposes upon the Summit Conference the
obligation to give to the Committee of Ten on Disarmament, when it
resumes its meeting, clear and unmistakable directives on an equitable
starting-point in disarmament, or at least, an agreed and promising starting point in negotiations.[19]

EAST-WEST INTERCHURCH CONFERENCES

Besides these WCC statements, which were directed specifically
to atomic energy questions, there have been a number of East-
West interchurch meetings in which nuclear disarmament and
bomb-testing have come up for major discussion. Since very
little information on these important East-West meetings has
been disseminated in our own country, we shall try here to
indicate some of the conclusions reached during these talks.

On the initiative of the Ecumenical Council of Churches in

[18]WCC Release, New York, Nb/4-60, Feb. 10, 1960.
[19]WCC Release, Geneva, Nb/21-60, May 10, 1960.

Czechoslovakia, some representatives of the Christian churches from the German Democratic Republic, the German Federal Republic, Poland, Hungary, Bulgaria, Rumania, the Soviet Union, the Union of South Africa, and Czechoslovakia gathered for a conference in Prague June 1-3, 1958. The purpose of the meeting was to discuss ways and means by which the members of Christian churches might help to moderate international tension and to surmount the dangers presented by the discovery of atomic and thermonuclear weapons and their application to warfare.

A "Message from the Christian Peace Conference in Session" at Prague read as follows:

Jesus Christ deprived death of its power and brought life and immortality to light through the Gospel. Therefore all those who wish to obey His commandment to love and truly belong to Him are called to serve with all their strength in order that all men, believing und unbelieving, may have life.

This ancient mission of God's people stands all the more urgently before us when we reflect on the terrible possibilities of destruction, yea, the very annihilation of the entire human generation, which have been opened up by nuclear weapons, by the entire war technique of today. In this situation, we must clearly see that war means death, while peace means life. To toy with the idea of atomic war and to prepare for it, therefore, is rebellion against God and a crime against the life of mankind for whom Jesus Christ died and rose from the dead.

Through Him the world is reconciled with God. Let us therefore strive for the nations to become reconciled one to the other and for us, the Christians of all nations, to make a beginning in this.

Jesus Christ loved us and freed us from all fear. Let us, therefore, help people and nations to rid themselves of mistrust, to have respect and understanding one for another and to behave truly in a brotherly way to one another.

In His name we may call out to the Lord God in peace. Let us, therefore, pray again and again for world peace. But let us not ever forget that we are ourselves obligated by this prayer, in order not to pray for something that we deny by our deeds.

Jesus Christ has led us to be sober. Therefore, let us not allow ourselves to be misled by an underestimation and belittling of the atomic danger. Let us not be misled by the false belief that it would be possible to solve the great problems of the world by force or pressure through the cold war.

In view of the mortal danger threatening mankind today, let us come forth and ask our governments for the establishment of an atom-free zone for the relaxation of today's tension, for a ban on atomic weapons tests, for the outlawing and destruction of atomic weapons, and for the early meeting of statesmen at the highest level to solve world problems.

All peoples long for peace. Glory, honour, and peace to every man that worketh good (Romans 2:10).[20]

To this statement were added special pleas to Premier Khrushchev and President Eisenhower:

A serious and conscientious examination of the situation today has strengthened us in our conviction that mankind needs nothing so much as, and yearns—consciously or unconsciously—for nothing more than liberation from anxiety about weapons of mass destruction.

For this reason the participants of the Conference, in profound Christian responsibility, are in accord with the thousands of scientists who have raised their voices in this question to bring about the abolition of means of mass annihilation. We are convinced that it is unconditionally necessary for the strengthening of mutual confidence among the nations, that all further tests of thermonuclear weapons be stopped immediately, that the political situation be relaxed through the formation of atom-free zones, and a conference of responsible statesmen be called on the highest level.

To Mr. Premier: "We welcome with gratitude the decision of the government of the Soviet Union to put an end to tests of atomic weapons. This step is, in our opinion, a decisive contribution to the alleviation of tension and strengthening of peace. We ask the government of the Soviet Union not to relax in these efforts. We consider the presentation of this request our Christian duty."

To Mr. President: "We realize . . . all that has already been done in this matter by Christian churches, particularly through the Central Committee of the World Council of Churches in New Haven in the summer of 1957. Therefore we take the liberty, Mr. President, of addressing ourselves to you in the unity of our Christian faith, with the urgent plea that you undertake everything possible on your part to promote these matters and to fulfill the wishes of millions. Since one State has already ceased testing atomic weapons, it would be a deed of immense and far-reaching significance if the United States were also to put an end to its tests."

On the invitation of the Evangelical Church of Westphalia, twenty conference participants representing ten nationalities met in August of the same year for an East-West theological peace conference in the international Freundschaftsheim at Bückeburg. Represented at this meeting was the Russian Orthodox Church of Moscow, the Lutheran Orthodox Churches of Latvia and Estonia, the Evangelical Lutheran Church of Germany, the Reformed Church of Hungary and of Holland, the American and British Friends, United States Presbyterian, French Roman

[20]*Task and Witness,* a report on the Prague Peace Conference, June 1958, edited by Bohuslav Pospisil, director of the Ecumenical Institute of Prague, Czechoslovakia. See also the 1959 report—*Elige Vitam.*

Catholic, International Fellowship of Reconciliation, New Zealand Methodist, and Mennonite Central Committee.[21]

The second East-West theological conference to be held in Germany met January 10-13, 1959, at Frankfurt. Participants from France, Great Britain, Czechoslovakia, Russia, Hungary, United States, Canada, and Germany signed the following statement relative to the use of nuclear weapons.

We hold that it is politically and humanly wrong to arm Central Europe with nuclear weapons; that to do so will put unpredictable obstacles in the way of a developing understanding between East and West and will long delay a peaceful settlement.

We hold that atomic energy which might be a great blessing to the increasing population of the earth must never be used, under any circumstances or by any nation, for purposes of destruction.

We hold, as children of God, and hence as brothers, that we cannot recognize the division of our one world into East and West, into the just and the unjust, into the elect and the rejected, into the so-called believers and the so-called godless. We wish to stand with our fellowmen who want to put an end to the cold war and who, because they believe that the only victory is reconciliation, reject the concept of "friend-and-enemy" as obsolete and reckless, a concept which must be eliminated from political speech and action.[22]

During the conference discussion it was learned that the Russian Orthodox Church had unanimously and unconditionally condemned nuclear weapons from the very beginning. Specific reference was made to the declaration which had been issued by Metropolitan Nikolai: "In the name of the Orthodox Church we have been compelled to declare that the existence of nuclear weapons is irreconcilable with the spirit of the Gospel." Professor Pakozdy of Debrecen, Hungary, called attention to the fact that his church also had made a decisive declaration against the use of nuclear weapons. He stressed the point that the Eastern churches did in fact have the freedom to make such pronouncements.

Speaking for the Czechoslovakian Brotherhood, Pospisil of Prague said:

Our Christian neighbors might well speak out against nuclear armament out of fear of losing their human existence, but we as Christians

[21]Clarence Bauman (European Peace Section Representative of the Mennonite Central Committee), "East-West Theological Peace Conference," An Informal Report, Aug. 1-6, 1958.

[22]"Frankfurter Konferenz zur Verständigung zwischen Ost und West," Communication from C. Bauman.

must go much further than that, for our very eternal salvation is at stake in such action. It is not the fear of losing our life in a bombing attack but a very different issue, namely, that of facing God. Another somewhat different factor enters and that is the fear of living in an atomic age, a fear somewhat comparable to the fear of Communism, or, one could simply say, the fear of an insecure and unknown future. But we must not forget that it takes courage to live in this future, and we must believe that the church can survive an atomic era. The church must continue to proclaim the same Gospel in hope and in courage . . . . What I wish to say is that we as Christians must be concerned about more than the fear of facing the unknown future.[23]

A second Prague meeting of the East-West Christian Peace Conference convened April 16-19, 1959. The "message" which was released reads as follows:

We think the time has come that the churches should meet, in a way transcending the present form of their co-operation, for an All-Christian Assembly for the Peace of the World. . . . We are . . . convinced, that such an assembly, if wisely planned, will further the ecumenical movement and will strengthen all the forces for peace in the world.

In a subsequent report by Heinz Kloppenburg of Germany, this Prague conference was referred to as "the miracle of reconciliation through the Cross which has a greater reality and depth than the antithesis of East and West." Kloppenburg remarked that men had come to the meeting not as official representatives of their western churches, but as "living representatives of their risen Lord." They had gathered from all denominations not only to speak their minds freely, but to present a united voice in the midst of a divided world.

The 1959 Christian Peace Conference in Prague also included in its agenda a day of world penitence and prayer on the anniversary of Hiroshima. Some of the Western delegates feared that coming from behind the iron curtain this would be badly received in the West and especially in the United States. The call from Prague read as follows:

All of us share the guilt. . . . We have not loved Him Whom God loved so much. Being of little faith we have thought that weapons and human power were our help. . . . The bomb has become a summons.

When, therefore, we come together with our congregations and

[23]An abridged report of the discussions at the Frankfurt and Prague East-West Theological Peace Conferences of 1958 and 1959 is given in a reprint of 50 pages published in Switzerland and compiled in translation by C. Bauman.

churches on the day of Hiroshima this year to hold a service of penitence and prayer, we ask all of you, both in East and West, and all over
the world, not to withhold your communion from us.   Let us stand
together before God as His children and make a new beginning through
His forgiveness. . . .

The Hiroshima day of repentance and prayer was very widely
observed in 1959 in Europe, both East and West.   In America
it was observed almost not at all, and the Prague Conference
itself was widely ignored in the American press, both secular
and religious.

We have seen that the East-West theological peace conferences
were motivated by the compelling conviction that Christians,
who profess to believe in the miracle of the church, the power
of forgiveness, and the victory of reconciliation, must in their
relations to one another transcend the friend-enemy categories
of ideological propaganda.   At these small meetings, many concerns and differences were discussed with unusual frankness and
in an atmosphere of personal confidence which is not always
possible in larger official conferences.

THE GERMAN CHURCH BROTHERHOODS

Within German Protestantism itself, the German Church
Brotherhoods, or so-called *Kirchliche Bruderschaften* have concerned themselves in a very direct manner with questions related
to atomic weapons and testing.[24]   These brotherhoods, an extension of the revived Confessing Church, stem partly from the
days of the resistance movement, the *Kirchenkampf,* and partly
from the oppositions to nuclear rearmament for the German
Republic which began in 1957.   Perhaps the most influential
figure in the *Bruderschaften* is Professor Helmut Gollwitzer of
Berlin.[25]

In April of 1958 the Synod of the Evangelical Church in
Germany was challenged by the brotherhoods to publicly and
fearlessly oppose German nuclear armament on the same basis
on which the church had been compelled to take a clear stand
against anti-Semitism in the 1930's.   The appeal to the members
of the synod contained ten articles, which, if not acceptable,

[24]For the official documents of this group consult *Christusbekenntnis im
Atomzeitalter,* Theologische Existenz Heute, Heft 70 (Munich, 1959).
[25]See Helmut Gollwitzer, *Die Christen und die Atomwaffen* (Munich,
1957).

were to be refuted on grounds of Scripture, confession of faith, and reason.[26]   One of the articles stated that a neutral attitude on the issue of nuclear armament was a sin against God and a denial of all three articles of the Apostles' Creed.   The synod took no action, but only stated that the depth of the rift between its members on this issue was so deep that either side considered its position an absolute one.

The brotherhoods thereupon resolved to clarify their own theological reasoning in a meeting in Frankfurt (October 2-4, 1958) which was devoted to the theme "The Unity of the Church in Faith and Obedience."   In response to the question, What does it mean to confess Jesus Christ in a world of atomic threats? the brotherhoods agreed on two main theological points: 1) The Christian church should confess its faith and obedience to the one and only revelation of God through Jesus Christ. 2) Justification and sanctification are really inseparable and no area of man's life may be divested from the obedience of faith.

Applied to the sphere of political responsibility, the brotherhoods stated that the function of the state was not to guarantee the proclamation of the gospel but to maintain and protect human life.   Christians, they said, should accept this fact and give their allegiance to the state insofar as the state fulfills its function of maintaining life.   But, said the report:

We must confess that for the state to incorporate the means of mass destruction into their power threats and power practices can only result in the actual denial of the will of God. . . . Such action is not Christian.   The standpoint of neutrality in this matter, upon which we look as sin, is not compatible with confessing Jesus Christ.   Every attempt to justify such action and such neutrality theologically will lead to false doctrine, cause corruption, and deny the will of the triune God. Whoever takes our warning of the means of mass destruction as an invitation to the belief in the promises of the Gospel, has understood us correctly.   The knowledge thus acquired through the word of God binds us to witness together and commits us to corresponding action.[27]

It is important to make specific mention of the fact that the brotherhoods have maintained a sharp distinction between the functions of church and state—this, in a country where the *unity* of church and state has always been considered to be

[26]*Christusbekenntnis, loc. cit.* pp. 100-108; also East-West Theological Peace Conference held at Frankfurt, edited by C. Bauman, pp. 13-36 and Appendix B, pp. 42, 43.
[27]*Christusbekenntnis, loc. cit.,* trans. by author, pp. 15, 16.

something quite evident. The Frankfurt meeting of the brotherhoods served, among other things, to inform the pastors of the churches of the synod what some of the main issues in the separation of church and state were. There was much difference of opinion on almost all points which were raised. Indeed, it was inferred by some that the motives of the brotherhood's misguided *Schwärmerei,* the "theology of disarmament," was more political (viz., to oppose Adenauer) than based on the Word of God.

Eventually the witness of the brotherhoods came to be looked on more as a dissenting vote to be tolerated within the church. The Bavarian group, for example, complimented the pacifist brotherhoods for daring to be fools for Christ on the assumption that every church must have a few odd prophets and fools. As *Oberkirchenrat* H. Kloppenburg said at the Frankfurt East-West meeting in 1958, the problem only becomes acute when "these so-called fools for Christ want to be the whole church! Then they [the nonpacifists, will] say, 'For God's sake, do not convert all respectable Christians into fools for Christ.' "

Dr. Ullmann, a Quaker of Birmingham, England, remarked while attending the East-West Frankfurt session, that he was convinced that something truly remarkable was taking place among the brotherhoods in Germany. He said:

Somehow, despite the intellectual overtone, I could not get rid of the impression that that meeting resembled the Diet of Augsburg. And I was tempted to write it up as the "Confession of the Diet of Frankfurt!" I received the remarkable impression that what is taking place here after four and one-half centuries is actually a movement from the Right to the Left Wing Reformation. Here we witness a development (and now I speak as a sectarian *Schwärmer*) towards the ideals upheld by the Anabaptists, while Zwingli and Luther, fearing the consequences, retreated to the Middle Age compromise, in a sense to a Constantinian compromise with state, with culture, and with all that this implies. Now in the midst of the 20th century, challenged by the atom bomb and steeled by resistance to Hitlerism, the Brotherhoods attempt to break this unholy alliance (of church and state) and to take the church along in this process—not to create a new church but to take the established church along in this process. And this is extraordinarily difficult. . . . I would like to say by way of explanation that the Brotherhoods have no pacifist conception so far. They proceed rather from what we are accustomed to refer to as an ethic of the *Situationsethik*. But I believe, nevertheless, that despite this fear of 'isms' there is noticeable a definite movement toward a full peace testimony. I would say that this development very much approaches a Quaker orientation, as we also say the Holy Spirit calls one to decision within the situation itself.

To Seize the Initiative in War Prevention

We now turn our attention to the Protestant concern for atomic energy as expressed by the statements of various church councils within the United States. Foremost among these is the National Council of the Churches of Christ in the U.S.A. (NCC) which has taken a somewhat less decisive stand on nuclear weapons and nuclear tests than the World Council of Churches. In general, the NCC advocated atomic energy legislation and disarmament within the framework of the United Nations, the International Atomic Energy Agency, and the United States Atomic Energy Commission.

As early as 1951, an appointed commission within the Federal Council of Churches of Christ in America (now a part of the NCC) released a report which attempted to define the circumstances under which the use of atomic weapons could be condoned. The report also outlined steps which might be taken to preclude the necessity of using atomic weapons. Two members of the commission subsequently submitted a minority report which proposed that atomic weapons be outlawed.[28]

In December 1957 a statement of policy on atomic energy was adopted by the NCC General Assembly in St. Louis. It was published by the Department of International Affairs for the NCC. Under the caption, "The Nature of the Present Crisis," we read the following:

> For us Christians, our faith and the fellowship of the Church press us to see life steadily and whole, to respond neither with complacency nor panic, but with confidence and appropriate action. . . . We declare that the present crisis with its dangers and opportunities, while partially military and scientific, is of broader and deeper nature. It is also educational, political, psychological, economic, diplomatic, and cultural. Even more fundamentally, it is moral and spiritual. It is related to faith and unfaith, the meaning of existence and history and the world, the understanding of God and His will, the nature of man and his destiny.[29]

Concerning armaments the statement had more to say:

> We hold that military might provides no sufficient security. While most of us think that our nation should maintain an adequate national

[28]*Bulletin of Atomic Scientists,* April 1951, pp. 115-118.
[29]*Some Hopes and Concerns of the Churches in the Nuclear-Space Age,* a pamphlet published by the NCC, Dec. 1957.

defense, some of us feel that all armament is futile, but we all agree that if there is a shield of arms, larger constructive work must be undertaken on many lines for peace with justice and freedom. Even when arming, our nation, we believe, must persistently seek workable agreements for universal, inspected controlled, reduction and regulation of all armaments, including nuclear weapons. We believe that the accelerating arms race which now grips our world may lead directly to a war which will destroy civilization, and that efforts must be re-doubled to realize the final goal of world-wide disarmament in the framework of the U. N.

The General Board of the NCC, meeting in Minneapolis in June 1958, adopted a statement of policy which called for the universal reduction and regulation of weapons, including nuclear weapons. It was suggested that adequate controls and inspection be undertaken, while pressing toward ultimate disarmament within the framework of the United Nations. Other concerns which were set forth included fuller dissemination of information and more candor in issues posed by the nuclear space age, including the facts about tests; the means of disarmament; the "frank disclosure as to the contribution, if any, to peacetime usage made by such tests, as well as the extent to which they are actually essential to the development of tactical weapons and of relatively radiation-free explosions", the frank public exposition of obstacles obstructing "international agreements to place atomic tests under the International Atomic Energy Agency"; and the "establishment of a civilian agency in the United States government with primary responsibility among United States agencies for exploration and developments in the use of space."[30]

In November 1958 over five hundred representatives, lay and clergy church leaders from thirty-three denominations within the NCC, met in Cleveland for the Fifth World Order Study Conference to discuss "Christian Responsibility on a Changing Planet." Secretary of State Dulles, addressing the opening public meeting, defended American diplomacy and declared that his administration did not believe that peace could be achieved "by maneuvers or expediency or by power politics." The various delegates, representing special interests in international relations outlined a program calling for major changes in United

[30]*The Churches' Concern in Policies Related to the Control of Armaments and of the Use of Space,* a pamphlet published by the NCC, June 1958.

States foreign policy. The message which was released urged step-by-step disarmament by multilateral agreement, going beyond the suspension of nuclear testing. The message also recommended eventual recognition by the United States of the People's Republic of China and its entrance into the United Nations. It urged a breakthrough in the stalemate produced by the cold war by advancing toward competition by means other than war, recommending co-operation where possible with more liberal economic aid to foreign countries.

We quote from the message which was adopted:

We have been moved to this meeting by that faith in the redeeming love of God revealed in Jesus Christ which requires us and enables us as Christians and citizens to live in the world as it is. We have come to Cleveland in the conviction that such faith mandates and strengthens us to make hard choices between real alternatives without self-deception or despair. . . . In the knowledge of God's mandate and in the strength of His promise we all must deal *now* with suddenly pressing problems, filled with unprecedented possibilities of good and evil in the life of our nation. Our troubled concern is for more than our nation. Because of the power of the United States, what happens here may bless or torment all the nations of the world. And our Christian concern is for every people. . . .

But it will not do to rehearse the promises, cross fingers, and hope for the best. Christians are not fools. They know that all the promises now tremble over one peril. . . .

The immediate task of every Christian is to seize the initiative in the prevention of war and the achievement of peace in a world of intercontinental ballistics, thermonuclear weapons, and platforms in outer space for missile launching sites. . . .

We urge Christians to exhort their governments to continued willingness to meet and discuss the means of disarmament by multilateral agreement involving satisfactory inspection and control of nuclear weapons as well as the progressive reduction of conventional arms. . . . The suspension of nuclear tests under appropriate control and inspection is a first step toward halting the manufacture and stockpiling of nuclear weapons. . . .

Every agreement that is reached, no matter how small, can lead to confidence only as there is growth in good faith. . . . Vigilance and realistic precautions are necessary, but cynicism about the good faith of each other on all counts is a poisonous atmosphere in which to try to conduct negotiations. . . .

The procedures available through the United Nations provide the main new resource for settlement and peaceful change. . . .

Christians are counseled to support the United Nations in every way now open, and then to seek new ways to defend, sustain, and enhance the institution as a diligent, presently active servant of the world's welfare and as the most ready, best flexed instrument of reconciliation now available to the nations.[31]

The message, resolutions, and findings of this conference contributed background materials for a Nationwide Program of Education and Action for Peace sponsored by the Department of International Affairs in co-operation with the constituent communions of the NCC across the nation. The message adopted was the fifth in a series of historic documents developed by five World Order Conferences.

The General Board of the NCC, meeting in Detroit, Michigan, in December 1959, adopted a "resolution on disarmament" in line with its previously stated goals for a responsible system of world-wide reduction, regulation, and inspection of armaments, including nuclear weapons, within the framework of the United Nations.

In June 1960 the General Board of the NCC published a pronouncement entitled "The Churches and the Use of Nuclear Energy for Peaceful Purposes." This policy statement was by far the most comprehensive and thought-provoking pronouncement which has yet been issued by any church council in the United States.

The statement reads:

Christians view the advent of the nuclear age with hopeful realism. Modern man now has vast resources of nuclear energy at his disposal capable of both untold good and incalculable evil. It is clearly imperative for the Church to reaffirm its confession of God as the Lord of all creation and to proclaim to all men that they are responsible to their Maker for the ways in which they use, abuse, or neglect to use the tremendous potentialities inherent in the employment of nuclear energy for peaceful purposes.

Christians confess both the absolute sovereignty of God and the responsible stewardship of man. God alone is Creator. Christians look with reverent gratitude upon the well-nigh inexhaustible treasures of nuclear energy for peaceful uses.

But the Christian's response to nuclear energy can be distorted by a

---

[31]Department of International Affairs, NCC, *Christian Responsibility on a Changing Planet,* Report of the Fifth World Order Study Conference, Cleveland, Ohio, November 18-21, 1958, pp. 16-21. See also the *Study Guide for Christian Responsibility on a Changing Planet,* and the *Bibliography for the Nationwide Program for Peace* published in December 1959 by the NCC's Department of International Affairs for use in its nationwide program of education and action for peace in co-operation with the member denominations and state and local councils of churches from June 1959 to June 1960.

sense of fear and guilt sometimes associated with its initial war-time development and use. This compounds the moral issue with which we are faced. We must learn how to distinguish the goodness of the gift and the Giver from the tragic circumstances in which its early use was set; for out of the tragedy of war came the development of this power.

This lays upon all Christians both personal and social responsibility to exercise a faithful stewardship over this newly discovered source of energy now entrusted to man by the providence of God. As a creature of God, man is both permitted and encouraged to employ all his abilities and talents to make this world as fruitful as possible for the benefit of mankind and the welfare of future generations.

As man improves his standard of living, he requires increasing amounts of energy. He has in the recent past obtained this energy mainly from fossil fuels, such as coal, oil, and natural gas. Moreover, the rapidly increasing population and the industrialization of the world create future demands for energy that will consume fossil fuels at a greatly accelerated and even wasteful rate; for the world's supplies of fossil fuels can, in many instances, serve more appropriate uses than in the production of electrical energy. While there is no immediate shortage of such fuels, they are not inexhaustible. Man as a steward of the resources included in God's creation has a responsibility to conserve such resources by putting each to its best use.

The unlocking of the atom provides to man a new dimension of energy with sufficient breadth and depth to accommodate the needs of the world for centuries. Indeed, nuclear power helps mankind to open up the possibility for rapid economic and industrial development the world over.

We welcome the fact that resources are being developed and that the "peaceful" atom is making its way in increasing degree into vital industrial, agricultural, and other activities of our communities across the nation. A still greater challenge exists for extending these possibilities for good to areas of dire need around the world, as well as bringing the industrial potential to areas in our own country which now lack energy needed for their economic well-being.

In addition to the use of the atom as a source of power, scientists are already engaged in the utilization of atomic radiation and radioactive isotopes in a variety of day-to-day activities ranging from medical diagnosis and treatment to improving crop varieties and yields. Atomic radiation is engaged in countless industrial applications, both in the discovery of new products and in the improvement of manufacturing methods and techniques. Atomic energy is beginning to be used in the propulsion of ships, and its possible use for the propulsion of aircraft and space vehicles is being explored. Beyond these already comprehensible applications of atomic energy, there lie possibilities for future development still unknown to us—possibilities that may lead to destructive or constructive results still not capable of being imagined.

We therefore deem it our Christian responsibility, as faithful stewards, to work for an orderly development of nuclear energy for peaceful purposes for the benefit of all mankind. There is urgent need for ethical and political decision to be made regarding the continuance, control, or curtailment of nuclear development, production, and testing for defense purposes; yet the potentialities of nuclear technology for peaceful and constructive uses are so great as to require in themselves all prudent research and development.

The origin of this industry under government development and control has presented serious problems of incorporating it into our private economy. We believe that the relative roles of public and private ownership and operation of the industry should give due weight to two divergent forces: the equity of the public arising from the vast initial investment paid for out of public funds; and the desirability of the incorporation of the industry into our free economy. In the choices our nation makes regarding the use of both public and private resources, whether separately or in cooperation, the over-riding concern should be to develop to the maximum the public interest and the potential for human well-being.

The use of nuclear energy for peaceful purposes involves its own unique health and safety hazards and may involve hazards not only to this generation but to generations to come. Strong efforts should be directed to devise and use all feasible and reasonable safeguards against accidents, all protective and curative measures against injury. We recognize the safety record that has been achieved, but there should be no relaxation in our concern for safety. Required safety and exposure standards based upon recommendations by the foremost leaders in the field of radiation should be set by and enforcement insured by agencies of national governments and international organizations. Additionally, there should be a wide dissemination of knowledge as to the safety record and the dangers, risks, and safeguards involved.

The use of atomic energy even for peaceful purposes should not proceed more rapidly than a reasonably assured capability to guard against hazards to human life in future generations. The disposition of radioactive wastes in particular requires the utmost care in planning and handling. While the goal of each industry is to find full utilization for its waste products, this goal is still in the future in respect to the nuclear energy industry. We favor a national policy concerning the use and disposal of waste products which will exercise a high sense of responsibility toward later as well as the present generations in the disposal of high and low level radioactive wastes. Because of the international flow of ocean waters and our still limited knowledge of oceanography, we urge our government to encourage international cooperation in respect to such waste disposal in off-shore and other ocean waters.

We believe that persistent international cooperation is called for rather than selfish national competition. Nuclear energy is a gift from God to the whole human race, not a prize to be used by one nation-state to dominate or terrify other nation-states.

Americans should be humble in face of history, for many of the great nuclear discoveries were made through the work of Enrico Fermi, an Italian; Niels Bohr, a Dane; Albert Einstein, a German; and Leo Szilard, a Hungarian. Science is an international pursuit.

As we view realistically the need of vast areas of the world for health and medical services, for the increasing production and better preservation of food, and for energy producing resources, we are faced with a moral challenge to harness the constructive forces needed to meet these high goals of humanity, with even greater dedication than mankind has demonstrated in the recent past in mobilizing these resources for destructive purposes.

A concrete demonstration of the mid-20th century manner of sharing knowledge and resources with one's neighbor in a Christian way is seen in the gift of a nuclear reactor to a university in Asia through funds from one of our denominations.

One of the most obvious needs is for the nations to operate as fully as possible through the recently formed International Atomic Energy Agency. Through it both the nations that produce and those that use nuclear energy and its by-products have their most promising meeting ground. The United States initiated the concept which the International Atomic Energy Agency embodies; it should continue to be a major supporter of the Agency. International cooperation and world peace will be promoted by support of the International Atomic Energy Agency and regional atomic agencies.

Christians believe and rejoice in the knowledge that God's gifts are intended for the enrichment of all mankind and for the Glory of God. We call upon the churches to lead their people to an ever-clearer understanding of Christian responsibility to serve their fellow men that all may share in the development of the peaceful uses of atomic energy.[32]

Simultaneously the General Board of the NCC in June 1960 adopted a pronouncement entitled, "Toward a Family of Nations under God; Agenda of Action for Peace." This message intended for use in the churches on World Order Sunday, October 23, 1960, contained the following statements relative to atomic issues:

Our responsibility as Christians involves learning the facts, appraising them fearlessly, seeking humbly to apply to them the moral principles which our faith inspires.

The United States must persevere in the quest for enforceable agreements to eliminate weapons of death and to reduce the burden of armaments. At the same time, the need for alternatives to the use of military force requires the development of institutions for collective security and the strengthening of peaceful processes.

War has never been a morally acceptable instrument for the pursuit of national policy, even though the capacity for self-defense has been recognized as necessary to survival. The dilemma of defense is sharpened by the existence of ultimate weapons, which threaten victim and aggressor alike with mutual suicide.

What, then, are the alternatives to appeasement or surrender? The

[32]The General Board of NCC, *A Pronouncement: The Churches and the Use of Nuclear Energy for Peaceful Purposes,* 25.3-1 and 25.3-2, June 2, 1960.

quest for enforceable disarmament clearly is part of the answer. We
have sought, and must continue to seek, enforceable agreements pertaining to the production, testing and means of delivery of weapons of
mass destruction, as well as more inclusive agreements.

"Disarmament" in reality means the reduction of national military
power and acceptance of limits upon the use of such power. No nation
will voluntarily agree to weaken its relative strength, if it lacks confidence in existing processes for security and for orderly change.

The objective of general disarmament can, therefore, be achieved
only in relation to a relatively stable international order. This, in turn,
depends upon strengthening institutions to build the foundations of peace
and more effective use of processes to keep the peace and assure justice.

The United Nations and other international processes cannot be wished
into maturity. They grow only with use, encouragement and support.
They atrophy when neglected or by-passed in the areas of their greatest
service to humanity: mutual economic and technical assistance, promotion of human rights, development of the atom for peaceful uses, co-
operation in the use of outer space, and faithful use of international
juridical, political and economic agencies.

The United States should respect the competence of the International
Court of Justice, without self-appointed powers of reservation, such as
the Connally Amendment. Until the Amendment is repealed, we should
use the reserved power with utmost restraint.

Improvement of standards of life of our fellowmen is a privilege
the United States shares, not a benefit it confers. Moral principle even
more than concern for our own national welfare impels an abiding
interest in our neighbors on a crowded planet. Their growth is part
of our growth and their partnership for peace is essential to all security. . . .

Communications of ideas, exchanges among peoples, and willingness
to negotiate at all levels, assume greater urgency, the more ideas clash
or political tensions mount. Communication does not imply approval,
exchanges do not corrupt men of principle, and negotiation need not
mean appeasement. The basic Christian concept of reconciliation must
be persistently pursued. . . .

Appeasement consists in the surrender of principle, not in the discussion of differences. Our government should, therefore, be ready
to confer at all levels with all governments, on any issues which affect
our national interest or international order, including disarmament, the
prohibition of nuclear tests, and the peaceful uses of atomic energy,
all of which require cooperation of the major powers, including those
which are not officially recognized by the United States.[33]

[33]Department of International Affairs, NCC, *Agenda of Action for
Peace: Toward a Family of Nations Under God,* CO 2-93, New York,
June 1960.

No Agreements with the Atheistic Kremlin

The strongest American opposition to the above stand of both the WCC and the NCC was taken by the American Council of Christian Churches (ACCC). This is a schismatic group of extreme fundamentalists who have the reputation of being "church splitters" in the mission field. Carl McIntire, pastor of the Bible Presbyterian Church of Collingswood, New Jersey, is editor of the *Christian Beacon,* a paper which speaks for the ACCC.

Three leaders of the ACCC, including McIntire, issued a press release on August 8, 1957, challenging one of the WCC pronouncements which was given above.[34] The ACCC statement reads in part:

The statement of the World Council of Churches, August 5, 1957, rests upon such erroneous moral presuppositions and offers such unsound advice to the nations that it cannot go unchallenged.

It is morally irresponsible to assume and propose that conditions of mutual trust can be established with an atheistic, anti-god, materialistic communism which recognizes no moral standard of any kind. To encourage the western world to believe that international confidence is possible in such circumstance involving our security and freedom is suicidal to the West.

To suggest that if one or more nations unilaterally forego atomic tests for a trial period might inspire a "new confidence" and "lay foundations for reliable agreements" is to mislead the people as to the real foundation needed for confidence and to open the way to the Russians further to deceive in their efforts to soften and deceive the West. . . .

Certain fundamental truths of Scripture are ignored by the WCC pronouncement. . . . Though the sin of man is mentioned, the (WCC) statement fails to recognize the total depravity of man as taught in the Scriptures and demonstrated in current history, particularly Russian oppression in Hungary. . . . God often has used a heathen power to destroy His people who compromised His moral law. . . . Nations have a right, in honoring God's law, to appeal for His favor and blessing. . . . The Bible constantly warns the Christian against any "understandings" with the devil and his agents. The believer is always to be on his guard against Satan's devices and deceptions. And this whole realm of biblical truth is completely ignored by the WCC in its attempt to lead man to believe and hope that somehow the devil's agents in the Kremlin will agree to their own deception of "peaceful co-existence."

The path to peace and security in a moral world with the living God cannot be along the way of concessions and agreements at the hand of atheistic Kremlin tyrants. It can be pursued by restoring the power

[34]This was the WCC pronouncement discussed on p. 245f.

of government into the hands of the people. The energies and wisdom of the West should be directed to the end that the people shall direct and control their government's decision to make war and to use the atom. Only when the lawless, gangster forces are replaced can a sure basis for agreement, confidence and understanding make possible the foundations of peace and freedom men desire.[35]

At its sixteenth spring convention, April 29 to May 2, 1958, in Greenville, South Carolina, the delegates of the ACCC adopted a resolution registering opposition to summit meetings with Soviet Premier Khrushchev. At the same time they called "for leadership in the West that will base its conduct upon high moral principles and convince the world that the gangsters of the Kremlin are impossible to deal with in any trustworthy or genuine manner." On the question of nuclear tests, the statement reads:

Whereas, the example of God's Word, the Bible, calls upon nations and people to be prepared for the defense of those possessions which God has provided. And Whereas, our Government is being pressurized by pacifists, the World Council of Churches, and Communistic pressure, in an attempt to cause cessation of nuclear tests, *Be it resolved* that we call upon our Government to heed the admonition of God's Word and seek every avenue of preparedness that is necessary in the continuation of all such essential nuclear testing.

The same ACCC resolution also carried a statement condoning racial segregation in the following terms:

The American Council of Christian Churches . . . declares that so-called liberal Christianity today and the program of the National Council of Churches, calling for a non-segregated church and a non-segregated world, does violence to the true Gospel of Jesus Christ. Segregation within the church on racial, linguistic, and national lines is not unchristian nor contrary to the specific commands of the Bible. . . . It is time for Christian people to repudiate . . . false Christianity which is attempting to take from them their churches, their liberty, and ultimately their Christ.[36]

The National Association of Evangelicals, a conservative group "serving over ten million Bible-believing Christians," has (according to its executive director) issued no statements on the testing of nuclear weapons.

---

[35]International Council of Christian Churches *Press Release,* Aug. 8, 1957, pp. 1, 2.

[36]*Christian Beacon,* May 8, 1958.

New Light for a Sore Dilemma

The most important recent inter-Protestant statement on atomic energy was adopted by the Third National Conference of the Church Peace Mission which convened at Evanston, Illinois, April 20-23, 1959, for a study conference devoted to the theme: "The Word of God in a Nuclear Age." Present at this meeting were 230 pacifists from twenty United States and Canadian groups and denominations. The message which was adopted reads in part as follows:

Our own country and the world are threatened physically with the holocaust of nuclear war.

Today let the church unequivocally renounce war and take some decisive action to break the terrible circle of armament and counter-armament in which the world is trapped. Then peace will cease to be a painful and frustrating dilemma. It will be a challenge to meet with faith.

There are still a multitude of Christians. . . who sincerely hold that the church cannot now make a final break with nuclear war because atomic bombs and missiles must be retained as deterrents. But this presents a sore dilemma. If, on the one hand, the arms race and popular dependence on it continue up to the moment of the final awful choice, it is idle to expect that then the counsel to renounce these weapons will suddenly be heeded. If, on the other hand, the course is indeed to be rejection of the use of nuclear weapons, this fact must be made completely clear, risking no further delay during which tension will become intolerable and war may be precipitated. In this event atomic weapons lose their so-called deterrent efficacy. It is imperative that we proceed now while there is yet time to develop and apply creative alternatives in defense and in foreign policy which are responsive to the demand for justice and order, to imaginative service to human need, and to the aspirations of the oppressed.

The moral dilemma is far more serious. Christians cannot be content to await some frightful future crisis and then decide what to do. It is the Christian vocation now to reject the sin of involvement in nuclear war and to live today in simple obedience and faith, and carry out the work of love and reconciliation.

It is with a deep sense of our own unworthiness, our little faith, our halting obedience that at this Third National Conference of the Church Peace Mission we send this message to the churches and to our fellow Christians everywhere. But we believe that in response to faith, God will now, as in other times of man's sinning and despair, import new light and power to His Church and His people. The church will then be a channel of grace and renewal for the world, and Christian citizenship will acquire a new meaning.[37]

[37]*The Mennonite,* June 23, 1959.

OPEN-MINDED AND WILLING TO COMPROMISE

As in the case of Catholics and Protestants, the American Jewish congregations have been divided on atomic energy issues.

On recommendation of its Commission on Social Action, the Forty-third Assembly of the Union of American Hebrew Congregations meeting in Los Angeles in February 1955, adopted a statement which reads in part:

We confront the modern threats to peace, symbolized by the awesome power of thermonuclear weapons, with deep anxiety and concern but with undimmed faith in the even mightier power of God and man. . . .

We recognize that aggressive Communism is primarily responsible for . . . many of the tensions threatening world peace. That Communist imperialism is the chief threat to world peace does not, however, absolve the United States from the heavy responsibility of constantly examining our own policies and conduct to make sure that we do not, in discouragement and frustration, weaken in our determination to build a peaceful world. . . .

Accordingly, we urge that the United Nations be made in deed as well as in word the cornerstone of United States foreign policy. . . . Our task must be to strengthen the United Nations . . . to become truly a world organization which it cannot be until it becomes a council of all nations.

We urge that the United States not yield to despair in the search for universal peace. . . . We warmly commend President Eisenhower for his imaginative proposal for an atomic pool for peace-time purposes, and for our country's contribution of fissionable materials for peaceful uses. The United States should similarly seize the initiative in the quest for universal disarmament. Until a working, realistic program of world disarmament is in force, however, the United States must continue, in concert with other free nations, to maintain its military strength, including its atomic stockpiles. It is an ironic truth that these stockpiles may be the most effective present deterrent to a world war.

We urge that consideration of a preventive war as a possible instrument of American policy be rejected as immoral and a blasphemy both of religion and of democracy. We heartily commend President Eisenhower for repeatedly repudiating such an alternative, and for courageously urging patience and maturity in the pursuit of peace, but we are disturbed by the continued prevalence in places of high authority of a state of mind which seems to regard a preventive war as a solution to our difficulties. . . .

We urge the convening of an international conference of religious, educational, scientific, and civil leaders from all nations to discuss the threats of peace and to consider ways of strengthening the fabric of universal harmony. . . . The voice of religion, the message of salvation through righteousness and justice, must be heard above the clatter of the weapons of war.[38]

The Forty-fourth General Assembly of the Union of American Hebrew Congregations, meeting in Toronto (April 28 to May 2, 1947), also adopted a resolution on "Disarmament and Peace." They commended "the efforts of the United States, Canada, and other governments toward the achievement of universal, enforceable disarmament," and urged "that all such efforts be carried forward with the utmost urgency, imagination, and flexibility." The same resolution was reaffirmed in November 1959 at Miami Beach, Florida, when the Union of American Hebrew Congregations met for its Forty-fifth Biennial General Assembly.

The Commission on Justice and Peace of the Central Conference of American Rabbis (CCAR) in 1956 passed resolutions urging that "atomic energy be outlawed as an instrument of international warfare, and that the development of atomic energy remain forever under government ownership and civilian control and that the secrets of the release of atomic energy be shared with the world when proper controls have been set up by the United Nations." The report continued:

In the atom we see not only the threat of death, but also the promise of new horizons for undreamed of life. We urge the continued and unceasing efforts on the part of our government . . . to further the peace-time uses of the atom and to make its blessing felt in the farthest corners of the earth. . . . Be it resolved that the CCAR urge our government to continue its efforts for an international agreement to govern or abolish the testing of nuclear weapons.[39]

In June 1958 the same Commission of the CCAR adopted a statement relative to bomb testing:

We call for the immediate abandonment of the testing of nuclear weapons because we believe that it is wrong to continue contaminating the atmosphere and soil of the earth with radioactive poisons. There may be some difference of opinion in the scientific community as to the amount of risk involved. There is no disagreement about the fact that there is some risk, that the longer testing continues and the more countries that engage in it, the more individuals will be murdered or malformed now and in the future. Governments simply have no moral

[38]*The Achievement of a Just Peace, A Statement of Principles,* published by the Union of American Hebrew Congregations, Los Angeles, Feb. 14, 1955, pp. 1-3.

[39]*Justice and Peace,* revised edition, published by the CCAR (New York, 1956), p. 10.

right consciously and in peacetime to impose pain, crippling, and death upon innocent human beings.

The statement further emphasized the importance of halting bomb tests as a first step toward international agreement, the goal being total disarmament:

All this will have to parallel the evolution of the United Nations into an effective, supranational agency of inspection, control, and the enforcement of international law. We strongly urge such amendments to the charter of the United Nations as will make this possible. . . .

We should urge our fellow citizens to organize, to inform themselves, to band together to bring pressure to bear, through meetings, demonstrations and messages, upon the President, the State Department, Congress, urging the negotiation of agreements on test halting and the other phases of disarmament with all possible speed; urging that our government approach these negotiations with the intent to be flexible, open minded, and willing to make compromise.

From the report of the CCAR's Commission on Justice and Peace adopted June 1959 we quote:

We believe that it is wrong to continue scattering the radioactive debris of bomb tests, whether they are carried out beneath the earth or waters, in the air or in the stratosphere. Regardless of the debate raging in scientific circles about the tolerable levels of radiation it is evident that considerable risk is involved for a number of human beings. It is a sophistry to equate this with the other tasks of living. Deliberately to gamble with the health and lives not only of the present but of unborn generations is immoral. We commend the efforts of the representatives of our government at Geneva, and, despite the difficulties which they are encountering, we urge them to continue to work patiently for an agreement with the Soviet Union.

From the CCAR report of June 1960 we quote:

We deeply regret the recent breakdown of the Summit Conference. We hope that the channels of diplomatic communication and of cultural interchange between our country and the Soviet Union will be kept open. We urge that every possible effort be made at Geneva to arrive at agreements of reduced armaments and to ban the testing of nuclear weapons. We should not like to see our country be the first to resume testing.[40]

The National Conference of Christians and Jews has issued no public statements regarding nuclear testing. It has been the basic purpose of this organization to combat interreligious and interracial bigotry, and the statements which the conference has

[40]*Statements on the Testing of Nuclear Weapons,* CCAR, June 1958, June 1959, and June 1960.

issued in the past have dealt specifically with problems in those areas.

No Man Can Serve Two Masters

We wish finally to single out a number of specific reactions to atomic energy which have come from the historic peace churches. I refer to those religious organizations which seek to give a pacifist witness through their churches. Christian pacifism and nonviolence might be defined in this context as the refusal of participation in war, or as nonresistance to war, whether offensive or defensive, international or civil; war being defined as the organized killing of one group by another. Perhaps the term conscientious objector, as used during the last war, would more accurately characterize the emphasis of the war resister who seeks to express opposition to war through positive courses of action consistent with nonresistant religious principles.

Not all pacifists are motivated by religious principles. We might illustrate this by quoting from a statement issued by the War Resisters League which says: "We welcome to our movement Democrats, Republicans, and Socialists, Jews, Christians, and atheists, agrarians and industrialists, saints and sinners; and we leave every man to reconcile his own way of life with the repudiation of all war.[41]   In our treatment here we are considering only some Christian pacifist positions on nuclear warfare and bomb testing.

According to the tradition of the historic peace churches, the Christian's responsibility belongs first and foremost to God and his fellow men and not to any state. How this responsibility works itself out in the area of morality and the sphere of daily national and international living is largely a matter of the individual's interpretation of the Word of God in these matters, as tempered by the consensus of opinion which is established by the group of peace-minded Christians to which the individual belongs. Hence, the Christian cannot agree to offer to God merely those services which remain after the state has made its claims and demands on the individual. In practice, this virtually amounts to an absolute and uncompromising refusal to condone war threats, and to co-operate in active warfare and projects which make war possible—to the extent that this is humanly

[41]*Pacifica News*, Dec. 29, 1944.

feasible.. Whatever theological differences of opinion Christian pacifists may entertain, they all stand firmly united in their all-out rejection of the military use of atomic devices in any form whatsoever.

There have been a number of joint historic peace church pronouncements on the question of nuclear warfare. For example, in 1954 in the *New York Times* and other newspapers, the American Friends Service Committee (AFSC), the Brethren Service Committee (BSC), and the Mennonite Central Committee (MCC) jointly issued a plea for outlawing nuclear weapons "unconditionally and permanently." The statement, beneath a drawing of a cross and an atomic bomb mushroom, read as follows:

No man can serve two masters. Today, the cross of Christ stands in the shadow of the cross of hydrogen, calling us back to the meaning of Calvary.

Two crosses: one standing for redemptive love and forgiveness, for the acceptance of suffering, for hope, for life; the other for hatred and massive retaliation, for the infliction of suffering, for fear, for death. One proclaims that evil is overcome with good; the other that evil can only be met with evil.

Man cannot serve both Christ and the bomb. He must choose which is to be his master. Let us choose the cross of Christ. Let us cease deluding ourselves: peace cannot be built from fear. Men do not gather grapes from thorns. Let us be done with these fearful weapons, regardless of what others do. Whether the bomb is a tool to deter or to destroy, it is not the sign by which men conquer. "Not by might, nor by power, but by my spirit, saith the Lord."[42]

Four years later, in May 1958, essentially the same challenge was repeated and published in *The Washington Post*.[43]

In July 1958 at Kassel, Germany, the three above-mentioned historic peace churches and the International Fellowship of Reconciliation met for a conference entitled "Recognition of Conscience in Church and State." They then drafted a statement on nuclear armaments and testing which was submitted to the Central Committee of the WCC on August 7, 1958, in time for their session at Nyborg, Denmark, where this issue was under discussion. We quote from this joint statement:

In our deliberating together we have been reminded of the responsibility resting upon all Christians today to protest against the sin of manufacturing nuclear weapons, to witness by word and deed to that

[42]*New York Times*, April 16, 1954.
[43]*MCC News and Notes*, May 16, 1958.

spirit and power of Christ which takes away the occasion of all war. . . .

On grounds of Christian conviction, we believe that war itself must be abandoned.

To acquiesce in the manufacture and use of these weapons is, we believe, a sin against God, a sin against our fellow-man, a sin against generations yet unborn.

We are deeply concerned because of the threatened destruction of civilization; we are concerned for the victims who will suffer on account of the widespread torture which will be involved; we are concerned for those who will be responsible for inflicting untold suffering on mankind, and we have been led to share our concern with you.

We would plead with you, the World Council of Churches Central Committee, to speak at this time both to governments and to people, urging the total renunciation of all nuclear weapons and reaffirming, in no uncertain terms, the conviction . . . that war is contrary to the will of God and incompatible with the precepts and example of our Lord, Jesus Christ.[44]

It was at the 1958 Nyborg session that the WCC document was released. We have already referred to that session above.[45]

Reinforce the God-given Capacity for Good

Among the historic peace churches, the Friends or Quakers have been by far the most persistent, most vocal, and most active group opposing nuclear arms and weapons testing. Disarmament is an old concern of the Quakers—atomic disarmament is a new urgency. The Quakers have issued special messages on disarmament as a conference. They have carried on a worldwide program in the dissemination of literature through various agencies. They have initiated a number of attempts to increase the exchange of information and mutual understanding behind the iron curtain. As individuals and in groups the Quakers have sent representatives to international atomic energy conclaves and congresses, supported peace-time atomic energy projects, circulated nuclear test-ban petitions, and picketed atomic installations.

We saw in the last chapter that the Friends have also been actively engaged in collaborating with scientific organizations which oppose atomic energy programs oriented toward the military. Most outstanding perhaps among Quaker scientists in this regard is Professor Kathleen Lonsdale, a British crystallog-

[44]Communication from C. Bauman.
[45]See p. 246.

rapher, who spent one month in Holloway prison in 1943 for refusal to register for civil defense duties and who has been most active since then both in organizing scientific opinion for nuclear disarmament and in writing on the subject.[46]

An event which elicited world-wide response to end weapons testing requires special mention. This took place on May 7, 1958, when four Quaker crew members of the vessel "Golden Rule" were arrested off Honolulu and sentenced for criminal contempt of court for sailing into the area of the Eniwetok proving grounds as a protest to the testing of atomic weapons by the United States government.[47]

Relatively few people recognize what a broad and far-reaching program accompanies the Friends' approach to organized non-resistant action. Devoted to a philosophy rooted deeply in Quaker religious faith and experience and based on a respect for the personality of each individual, the Friends now operate nonpartisan projects in many countries around the world. These project activities include aid to refugees and others in need overseas; social and technical assistance; work and study projects for young people; promotion of international understanding through school affiliations, seminars, international centers and peace education; and efforts for improved community relations, with full opportunities for racial minorities. The Friends' Christian philosophy of active love in place of violence to overcome evil is one which dramatically opposes the manufacture, testing, and use of nuclear weapons in any form.[48]

In 1957 the Executive Council of the Friends Committee on National Legislation opposed civil defense programs in this country on the grounds that they served as preparations for war. The statement on "Civil Defense and Peace" which was drafted in March 1957 at Germantown, Pennsylvania, is quoted here in part:

In our view the civil defense program is not consistent with . . . the overriding need to achieve lasting peace and avoid the sufferings of

[46]Kathleen Lonsdale, "Disarmament," *The New Scientist,* Nov. 1957; numerous articles in the *Bulletin of Atomic Scientists; Removing the Causes of War* (London, 1953).

[47]Norman Cousins, *The Saturday Review,* May 17, 1958, p. 24.

[48]An informative series of analyses of international events and policies was begun by the AFSC in 1949: *The United States and the Soviet Union,* 1949; *Steps to Peace,* 1951; *Towards Security Through Disarmament,* 1955; and *Speak Truth to Power, a Quaker Search for an Alternative to Violence,* 1958.

war . . . and we cannot endorse it. The available evidence indicates that
this program is primarily motivated by fear for our own safety and a
desire to prepare for the consequences of another war. . . . By preparing people psychologically for war, by increasing their fear and
hatred of an enemy, civil defense is in fact increasing the danger of
war by creating the sort of climate that will produce it. The civil
defense program thus seems to us to be yet another phase of war
preparation. . . . The only realistic defense efforts are those which
prevent a nuclear attack by abolishing war itself. . . . With faith in
our fellow man, we in the United States should use our time, energies
and resources to prevent the bombs from falling and to build the conditions of lasting peace. This is our only real defense.[49]

As another example of Friends concern for atomic disarmament, let us refer to the message of the Friends Conference on
Disarmament attended by 145 Friends from twenty-one yearly
meetings in the United States held in Germantown, Ohio,
March 13-16, 1958. We quote:

The witness of Friends for peace is deeply rooted in the basic religious insights of our Society. The sacredness of human life and the
essential brotherhood of all men demand a rejection of war. The
Quaker understanding of the Christian gospel leads to a complete renunciation of war and preparation for war.

Disarmament is everyone's responsibility, because we are all now involved in preparation for war. Each of us shares the blame for the
climate of fear which has resulted in reliance on military defense for
security, in an inflexible foreign policy, and in a weakening of democracy at home. Each of us shares the obligation for asserting the religious
faith from which will issue creative steps toward peace. We are not
alone. We are never helpless. God works in history through men,
and we feel we are under His leading.

The steps toward an unarmed world cannot all be foreseen, but two
seem to us necessary and possible now: ending nuclear weapons tests;
banning ballistic missiles by placing the use and exploration of the
upper atmosphere and outer space under the supervision of the United
Nations.

Steps which we believe can follow in the near future, either singly
or together, include: ending the production of nuclear weapons; re-
stricting stockpiles of nuclear weapons to countries which made them;
beginning the conversion of existing nuclear weapons to peacetime uses;
reducing conventional armed forces and terminating conscription; banning shipment of arms to tension areas; withdrawing NATO and Soviet
armed forces from Central Europe and demilitarizing this and other
strategic areas; creating machinery for inspection and control of these
measures.

We recognize the complex problems facing nations even after they

[49]*Bulletin of Atomic Scientists,* May 1957, p. 176.

decide to move toward a disarmed world. There is no easy answer to the question, How do you meet the threat of potential aggression? There is no blueprint for the uncharted region between our disturbed world and a world of peace and justice under law. But the risks we encounter in this venture are better justified than the risks of continuing the arms race.

In 1958 the AFSC distributed a mat, which was widely published in newspapers and magazines. It was entitled *Stop this Fatal Race!* We quote from this statement:

Let us have faith in the strength of freedom and the power of righteousness. This new approach would involve enormous risks. But they are not as great as those involved in continuing to balance on the knife edge of terror. Recognizing man's capacity for evil, we must seek to reinforce his God-given capacity for good.

We could: 1. Cancel our nuclear weapons tests, because they are hurting men now and may warp the bodies of our grandchildren *and because our souls are betrayed when we use our minds to plan the destruction of God's creation.* 2. Start disarmament—by steps WE can take, because there will be no real peace without world disarmament, and no disarmament unless some nation starts *and because it is wrong to prepare to kill other men.* 3. Share our resources more fully, because helping people help themselves is a genuine answer to the appeal of Communism *and because it is wrong to keep so much when two-thirds of the world is sick and hungry.* 4. Consider the problems of men more important than the promotion of alliances, because a solution in Algeria is more important than NATO; settling refugees in the Middle East is more important than sending arms; *and because we are men and we know that men should live in peace and love one another.* 5. Strengthen the United Nations as an inclusive and responsible agency for peace, because nations in conflict need a common meeting ground *and because mankind is indivisible.* 6. Seek ways to bring men together across iron and bamboo curtains, because everyone would gain from commercial, scientific, cultural and religious contacts *and because the major foes of understanding are ignorance and bigotry.* We could. Will we?

In a pamphlet by the Labor-International Affairs Program of the AFSC, which was designed to "Support the Pickets against H-bomb Tests," in 1958 we read:

Be it . . . resolved: 1. That the United States should halt all nuclear weapons tests immediately, and invite the Soviet Union and the United Kingdom to join in a declaration of unconditional cessation of nuclear weapons tests, with inspection. 2. That the United States should invite the United Kingdom and the Soviet Union to enter into immediate negotiations for the establishment of an international inspection system to police the test ban. 3. That such negotiations should be conducted within the framework of the United Nations and under the guidance of the Secretary-General.

During 1960 the International Affairs and Centers Program of the AFSC in Philadelphia issued a series of informative papers entitled *Background on Disarmament, 1960*. The statements in this series were prepared by different authors and covered the international and political situation regarding universal disarmament and nuclear testing. Included also were the current attitudes of the presidential candidates and other American and foreign statesmen.

Among the foremost Quaker publications which have dealt with problems connected with atomic energy, bomb testing, and disarmament we cite *AFSERCO Notes,* a quarterly digest of news and views from Quaker centers around the world, published in Philadelphia; and the *Washington Newsletter* published by the Friends Committee on National Legislation. There are also the special publications of the Educational Service of the AFSC, of the Peace and Social Order Committee of the Friends General Conference, and of the Friends Peace Committee of the Society of Friends in London.

In addition, the Quakers on a number of occasions have worked in collaboration with organizations such as the International Fellowship of Reconciliation (IFOR), a Christian pacifist organization which seeks especially to give the pacifist witness in and through the churches; the Anglican Pacifist Fellowship, a fellowship of pacifists in the Church of England; the Peace Pledge Union (London); the Women's International League for Peace and Freedom; the Peacemakers; the War Resisters League; the Committee for World Development and World Disarmament; the Society for Social Responsibility in Science; Nonviolent Action Against Nuclear Weapons; and the National Committee for a Sane Nuclear Policy.

A PERIL TO QUIET SOULS

The second of the historic peace churches which merits our attention is the Church of the Brethren. We have already mentioned this group in connection with the joint statements by the American Friends Service Committee, the Mennonite Central Committee, and the Brethren Service Committee.

In 1954 the Annual Conference of the Church of the Brethren, meeting at Ocean Grove, New Jersey, issued the following statement:

As Christians we believe we cannot remain indifferent to the perplexing problems of our society. We believe it is our duty to study these problems, to voice our concerns, and to explore the possible means of solution.

We are also living in the midst of severe international tension. We are glad the President of the United States and other of our governmental heads feel the need to seek divine guidance. We commend our leaders for every effort they make to resolve tensions through the medium of negotiation. We urge that our government genuinely negotiate from a more flexible basis in matters of foreign policy. We commend the President for the proposal he made in his speech before the United Nations on December 8, when he called for an international pool of atomic energy for peaceful purposes. We urge that more be done toward the implementation of this proposal and that a constructive plan be placed before the United Nations Disarmament Commission, including a standstill agreement on atomic and conventional arms— a first step looking toward complete disarmament.

The development of the hydrogen bomb, the cobalt bomb, biological warfare, and other military devices threatening mass murder and collective suicide indicate that war cannot be used among nations as an instrument of national policy for securing international peace and justice. The Brethren, as a church, long ago renounced war as incompatible with the teachings of Jesus. At this crucial moment in our history we wish to reaffirm our conviction that "all war is sin." We believe this position finds an echoing chord of sympathy and agreement in many communions. We invite all such to join us in making facts and convictions known to our government. We believe the time has come when the Christian people of the world should urge their governments to join in an all-out effort to discover means whereby another war may be prevented. In keeping with this we would humbly suggest to the Congress and the President of the United States the establishment of a national department of peace.[50]

In 1955 the Annual Conference of the Church of the Brethren, meeting at Grand Rapids, Michigan, issued a second statement:

We pledge ourselves to the intelligent support of every effort of our government and of the United Nations to enhance world co-operation and understanding. We commend all efforts which have been made by our government to bring about and to enter into peaceful negotiations between peoples and nations. We urge our nation to lead out courageously in disarmament proposals and action. We further urge our government to discontinue all undertakings which seem to be gestures of belligerence or threatening displays of military might; we urge the government to curtail and discontinue the testing and stockpiling of nuclear and other lethal weapons. We commend our government for the studies of the constructive use of atomic power. We urge our national leaders to seek to lead the way toward a world of co-

[50]Church of the Brethren, *168th Conference Minutes,* June 1954.

operation rather than to be a continuing factor in a world of fear.[51]

At the same time, the General Brotherhood released the following *Statement on Modern Weapons*:

With the recent and current development of bacteriological weapons, of nuclear weapons, and of other lethal instruments of mass destruction, the human race is confronted with new possibilities of unheard-of destructiveness on a world scale. However, nuclear fusion and other current technological developments have also introduced new possibilities of unparalleled creativeness, also on a world scale. So far the major emphasis has been on the destructive aspect. There is a real danger that the arms race between the USA and the USSR may break into a war where one or more of these weapons will be used.

Some scientists believe that most of the human race, civilians and soldiers, could be annihilated just by the pushing of buttons; some believe that all life could be destroyed, if not immediately, then by destructive genetic efforts in future generations. Our own children, the children of the world, and their children—if they should survive—are innocently involved. Many Americans, even Christians, are caught in the grip of fear of what might happen.

Some political leaders hold that a major war has been avoided so far by the existence of these deadly weapons in the hand of potentially enemy nations. We are grateful for any avoidance of war, whether for this or other reasons, but we do not want our present security bought at the cost of the future. The mounting fear and distrust generated by the competitive development and stockpiling of these weapons fills us with grave concern for the immediately ensuing years.

We cannot with consistency place our trust in both God and modern military weapons. In our time and place, as in the days of old, God's will comes to us in terms of "not by might, nor by power, but by my spirit, saith the Lord."

Brethren have a heritage of opposition to war with a central doctrine and a serious effort toward peace. Although this effort at its best has been far too small, peace is still the goal of our striving.

We call upon our whole Brotherhood to work and pray with renewed vigor toward fulfilling our peace heritage and toward helping to turn mankind from the ways of destruction and toward the ways of our Lord and Master, the Prince of Peace.

We also call upon our Government to stop the making of these weapons of mass destruction, and to turn toward disarmament and world rehabilitation.[52]

In 1956 the Annual Conference of the Church of the Brethren, meeting at Eugene, Oregon, issued a third statement:

We commend our president for his personal support of a program of international disarmament and urge him to continue efforts in this

[51]Church of the Brethren, *169th Conference Minutes,* June 1955.
[52]Church of the Brethren, *Statement on Modern Weapons,* June 1955.

direction. We commend the leadership of our government in taking such initiative in encouraging the uses of atomic energy for peaceful purposes and in bringing about the recent international agreement on the use of atomic energy. However, we feel that the continuation of H-bomb tests is not in keeping with this avowed purpose. Therefore, we recommend the cessation in the interests of creating an atmosphere more conducive to world peace. We encourage our government to shift its policy from one of dependence upon military power and aid, to economic aid, especially of underdeveloped areas, and to separate all foreign economic aid from military aid. In this connection, we also encourage our government to pool its economic aid with that of other nations through the United Nations in multilateral agreements rather than bilateral agreements.[53]

In 1957 the Annual Conference of the Church of the Brethren, meeting at Richmond, Virginia, adopted resolutions pertaining to bomb tests. We quote:

The testing of large nuclear weapons now constitutes a health hazard to our own and future generations that dare not be minimized. While there is some disagreement as to the exact extent of danger to the human race involved in bomb testing, there is no question that serious damage has already been done and that continued testing will increase the danger. We would add our voice to the appeal of thousands of scientists, churchmen, and humanitarian leaders urging our government not only to end its testing program but to take the initiative in securing similar agreements by Great Britain and the Soviet Union. The perils of continued manufacture and testing of nuclear weapons rest not only in physical danger to ourselves and our descendants but also in our relations with other nations, especially those in the Pacific area. We discern a peril to our foreign mission efforts if our nation continues to disregard the frequent appeals that have come from smaller countries around the world. Even more alarming is the peril to our own souls if we stand quietly by without protest while ever larger and more lethal weapons are designed, manufactured and tested.

We reaffirm our belief that the United Nations and its agencies offer many real opportunities to lay the foundation of peace and to prevent the outbreak of hostilities. In order for such an international organization to be more effective, all nations should eventually become universal. We urge our government to join with other nations in favoring the admission to the United Nations of any nation that desires membership and is willing to accept the conditions of membership set forth in the United Nations Charter.[54]

In March 1958 the General Brotherhood Board of the Brethren passed a "resolution on disarmament" which stated:

We commend our government for taking the following steps to help

[53]Church of the Brethren, *170th Conference Minutes,* June 1956.
[54]Church of the Brethren, *171st Conference Minutes,* June 1957.

develop an atmosphere of trust and confidence between our nation and the Soviet Union: 1) participation in the agency for the peaceful use of atomic energy, 2) participation in the International Geophysical Year and 3) the conclusion of a cultural exchange agreement.

However, we deeply regret that the arms race continues unabated. We therefore urge the government to proceed with all possible deliberate speed to negotiate with the Soviet Union for an end to the testing of nuclear weapons as a first step toward genuine disarmament. The Christian conscience calls out for a halt and a retreat from the present suicidal arms race while there is yet time and opportunity.

The Annual Conference of the Church of the Brethren, meeting in 1959 adopted the following statement on nuclear testing:

In view of the disquieting uncertainty about the ultimate genetic effects of continued experiments with nuclear weapons, and the belief of responsible Christians that further experimentation will only take us closer to nuclear war, we express our earnest and unalterable opposition to further testing of nuclear weapons. We call upon the government of the United States to take the lead in permanent abandonment of such tests.

In November 1959 the General Brotherhood Board of the Brethren issued a resolution on disarmament which was passed on to the National Council of Churches. This resolution petitioned the NCC to reidentify itself with its previously stated goals of universal and total disarmament with an adequate international system within the framework of the United Nations. The Brethren also requested that the Department of International Affairs of the NCC suggest means by which churches and church members could help our nation to fulfill its responsibility in achieving the goals of nuclear disarmament. This Resolution on Disarmament was then adopted by the General Board of the NCC at its meeting in Detroit, Michigan, on December 3, 1959. As mentioned above, it was at this meeting that the NCC's Department of International Affairs launched its Nationwide Program of Education and Action for Peace.

In the Name of Christ

It is appropriate, finally, that we consider the third of the historic peace churches, viz., the Mennonites, in order to examine the steps which they have taken to express their concerns relative to the question of nuclear warfare and atom-bomb testing.

As in the case of the Quakers and the Brethren, so also among the Mennonites, we recognize that there are a number of groups which have been relatively unconcerned and indifferent about atomic energy matters in relation to war. In America these groups are to be found mostly among those of the last generation who have moved away from the strong historic nonresistant emphasis toward a closer identification, on the question of war, with other churches within their own religious environments.

This is notably the case for those groups which have adopted the outlook, perhaps unwittingly, that capitalism as a political system is peculiarly congenial to the spread of the Christian religion. This, of course, is precisely what the Marxists would like to believe. For, to the extent that there has been an identification of the Christian religion with capitalism in the West, the Communists have succeeded in driving democracy and the social gospel further apart than they were at the beginning of the century.

Communists are as pleased to see the church engaged in its own internal and ecclesiastical matters as to see it abandon its ideals for the reconstruction of society in order to devote itself exclusively to the salvation of lost souls. To the Communists, the issues between "fundamentalists" and "modernists" and their differences in the interpretation of Scripture are uninteresting. But the church becomes a threat to Communism when it begins to concern itself with the political, social, and economic affairs which affect human relations.

It is possible to argue, therefore, as Milton Mayer has done, that one of the most crucial current issues among Christians, in the East and in the West, is between those who want to see the social gospel preached and those who want to see the social gospel unpreached. In terms of our specific problem here, I believe that most Mennonites would say, "In Christ there is no East or West." They would say that the troubles of the world are so deep and so desperate that there is something which neither capitalism nor Communism can do. Only Christian brotherhood will suffice.

On the whole, among the Mennonites, it is the Mennonite Central Committee (MCC) which has concerned itself with the larger problems connected with the international state of affairs brought about since the development of atomic energy.

The MCC, an "agency for relief and other Christian services," was organized in 1920 and incorporated in 1937 to speak for Mennonites in every area of the globe. The Peace Section of the MCC is concerned with all matters relating to the historic Mennonite nonresistant principles and their applications, such as war and preparation for war, industrial relations, church and state relations, and racial strife. The policy of the MCC is less given to issuing official statements or pronouncements on atomic energy than to counteracting the effect of the nuclear arms race by means of active involvement in peace and relief missions at home and abroad. The emphasis has been on pacifism and nonresistance, with its theological basis rooted in both the redemptive work of Christ and in His outgoing love toward mankind. In practice this has meant total commitment to and total involvement in biblical nonresistance, the mission and peace witness of the church being inseparable.

In Europe the MCC operates today through some seventeen distinct types of correlated programs with central offices in Amsterdam, Kaiserslautern, Basel, Vienna, and Berlin. The MCC, working "in the name of Christ," carries out its pacifist mission in Europe through a wide variety of programs which are dedicated to positive work of construction and to the dissemination of the gospel in the spirit of dedication and service to all peoples in need of help.

A bird's eye view of the MCC program in Europe would include: a group of young "Paxmen" who are building houses and churches for German refugees and who are giving agricultural assistance to Greek villagers; a refugee home for mothers and children in Berlin; food, clothing, church building gifts and loans for refugees settling in West Germany; youth workshops, retreats, and conferences; distribution of supplies to Yugoslavia and Hungary; the *Mennonitischer-Freiwilligendienst* (MFD), sponsoring international work camps with people from twenty-three countries; travel service agencies in Amsterdam and London; an International Christian Service for Peace (called Eirene) —a co-operative venture among several peace groups (including the Brethren Service Committee) for conscientious objectors serving in underdeveloped rural Morocco in northeast Africa; homes for needy children in Bad Duerkheim, Germany, in Valdoie and Weiler, France; the publication of an international Mennonite periodical—*Der Mennonit,* Frankfurt; a Bible school near Basel; student and trainee exchange with the United States; the *Agape Verlag*—a publication house in Basel for German and French materials; an international Mennonite relief organization

(operated by German and Dutch Mennonites and the MCC);
an international peace center at Heerewegan, Holland (operated
by the Dutch Mennonite Peace Committee and the MCC)
which arranges peace seminars and conferences and which produces and distributes peace literature; and an East-West office
in Frankfurt for tracing missing persons and for setting up liaison
with Christians behind the iron curtain. Although the MCC
operates its main program through its European offices, MCC
personnel are also active in North and South America and the
Near and Far East.

Let us now mention a number of instances in which the
Mennonites have taken specific action on the question of nuclear
energy and warfare. In December 1955, the Mennonite international magazine, *Der Mennonit*, carried and commented favorably on the text of the resolution relative to atomic weapons
which had been adopted on July 25, 1955, in Göttingen at the
annual meeting of the *Arbeitsgemeinschaft Deutscher Friedens-
verbände*, a German peace society made up of a number of
German and international peace organizations. This resolution
supported the statements relative to atomic disarmament and
test ban which had been made in the Albert Einstein-Bertrand
Russel statement, and the Mainau manifesto of Nobel Prize
winners, to which we referred in Chapter 8.

We have already had occasion to mention the statement on
nuclear disarmament and the test ban which the Mennonite
Central Committee (MCC) issued jointly with the Quakers and
the Brethren in 1954 and 1958.

At the Sixth World Conference of Mennonites, in Karlsruhe
(August 1957), the International Mennonite Peace Committee
through its European and American delegates expressed the
desire to join the World Council of Churches and Christian
groups in many lands who had already voiced their concern over
the development and testing of nuclear weapons. The Mennonite statement reads in part as follows:

For centuries the Mennonites have refused to take part in war on the
basis of their Christian belief. We are of the conviction that as Christians we know of no higher duty than the one towards Jesus Christ; that
no kind of warfare can agree with His spirit and His teaching. We know
how to value the tolerance which certain states have shown towards conscientious objectors. Nevertheless, our problem today does not concern
ourselves, but rather the dangers which threaten all mankind through the
spread of radioactivity released by nuclear explosions.

To a great extent every use of atomic weapons, as for example in war, not only results in the direct mass annihilation of life, but could produce sufficient amounts of radioactivity to threaten the health of all peoples on earth, and that for generations to come. Even if scientists are not yet completely clear about the risks of radioactivity to human life and health, enough is known today to recognize that a potential danger exists, not only for humans who come in direct contact with the rays but also for their descendants. Therefore the mere development of atomic weapons and the accompanying tests of the weapons already impose on those states, which develop them, the responsibility for the health of peoples beyond their own national borders, and even of generations of unknown humans, including people who in no way are concerned with any specific military objective. It has been asserted that the risk of danger from radioactivity produced by nuclear tests is less than the risk to a nation which is not equipped with superior might. But such superiority also brings with it the greater risk of a world war in which nuclear weapons are used to destroy to a great extent all participants. Therefore we would call in question such arguments of political expediency for the production of nuclear weapons on the basis of their own demonstrations. In addition we would call to the attention of governments their moral obligations which reach far beyond the level of mere political expediency.

Consequently we would urgently request that the development and testing of nuclear weapons be immediately suspended and that every thought of their employment be abandoned. We would direct this urgent entreaty and request alike to all the nations which are engaged in the development and testing of nuclear weapons.[55]

A second resolution on the atomic question was addressed to the presidency of the Sixth Mennonite World Conference by the *Frauentagung*.[56] The statement which was adopted embodied an earlier resolution which had been issued by the Dutch Mennonite Brotherhood. All Christians were admonished to oppose nuclear weapons development and testing and to bear witness to the Christian's calling, dedicated to the reconciliation of the nations.

Many Mennonites the world over will be looking for deeper discussions on the atomic energy question when the Seventh Mennonite World Conference convenes in Kitchener, Ontario, in August of 1962 to explore the theme, "The Lordship of Christ."

Among the Mennonite churches in North and South America,

[55]*Das Evangelium von Jesus Christus in der Welt,* Vorträge und Verhandlungen der sechsten Mennonitischen Weltkonferenz. Author's translation, pp. 364, 365 (Karlsruhe, 1958).
[56]*Ibid.,* p. 187.

we find, to date, that only the General Conference Mennonite Church has notably addressed itself to the question of the Christian's responsibility toward nuclear weapons and bomb testing. The Conference of Mennonites in Canada, which belongs to the above-mentioned General Conference, although it is a separate organization, has not registered any official protest or opinion on nuclear disarmament and bomb testing. However, at the June 1958 Conference session in Saskatoon, a resolution was submitted, asking the Conference to express its position on this question. The matter was referred to the Canadian Board of Christian Service, and it is likely that a statement will be forthcoming.[57] The Mennonites of Brazil, Paraguay, Uruguay, Colombia, and Argentina have not published any statements relative to nuclear disarmament.[58]

The Committee on Peace and Social Concerns of the Board of Christian Service of the General Conference Mennonite Church, meeting in Chicago in 1958, expressed its attitude as follows: "We feel a tension within ourselves in carrying our responsibilities as Christian citizens. We should represent a certain type of conscience to the nation; yet as Mennonites we are theologically perplexed in trying to witness to a government that adheres to a fundamentally different policy." The committee wisely cautioned against expressing "a naive activism without any understanding of the complexity of the issues."[59]

The Pacific District Conference of the General Conference Mennonite Church at its annual meeting in Ritzville, Washington, issued the following statement in 1958:

Believing that the testing of nuclear weapons and their threatened use is immoral and degrading to our nation, and seeking to be obedient to our calling as Christ's disciples, we recommend:

That this session . . . uphold the President of the United States in prayer and send a letter to him stating our concern and imploring him to halt and to ban the testing of nuclear weapons.

That this session . . . petition the President of the United States to regard considerately the motive of the four men who, we believe, should be symbolic of the conscience and safety of the millions of men, women and children of the whole world who are being exposed to deformity and death, and who, in obedience to conscience, have been

[57]Communication from Frank H. Epp, editor of *The Canadian Mennonite*.

[58]Communication from MCC Director Frank J. Wiens, Paraguay, South America.

[59]Minutes of the Committee on Peace and 1-W, May 2, 3, 1958, p. 5.

imprisoned for attempting to sail a 30-foot ketch, The Golden Rule, into the Pacific bomb test area to protest with their lives the current series of tests by our government.

That our church members be encouraged to write to the President expressing their individual concerns, asking for a halt to the weapons testing.[60]

At its Centennial Conference in August 1959, the General Conference Mennonite Church, meeting in Bluffton, Ohio, adopted the following statement on nuclear power:

In our generation new dimensions of power have become available to man. This new power opens to men and nations terrifying possibilities for evil and violence, especially if war should come.

By a strange coincidence of history, science discovered how to split the atom just as the most destructive war of all time spread across the world in 1939. In this war, obliteration bombing became established military policy. By war's end, the split atom came forth as an atomic bomb; and obliteration bombing came to Hiroshima and Nagasaki. Since that war, the hydrogen bomb and the intercontinental ballistic missile make future war almost inevitably intercontinental in scope and an ominous threat to the very existence of man.

The Christian Faith: In such a time of urgency the Christian church cannot be silent. It must through its members voice clearly its Christian concern and proclaim fearlessly its conviction:

"The earth is the Lord's" (Ps. 24:1). God "made the world and all things therein" (Acts 17:24). He is the all-wise, all-good, and all-powerful ruler and sustainer of His creation. Evil men are not going to wrest it from Him. He is Lord of all, Lord even of history.

God is to be trusted and His infinitely wise will for men and the world is to be respected and obeyed. Obeying His will brings fullness of life (John 10:10). Defying or ignoring it invites ultimate and inevitable disaster (Gal. 6:7; Rom. 6:23).

God created man with amazing capacity to know, to understand, and to use his knowledge for His good purposes. "Subdue" the earth and have "dominion" over every living thing was part of God's creative purpose (Gen. 1:28). The scientist's tireless search to know and understand and to adapt to practical uses the secrets of nature is therefore in accord with God's good purpose. Unlocking the secrets of atomic energy and discovering how to release its power is in itself not an evil.

These discoveries of science have released to man a marvelous potential for good but also frightening possibilities for evil. Evil results may come upon men unexpectedly, perhaps even through well-intentioned people.

Only dedicated men of good will who love God with heart, mind, and soul and their neighbor as themselves and who respect God's holy will for man and the world can be trusted to use this power for blessing

[60]"Pacific District Conference Statement," 1958.

and not for horrible self-destruction (Matt. 22:37). Under God they have the will, the power, and the obligation to direct the use of this God-given power into channels of peace and blessing for all mankind.

Our Repentance: We confess our submission to the will of God has not always been complete. Fear, distrust, and national and racial tensions have all too often blurred our vision of God's will and purpose for us. We are too much involved in these pagan practices. Our silence in the face of these and other social evils condemns us. Our taxes support gigantic armaments programs. Our economic prosperity rests too much on these cold-war tensions. We are so entangled in all these sub-Christian trends that we cry out for light and for the leading of the Lord. Our devotion to God's great purpose in Christ Jesus is often feeble. We find it so hard to put our faith into action. In our repentance we ever take new hope and find new strength in the knowledge that God truly forgives and restores men to their rightful relationship to God and to one another.

Our Concern: As evidence of the sincerity of our repentance and profession of faith: We reaffirm our complete confidence in Jesus Christ as God's sufficient answer to man's need and to the whole perplexing problem of human relationship.

We reaffirm our belief that Jesus' way of unwearied, self-giving, understanding love and good will is, in God's moral order, the only effective cure for world tensions, fears, and distrust. This is the only power that can find a positive and effective answer to world tensions, fear, and distrust.

We reaffirm our faith as found in our historic Anabaptist-Mennonite heritage and in the peace statement adopted at Portland, Oregon, in 1953.

We pledge ourselves to live in this spirit, proclaiming in word and work God's reconciling purpose through a ministry of healing, preaching, and teaching, and through a service of love in areas of need, tension, and conflict. In this way we would help to quiet fears, allay distrust, and build mutual good will and co-operation for the good of each and of all.

We call upon our leaders in government to make permanent the ban on bomb tests. They are a serious threat to the health of peoples. They undermine mutual trust among nations. Most of all they are as contrary to the spirit and teachings of Jesus as war itself. War is sin and so are bomb testings because they belong to the war preparations scheme.

It is no less a sin to prostitute this marvelous power of the atom by stockpiling it in the form of bombs, spending billions of dollars for missiles and missile bases and cursing the soil confiscated for this purpose. Most shocking to the Christian conscience are the fantastic military installations in the very heart of the nation. Sin is sin. It will destroy a people which condones it. We oppose the use of any of God's natural resources for the purpose of warfare with our fellow men.

We earnestly urge our men in government to assume leadership in promoting the peaceful uses of atomic energy for the benefit of all peoples of the world.[61]

[61]*The Mennonite,* Sept. 8, 1959, p. 549.

In the light of all of the statements on atomic warfare and bomb testing that have come from the historic peace churches, it is evident that the Mennonites as a whole have done much less in the way of clarifying their position than have the Quakers and the Brethren.   This is particularly true of the Mennonites in Canada, the United States, and South America.

It is true that Mennonites in the United States, as individuals, have taken an active part in opposing bomb testing through letters of protest directed to the President, to Senators and to the Washington office of the AEC, but the various conferences have not to date given these problems a great deal of serious thought.

The Social Concerns Committee of the General Conference Mennonite Church met in Chicago in September of 1958 to discuss these problems.   This study received its initial impetus from those discussions, and it is to be hoped that our brief factual history of atomic developments and the reactions elicited by atomic energy will provide some of the essential informational background for intelligent thinking on the subject.

The Spirit of Christ Changeth Not

We might, finally, raise the question whether atomic energy has fundamentally altered the problem of dealing with wars. Wars were catastrophic enough even without the use of atomic weapons.   The atomic bombs which were dropped on Hiroshima and Nagasaki probably did not kill more civilians than were killed by the fire bomb raids on Tokyo in March 1945.[62]   Still, the situation of a monopolistic possession of nuclear weapons which existed in 1945 is now a thing of the past.   And this makes a difference.   While there may still be no fundamental changes in the methods of dealing with wars, it cannot be denied that atomic energy has magnified enormously the penalty of *failure* to deal with war.

Professor I. I. Rabi of Columbia University, Nobel prize-winner in physics for 1944, has said that even a combination of the best brains in our country from all fields of experience— scientific, business, religious, and ethical, as well as academic and political—is hardly equal to the task of mapping a wise course

[62]P.M.S. Blackett, *Atomic Weapons and East-West Relations* (Cambridge, 1956), p. 81.

through the tangle of mistrust and terror which has grown up in the postwar years. He says that it is customary to lay blame for most of our failures on the Russians and adds: "Indeed, I would be among the last to deprive them of their proper share of the blame, which is large. But we are not blameless. Although we cannot do much about reforming the Russians, we ought to be able to take steps to set our own house in order, for our policy is far from clear, even to ourselves."[63]

Presidential Science Adviser Kistiakowsky, said recently:

The need to adjust public policy to changing human conditions, of course, is not new. What is new today is the rapidity with which the developments of science are altering the human conditions, the rapidity with which policy, particularly foreign policy, must adjust to the changes being wrought by the pace of scientific advance. Not only must it adjust; policy must prepare for, must predict, the impact of scientific discovery and must also in some sense attempt to guide it.[64]

With a world split in two by democratic and communistic powers, each in possession of atomic weapons powerful enough to annihilate each other, where shall one locate the basis for a practicable resolution for public policy which will lead to agreement or even coexistence? We have seen that suggestions to deal with the East-West conflict range all the way from a gentle, courteous, nonviolent response at one extreme to the rudest and most violent get-tough policy on the other. One feels that there is a certain absurdity in resting one's security on a type of weapon, which, if it were extensively used in war, would mean suicide for both sides. There are many who would prefer to gamble for that security. Max Born has said that it is a "crazy situation in which we find ourselves, [and] it looks as if our civilization were condemned to ruin by reason of its own structure."[65]

In the last analysis, the most compelling reasons for putting the wartime atom aside are of a religious and philosophical nature. The cultivation of weapons of mass destruction, which threaten civilization involves, as Kennan says, "an egocentricity on our part which has no foundation either in religious faith or political philosophy."[66]

[63]I. I. Rabi, *Atlantic Monthly*, August 1960, pp. 39-42.
[64]G. B. Kistiakowsky, "Science and Foreign Affairs," *Science*, April 8, 1960, p. 1020.
[65]Max Born, *Bulletin of Atomic Scientists*, June 1957, p. 192.
[66]George F. Kennan, *The Listener*, Oct. 29, 1959, pp. 711-713.

If Christians believe that they cannot personally construct or use atomic weapons, they can hardly maintain that others should do so. It would likewise appear to be inconsistent to hold that nuclear arsenals be maintained merely to threaten others. If Christians feel that it is God's will that men everywhere should enjoy the benefits of civilization, they ought to be committed to a fair and reasonable distribution of the peacetime uses of atomic energy. Christians could also give their support to the building of a world of really free nations through an atoms-for-peace program.

But, of course, even all this is not sufficient in a world where people are remote from each other and where they are taught to hate each other merely because governments are committed to different political and economic ideologies. There are very few facts which would stand up to show that one national fanaticism can be defeated by a rival fanaticism. Is it not too radical, then, to ask a government which wishes to defend its values against destruction to set aside those values in order to carry out its defense? Our so-called Christian nation could expose the hypocrisy of the Communists and win the uncommitted world by ending its own hypocrisy.

And so it seems to me that Christians ought to be willing to push aside the use of atomic energy for national defense and to accept rather all the measures of risk and discomfort to which that might lead. It is by no means certain that such an action would solve the political problems which rest at the heart of the cold war. But I do feel that it would remove a major share of the fear and danger which now besets mankind. We do not own this planet. We are only the custodians of what God has given us, and it would be preposterous to pollute and destroy the world in the attempt to clutch it to ourselves.

Finally, it would seem desirable that Christians do everything within their power not only to convince others of the strength of nonviolence, but to encourage those who are able to do so, to work out the technical requirements and details of feasible methods to control atomic energy in war and peace. In large measure this task will fall upon the scientists themselves—who on the whole, to be quite realistic, are now almost the only individuals in our society equipped to handle the mechanics of effective atomic energy controls which will appeal to both East and West. Strong feelings accompanied by determined wills may result in action; but, if there is no guiding thought, it is very likely that the action will be blind and misdirected and, therefore, ineffective. The Christian may well believe that science without religion cannot see what needs to be done. But religion without science has not the power to do it.

Science today is one of the few common languages of all mankind. It is a language which can provide a most important basis for the communication of ideas between people of different political and ideological convictions. In their work, scientists the world over place the highest premium on intellectual honesty, personal integrity, hard work, tenacity, concentration, imagination, insight, and curiosity—characteristics which Christians would do well to emulate in their search for opportunities to "speak truth to power" and to work for peace. If Christians everywhere would throw themselves wholeheartedly into the building of a world community without regard to national interests, their actions would go a long way toward the creation of a world free from war.

Modern wars are so horrible not only because they cause so much suffering, but because the killing can be accomplished so easily without much feeling. George Sarton, the distinguished historian of science wrote during the first world war: "The act . . . of fighting is a monstrous thing; but what surpasses everything in horror and monstrousness is when the act of fighting becomes a moral duty, and the collective crime becomes for the moment the highest duty of the citizens."[67]

In 1660 the Quakers sent a declaration to Charles II which is still meaningful for our day:

We utterly deny all outward wars and strife, and fighting with outward weapons, for an end, or under any pretense whatever; this is our testimony to the world. The Spirit of Christ by which we are guided is not changeable, so as once to command us for a thing as evil and again to move unto it; and we certainly know and testify to the world, that the Spirit of Christ, which leads us into all Truth, will never move us to fight and war against any man with outward weapons, neither for the Kingdom of Christ nor for the Kingdoms of this world.

[67]May Sarton, *I Knew a Phoenix* (New York, 1959), pp. 84, 85.

BIBLIOGRAPHY

ALEXANDER, PETER. *Atomic Radiation and Life.* Harmondsworth, Middlesex: Penguin, 1957.

ALSOP, JOSEPH AND STEWART ALSOP. *We Accuse! The Story of the Miscarriage of American Justice in the Case of J. Robert Oppenheimer.* New York: Simon and Schuster, 1954.

AMRINE, MICHAEL. *The Great Decision: The Secret History of the Atomic Bomb.* New York: Putnam, 1959.

BERTIN, LEONARD. *Atomic Harvest: A British View of Atomic Energy.* San Francisco: W. H. Freeman, 1957.

BIGELOW, ALBERT. *The Voyage of the Golden Rule: An Experiment with Truth.* Garden City, N. Y.: Doubleday, 1959.

BISHOP, AMASA S. *Project Sherwood: The U. S. Program in Controlled Fusion.* Reading, Mass.: Addison-Wesley, 1958.

BLACKETT, PATRICK M. S. *Fear, War and the Bomb: Military and Political Consequences of Atomic Energy.* New York: Whittlesey House, 1949.

BLACKETT, PATRICK M. S. *Atomic Weapons and East-West Relations.* Cambridge: Cambridge University Press, 1956.

BOER, HANS A. DE. *The Bridge Is Love: Jottings from a Traveller's Notebook.* Translated from the German. London: Marshall, Morgan and Scott, 1958.

BRAUNBEK, WERNER. *The Drama of the Atom.* Translated from the German by B. J. Kenworthy and W. A. Coupe. Edinburgh and London: Oliver and Boyd, 1958.

BROWN, HARRISON. *Must Destruction Be Our Destiny? A Scientist Speaks as a Citizen.* New York: Simon and Schuster, 1946.

COMAR, CYRIL L. *Radioisotopes in Biology and Agriculture; Principles and Practice.* New York: McGraw Hill, 1955.

COMPTON, ARTHUR H. *Atomic Quest: A Personal Narrative.* New York: Oxford University Press, 1956.

COULSON, CHARLES A. *Nuclear Knowledge and Christian Responsibility.* Foundry Pamphlets Number 9. London: The Epworth Press, 1958.

CROW, JAMES F. *Effects of Radiation and Fallout.* Public Affairs Pamphlet No. 256. New York: Public Affairs Committee, 1957.

DEAN, GORDON E. *Report on the Atom: What you should know about the Atomic Energy Program of the United States.* New York: Knopf, 1953.

DICK, WILLIAM E. *Atomic Energy in Agriculture.* New York: Philosophical Library, 1957.

FEINBERG, JOSEPH G. *The Story of Atomic Theory and Atomic Energy.* New York: Dover reprint of 1953 ed., 1960.

FERMI, LAURA. *Atoms in the Family; My Life with Enrico Fermi,* Chicago: University of Chicago Press, 1954.

FERMI, LAURA. *Atoms for the World; United States Participation in the Conference of the Peaceful Uses of Atomic Energy.* Chicago: University of Chicago Press, 1957.

FOWLER, JOHN M. (ed.). *Fallout: A Study of Superbombs, Strontium 90, and Survival.* New York: Basic Books, 1960.

GAMOW, GEORGE. *Atomic Energy in Cosmic and Human Life: Fifty Years of Radioactivity.* New York: Macmillan, 1947.

GELLHORN, WALTER. *Security, Loyalty, and Science.* Ithaca: Cornell University Press, 1950.

GLASSTONE, SAMUEL (ed). *The Effects of Atomic Weapons.* (Prepared by the U. S. Dept. of Defense and published for the U. S. AEC.) Washington, D. C.: Govt. Printing Office, 1957.

GLASSTONE, SAMUEL. *Sourcebook on Atomic Energy.* Princeton, N. J.: Van Nostrand, 1958.

GOLLWITZER, HELMUT. *Die Christen und die Atomwaffen.* Theologische Existenz Heute, Heft 61. Munich: Chr. Kaiser Verlag, 1957.

HAHN, OTTO. *New Atoms: Progress and Some Memories.* New York and Amsterdam: Elsevier Publishing Co., 1950.

HECHT, SELIG. *Explaining the Atom.* Revised with four additional chapters by E. Rabinowitch. New York: Viking Press, 1954.

HECKSTALL-SMITH, HUGH W. *Atomic Radiation Dangers and What They Mean to You.* London: J. M. Dent & Sons, 1958.

HERSEY, JOHN R. *Hiroshima.* New York: Knopf, 1946.

HERZ, JOHN H. *International Politics in the Atomic Age.* New York: Columbia University Press, 1959.

HOLCOMBE, ARTHUR N. (chairman). *Organizing Peace in the Nuclear Age.* (Commission to Study the Organization of Peace, eleventh report.) New York: New York University Press, 1959.

HUGHES, DONALD J. *On Nuclear Energy: Its Potential for Peacetime Uses.* Cambridge: Harvard University Press, 1957.

HUGHES, DONALD J. *The Neutron Story.* Garden City, N. Y.: Doubleday Anchor, 1959.

JUNGK, ROBERT: *Brighter than a Thousand Suns: A Personal History of the Atomic Scientists.* Translated from the German by James Cleugh. New York: Harcourt Brace, 1958.

KENNAN, GEORGE F. *Russia, the Atom and the West.* New York: Harper, 1958.

KISSINGER, HENRY A. *Nuclear Weapons and Foreign Policy.* Garden City, N. Y.: Doubleday, 1958.

KRAMISH, ARNOLD. *Atomic Energy in the Soviet Union.* Stanford: Stanford University Press, 1959.

LANDSDELL, NORMAN. *The Atom and the Energy Revolution.* Harmondsworth, Middlesex: Penguin, 1958.

LAPP, RALPH E. *The Voyage of the Lucky Dragon.* New York: Harper, 1958.

LAPP, RALPH E. *Roads to Discovery.* New York: Harper, 1960.

LATIL, PIERRE DE AND JACQUES BERGIER. *Quinze Hommes . . . un Secret.* Paris: Gallimard, 1956.

LAURENCE, WILLIAM L. *Men and Atoms: The Discovery, the Uses and the Future of Atomic Energy.* New York: Simon and Schuster, 1959.

LOT, FERNAND. *Radioisotopes in the Service of Man.* (United Nations Educational, Scientific and Cultural Organization, Publication No. 16.) Paris, 1959.

MILLER, MERLE AND ABE SPITZER. *We Dropped the A-Bomb.* New York: Y. Crowell, 1946.

MODELSKI, GEORGE A. *Atomic Energy in the Communist Bloc.* Melbourne, Australia: Melbourne University Press, 1959.

MUMFORD, LEWIS (ed). *Alternatives to the H-Bomb.* (A Symposium.) Boston: Beacon Press, 1955.

MURRAY, THOMAS E. *Nuclear Policy for War and Peace.* Cleveland and New York: The World Publishing Co., 1960.

NETSCHERT, BRUCE C. AND S. H. SCHURR. *Atomic Energy Applications with Reference to Underdeveloped Countries: A Preliminary Survey.* Baltimore: Johns Hopkins Press, 1957.

NOEL-BAKER, PHILIP J. *The Arms Race: A Programme for World Disarmament.* London: Stevens, 1958.

OSADA, ARATA (compiler). *Children of the A-Bomb: Testament of the Boys and Girls of Hiroshima.* Translated from the Japanese by Jean Dan and Ruth Sieben-Morgan. Tokyo: Uchida Rokakuho Publishing House, 1959.

PAULING, LINUS C. *No More War!* New York: Dodd, Mead, 1958.

PIRIE, ANTOINETE (ed). *Fall Out: Radiation Hazards from Nuclear Explosions.* London: MacGibbon & Kee, 1958.

RABINOWITCH, EUGENE I. (ed). *Minutes to Midnight: The International Control of Atomic Energy.* Chicago: Bulletin of the Atomic Scientists, 1950.

RUGGLES, MELVILLE J., AND ARNOLD KRAMISH. *The Soviet Union and the Atom: The Early Years.* Santa Monica, Calif.: Rand Corporation, 1956.

SACKS, JACOB. *The Atom at Work.* New York: Ronald Press, 1951.

SCHURR, SAM H. AND JACOB MARSCHAK. *Economic Aspects of Atomic Power: An Exploratory Study.* Princeton: Princeton University Press, 1950.

SCHWARZENBERGER, GEORG. *The Legality of Nuclear Weapons.* (Published under the auspices of The London Institute of World Affairs), London: Stevens, 1958.

SINGH, NAGENDRA. *Nuclear Weapons and International Law.* (Published under the auspices of the Indian Council of World Affairs, New Delhi. New York: Praeger, 1959.)

SMYTH, HENRY DE WOLF. *Atomic Energy for Military Purposes: The Official Report on the Development of the Atomic Bomb under the Auspices of the U. S. Government, 1940-1945.* Princeton: Princeton University Press, 1945.

TELLER, EDWARD AND ALBERT L. LATTER. *Our Nuclear Future: Facts, Dangers and Opportunities.* New York: Criterion Books, 1958.

THIRRIG, HANS. *Energy for Man; Windmills to Nuclear Power.* Bloomington: Indiana University Press, 1958.

TOYNBEE, PHILIP (ed). *The Fearful Choice: A Debate on Nuclear Policy.* London: Victor Gollancz, 1958.

WALLACE, BRUCE AND TH. DOBZHANSKY. *Radiation, Genes, and Man.* New York: Holt, 1959.

WEIZÄCKER, C. F. VON. *Ethical and Political Problems of the Atomic Age.* (The Burge Memorial Lecture.) London: SCM Press, 1958.

WOLF, ERNEST (ed). *Christusbekenntnis im Atomzeitalter?* (Im Auftrag des Arbeitskreises Kirchlicher Bruderschaften, Theologische Existenz Heute, Heft 70. Munich: Chr. Kaiser Verlag, 1959.

WORLD COUNCIL OF CHURCHES—Division of Studies, A Provisional Study Document on *Christians and the Prevention of War in an Atomic Age: A Theological Discussion.* (Central Committee action of August 27, 1958).

INDEX

Acheson-Lilienthal Plan, 151
Advisory Committee on Uranium, 8, 9
Aggression, 132, 161, 193
Alamogordo Air Base, 24
Alpha particles, 3ff., 63
American College of Radiology, 87
American Council of Christian Churches, 264, 265
American Friends Service Committee, 275, 276
Amrine, Michael, 22
Anderson, Clinton P., 81
Anglican Pacifist Fellowship, 276
Appeasement, 140, 263
Argonne National Laboratories, 164
Armaments race, 132, 133, 135, 158, 159, 193, 194, 216, 219, 221, 222, 232, 236, 256
Aron, Raymond, 140
Association of Los Alamos Scientists, 205
Association of Scientists for Atomic Education, 208
Atomic bombs, 11, 14, 24ff., 30f., 42, 44, 48, 55ff., 161, 162, 203, 232, 245, 287f.; American monopoly, 152; emotional impact, 28; German research, 16; outlawing of, 148, 159; secrets of, 35; use of, 23f.
Atomic Development Authority, 153
Atomic energy, 7, 12, 19, 20, 26, 30, 32, 34, 36-39, 45, 99, 103, 107, 109, 110, 115, 131, 148, 168, 216, 268, 270, 284, 288, 290; control of, 33, 147-197, 206, 208, 210, 216, 290; control by civilian authorities, 147, 149, 206, 268; controlled release, 10, 99; co-operation in, 147, 221, 227, 244, 261; development of, 15, 268; domestic use of, 147, 150, 204; exchange of information on, 151;

explosions, 175; fission, 5f., 17, 83, 97; fuels, 99, 172; fusion, 14, 38, 107, 109f., 169, 171; history of, 3-20; industry and, 162, 205; legislation on, 256; licensing of, 151; medical use, 60; military applications of, 21, 43, 93, 205; misuse of, 151; monopoly of, 32, 151, 155, 157; peaceful use of, 17, 93-127, 141, 152f., 171, 172, 205, 215, 217, 259, 261, 263, 268, 279f., 287; pile, 99; policy, 23; political implications, 198, 207; for propulsion, 112ff., 192; power plants, 63, 99, 100; power production, 104, 205; reactors, 40, 55, 89, 98-101, 104ff., 113, 117, 125, 162; release of, 268; research, 15, 20, 40, 97f., 102, 153, 163, 205; resources, 105; secrecy, 31, 149, 168; submarines and, 44, 49, 112f., 137; war time use, 125f.; world control, 33, 205; in World War II, 21-40.
Atomic Energy Commission, 28, 33, 43, 49, 85-88, 90f., 96f., 102-104, 109, 140, 150, 165, 176, 182, 192, 288; Atomic Energy Act, 50, 161, 206; commissioners, 154; General Advisory Committee, 83; Oak Ridge, 84; Plowshare, 52
Atomic scientists, 41, 148, 150, 185, 200, 201, 204; loyalty of, 159; world politics, 154
Atomic Scientists' News, 208
Atomic warfare, 133, 216, 236, 283, 288; and accidental annihilation, 136; survival in, 29, 65
Atomic weapons, 23, 41, 44, 49, 51, 56, 58, 76, 77, 133-139; 150, 153, 161, 181f., 186, 222, 234, 241f., 278, 283ff., 288ff.; abolition of, 212; as absolute weapons, 31; agreement to ban, 166, 192, 223; contamination of, 47, 91; control of, 148, 153, 155,